# SEVEN PILLARS
## OF FREEDOM
# WORKBOOK

## BY DR. TED ROBERTS

### WITH DIANE ROBERTS AND HARRY FLANAGAN

PURE DESIRE MINISTRIES INTERNATIONAL | GRESHAM, OREGON

# SEVEN PILLARS OF FREEDOM WORKBOOK

By Dr. Ted Roberts

Other contributing writers:
Harry Flanagan
Diane Roberts
Linda Dodge

Published by
Pure Desire Ministries International
719 NE Roberts Avenue, Gresham, OR 97030
www.puredesire.org | 503.489.0230
ISBN 978-0-9840755-5-3

4th Edition with revisions, September 2015

The stories presented of individual lives in this workbook are true and accurate. The details have been adjusted to prevent personal identification. In some cases the story presented is a compilation of the histories of several individuals. The compilation, however, doesn't affect the clinical or theological veracity of the stories.

# TABLE OF CONTENTS

# ACKNOWLEDGMENTS

The acknowledgments are not extensive or lengthy, because very little in this workbook is totally original.

The foundations of the workbook were taken directly from the Word of God. Some might say that the observations concerning the Word of God were original to me, but the truth is if there is any biblical wisdom found in these pages it came from the Holy Spirit. I either recognized the truth during my devotions or in the middle of a counseling session. I have long ago realized I am just not that smart. I take notes during most counseling sessions because I never know when the Holy Spirit is going to open my eyes, not just my client's eyes.

*Thank you Lord for the living and giving truth of Your Word!*

The clinical insights as well are not original to me. Dr. Patrick Carnes has been my mentor for years. This national known researcher and clinician has been so gracious in pouring his wisdom and insights into my heart. I have attempted to reference Dr. Carnes' work where I have directly used it. If I have missed some references, my apologies to my friend.

*Thank you Lord for the touch of Dr. Carnes in my life; may this workbook not only honor him but also result in thousands of men who love You being set free!*

*Special thanks to my wife Diane.*

Finally, some pillars are written by my dear friend and colleague Harry Flanagan.

*Thank you Father Flanagan!*

Dr. Ted Roberts

# INTRODUCTION

## WELCOME

Joining a Seven Pillars of Freedom men's group may be one of the most difficult decisions you have ever made. It may also be the decision that will require the most courage. I believe that if you make a commitment to this group, complete your daily assignments, and invest in your recovery, this will be the best decision you have ever made.

The introduction sections of this workbook are vital pieces of your preparation for freedom and healing. They explain concepts and principles that lay the foundation for everything in this workbook and in your Pure Desire group. If you have not completed the *Conquer Series: A Battle Plan for Purity* (puredesire.org/conquer), including watching all DVDs in that series, please read the lessons titled "A Sexy Brain" and "Help! Someone Hijacked My Brain!" in Appendix One before continuing with the *Seven Pillars of Freedom Workbook*.

It is absolutely essential that you read ALL the materials in the introduction BEFORE you begin working your way through the lessons in Pillars of Freedom One through Seven.

## INTRODUCTION

In 1993, East Hill Church in Gresham, Oregon, took on the issue of sexual addiction. We had no road map because we knew of no other church that had walked down this path. The original focus was working with men who were trapped in sexual bondage. Quickly, we realized we also needed to support women who had been betrayed by their husbands, as well as women trapped in sexual bondage.

For 23 years, the Lord has led Pure Desire in a ministry of support, healing, and restoration to churches around the world. Through the development of curriculum—uniquely designed to provide a theologically and clinically proven process—and training conferences, shame is losing the battle and hope is increasing. The message of grace and freedom is becoming visible in small groups all over the country.

Families are experiencing change from negative family systems that have dominated for generations. Pure Desire groups, led by courageous lay leaders in the church, are answering the call of the wounded and offering a safe place where vulnerability is appearing in many lives for the first time.

With the explosion in brain research, it is now possible to understand the devastating effectiveness of technology (Internet, video, etc.) on our culture. Pure Desire groups offer continuing education, resources, and training necessary to protect our families from sexual addiction and the unhealthy sexual messages that permeate our culture and bombard us everywhere we turn.

HARRY FLANAGAN
**Pastoral Sex Addiction Professional**
Pure Desire Ministries

# THE SEVEN PILLARS

Used by permission of Patrick J. Carnes

## RESTORATION PILLAR    LIFE COMPETENCY

| RESTORATION PILLAR | LIFE COMPETENCY |
|---|---|
| **1.** Break through denial | • Understands the characteristics of denial and self-delusion<br>• Identifies the presence of self-delusion in life<br>• Knows personal preferred patterns of thought distortion<br>• Accepts confrontation |
| **2.** Understand the nature of sexual addiction | • Knows information on addictive behavior<br>• Applies information to personal life<br>• Understands sexually compulsive patterns<br>• Knows specific stories/scenarios of the arousal template |
| **3.** Surrenders to process | • Acceptance of addiction in life<br>• Knows personal limitations<br>• Discerns difference between controllable & non-controllable events |
| **4.** Limits damage from behavior | • Has internal skills for anxiety reduction<br>• Develops resolution for change and commitment |
| **5.** Establish sobriety | • Uses clearly stated boundaries of sobriety<br>• Manages life without dysfunctional sexual behavior |
| **6.** The battle is in your mind | • Emotional healing |
| **7.** Develops and implements a spiritual growth plan | • Maintains a lifestyle of spiritual growth |

In order to have these Seven Pillars as the structure to our freedom, we need to understand a biblical truth these Pillars must be built on.

If you have ever looked closely at a classic Roman or Greek pillar you may have noticed they are not one solid piece. They rest on a massive foundation. Like the Roman or Greek pillars, none of these Seven Pillars will be effective in your life, or be able to bear the weight of the restoration process until you are gripped by God's grace.

Grace is not a doctrine or a theological concept, it is a person—Jesus Christ. Paul declares in Romans that the Law was given by Moses, but grace and truth came through Jesus Christ. Grace is the gospel. When the apostle Paul talks about the gospel, he talks about the gospel of grace. God's radical grace will never get a grip on your soul until you understand this truth.

# GROUP CURRICULUM RESOURCES

*The Conquer Series: A Battle Plan for Purity* is highly recommended as a launching point for all Pure Desire men's groups.

*The Seven Pillars of Freedom Journal* will reinforce the daily commitment to health that is vital to your sobriety and spiritual growth.

**Pure Desire** by Dr. Ted Roberts is used as a support resource that offers hope for establishing healthy personal boundaries with proven, practical applications.

*Genesis Process for Change Groups* by Michael Dye will help men open up to new levels of healing through lesson information and practical discipleship tools. This resource does not teach theology. However, it provides tools that promote growth and healing as we become more life Jesus.

*The Cure* (book, study guide, and DVD) by John Lynch provides excellent foundational material useful when starting Pure Desire groups. The eight-session videos and study guide provide an opportunity for a two-month break between the *Seven Pillars of Freedom* and *Genesis Process*.

These resources were limited and intentionally chosen to represent the very best cohesive materials that will help men break their cycle of addiction and bondage.

# THE FLIGHT GEAR YOU WILL ABSOLUTELY NEED!

You don't walk out to a fighter aircraft and just hop in. You have to be dressed for the challenge. You will have to become a master at using four essential pieces of equipment if you want to win the battle:

- The navigational compass
- The flight helmet
- The G suit
- The survival vest

The same is true for your journey of freedom. There are four essential tools that you must master if you want to truly break free from sexual bondage.

❶ **The navigational compass.** There are two sets of rules for flying any aircraft: Visual Flight Rules (VFR) and Instrument Flight Rules (IFR). Flying under VFR rules, the pilot can choose a flight path based on what they see out of the cockpit window. Flying under IFR, you must file a flight plan before take off and check your instruments often throughout the journey. In this journey of healing there will be days where you can clearly see where you are headed. Other days you will endure storms of the enemy's attacks. There will inevitably be some dark nights of confusion. You may find yourself asking the question, "Am I even headed the right direction?" In a Pure Desire group you must file a flight plan (Commitment to Change) each week and ask your group members for input. The Commitment to Change is like a navigational compass, no matter how dark the night, or how ominous the storm, your compass will keep you moving in the right direction.

❷ **The flight helmet.** The first time I put on an advanced model flight helmet it felt totally weird. I was flooded with information from a multiplicity of sources. Warning tones telling me of potential enemy antiaircraft missiles being fired my way. Alerts from radar warnings, pointing out that there were enemy fighter aircraft headed at me. Emergency calls on guard channel from friendly aircraft in trouble, and the normal radio chatter of the other aircraft in my flight in the chaos of combat operations. All of this information increased my "Situational Awareness," but it initially felt like an overload!

The latest flight helmets have taken this development of situational awareness to an incredible level. They fuse all the information coming from the plane's sensors with imagery fed by a set of cameras mounted on the jet's outer surfaces. This information is projected directly on the pilot's visor giving him an X-ray-like imagery. He has all the information to fly the plane to its maximum capabilities immediately available to him. And what is simply awesome is his weapons are bore sighted to where he is looking.[1] All he has to do is look at the enemy aircraft and fire. He doesn't have to do all the twisting and turning I used to do. He has total situational awareness!!

My point is this: once you learn to use the **FASTER Scale,** you will have the best spiritual helmet available. You will have an awesome awareness of how the enemy sets you up for the kill. You will start understanding why you relapsed again and again in the past. You will be able pick him up way before he can bring his weapons to bear on you. Most delightful of all, you will be able to turn and bore sight him and blow him away by the grace of God.

Using the FASTER Scale is a learned skill, so be patient with yourself. When I first put on an advanced flight helmet it felt uncomfortable and cumbersome. But, I realized I was totally blind to what was really going on in the battle without it. One of the hardest skills to learn for a guy coming out of sexual bondage is…being present. Realizing what they are feeling and why they are feeling that way. For so many years they have learned to medicate the pain in their life; thus, they have no situational awareness and end up going down in flames no matter how hard they try. Mastery of the FASTER Scale will give you the victory over the enemy; in fact, it will give you the ability to win the battle every time.

❸ **The G suit.** You could never withstand the stress of combat dogfighting without a "G" suit or as we used to call them "speed jeans." The object of a G suit is to take your legs and squeeze them up into your helmet, for the simple reason that the tighter you turn your aircraft to get on the enemy's tail, the more your blood will be pushed down to your legs and the lower part of your body because of the acceleration. This results in graying out (loss of vision) or the dreaded g-LOC (g-induced loss of consciousness). Who wins in a turning dogfight is not necessarily the guy who pulls the hardest, but the one who fights the smartest. The G suit enables you to stay conscious long enough to out-think your opponent. Being a great dogfighter is an art form; it involves balancing two conflicting choices. If you pull too hard you pass out and die. If you don't pull enough the enemy gets on your tail and blows you out of the sky!

Learning how to use the **Double Bind** in conjunction with the FASTER Scale will enable you to take on the most vicious attacks the enemy can throw at you and still come out on top. Once again, it is a learned skill. The Double Bind will help you to face your deepest fears. The typical guy doesn't like to admit he is ever afraid because that makes them feel weak. This is why he never seems to get unstuck. Freedom is about the courage to face our fears. The Double Bind will help your situational awareness to increase to such a level that the Holy Spirit can finally bring healing down to the very depths of your soul.

If your wife is in the Betrayal & Beyond group for women, she, too, will be learning the FASTER Scale and Double Bind. Often times, her Double Bind is to stop being a sheriff and face the fear of her husband's possible relapse. In order to help her with this Double Bind, we have created the Safety Action Plan that helps her begin to let go and trust her husband to God. The Safety Plan in turn will often feel like a G suit to her spouse; it will challenge him to be squeezed into new levels of integrity that might feel uncomfortable at first, but will ultimately help him to be the man of God he has cried out to be.

❹ **The survival vest.** The survival vest is for those times you find yourself in what we used to call "the weeds." Somehow you find yourself on the ground and you have to find a way to survive. The survival vest is packed with all kinds of stuff from first aid supplies, to water, to signal flares and what ever else they can pack into it. I managed to cram a 45-caliber pistol into mine. I thought the little 38-caliber pistol they normally included in the vest was rather wimpy. But the truth is, I wasn't really counting on shooting my way out of trouble. I knew the only way out was to call for help from my teammates. If I ever found myself on the ground running for my life, I knew I would pull out my survival radio, screaming out for fire support and someone to come and get me out of this mess!

Without your Pure Desire group and their support, your chances of making it to freedom are slim to non-existent. I have seen so many guys running through the jungle of their addiction trying to stay one step ahead of the enemy. They seldom or never make calls to their group members during the week, and don't really open up to the group. Then they wonder why they keep relapsing. A lack of situational awareness goes along with isolation. I always tell guys when they go into isolation, passivity, and withdrawal that they are kissing the snake. At some point you are going to get bit…bad!

Yet it is such a hard pattern to break because it is how we learned to survive as a kid, growing up in a dysfunctional home. Yes, we may have been raised in a Christian home, but it was about rules and performance instead of relationships and grace. Statistics show that 69% of sexual addicts grew up in a rigid, disengaged home; a great definition of such a home is an uptight evangelical home. As a result, they learned to be a loner. They frequently take on what I call the "Rambo" mentality. It is important to realize that Rambo was basically an idiot, a figment of Hollywood fantasies. He was such a loner that he would have lasted about ten seconds on the battlefield. And I don't know where they found all those dumb North Vietnamese for his movies. I never met one in combat who was dumb; they always operated in combat teams. Therefore, the **Small Group Guidelines**, the **Memo of Understanding,** and the **Covenant to Contend** are going to be essential tools in the challenge to breaking isolation and increasing your situational awareness. These tools our your spiritual survival vest when you find yourself in the weeds, fighting for your soul against the raging urges to act out again. They will keep you connected, alive, and eventually a victor in the battle to come out of the jungle of sexual addiction.

## THE NAVIGATIONAL COMPASS (YOUR COMMITMENT TO CHANGE)

When you are dealing with addictive behaviors, there is no such thing as standing still or maintaining the status quo. You are either working towards restoration or falling back into addiction. Failing to plan your next move forward is planning for relapse.

In the last twenty minutes of group time each week, you will need to complete a Commitment to Change for the week. This commitment will help further your restoration or address a challenge that you know you will be facing. If you are struggling with inappropriate Internet use, your commitment may be that you will install a filtering and accountability app. Perhaps you have the challenge of going on a business trip alone. What boundaries and accountability can you put in place as you prepare for the trip?

## THE FASTER SCALE/PHONE CALLS (YOUR FLIGHT HELMET)

The FASTER Scale is a tool for identifying relapse patterns and high risk scenarios. It helps us identify areas in our lives that are causing destructive problems. Each week, choose at least three days when you will commit to calling another group member. Before each call, review the FASTER Scale and identify how far down the scale you have been since the last call or group meeting, based on the emotions and behaviors you identify with. During your call, answer the following questions relating to where you are on the FASTER Scale:

- How does it affect you? How do you act/feel?
- How does it affect the important people in your life?
- Why do you do this? What is the benefit for you?
- What do you need to do to get back to restoration?
- How are you doing on your commitment to change?

## THE DOUBLE BIND (YOUR "G" SUIT)

The "G" suit helps you to out-think your opponent by helping to keep your head in the game. The Double Bind does the same thing in our battle with sexual bondage. It will help you to face your deepest and most profound fears and more importantly, to conquer those fears.

When I need to change a behavior, I would:

1. Identify the behavior I want to change.
2. Ask myself, "If I give up this behavior, what will happen?"
3. Ask myself, "What would I be feeling and thinking in that moment?"
4. Ask myself, "If I don't change this behavior, what will continue to happen?"
5. Ask myself, "What would I be feeling and thinking in that moment?"

If I need to stop procrastinating, the double bind would look like this:

1. Procrastinating
2. If I give up procrastinating, I will have to do a task that I fear I would fail.
3. I would feel embarrassed and ashamed. I would probably get angry at myself and the person who is compelling me to do the task to begin with.
4. If I don't change, I will be stuck right here.
5. I will constantly feel the dread of the unfinished task, and this would follow me wherever I go, whatever I do. I think I would feel depressed, and it might lead me back into my addictions.

The Double Bind tool allows you to grow in your internal awareness of what drives you. It will help you when you implement the FASTER Scale to your day.

## THE PURE DESIRE GROUP (YOUR SURVIVAL VEST)

Your survival vest is your Pure Desire group. Your group will be extremely important in your healing process. You will need the group to survive the powerful nature of your sexual bondage.

In our bondage, we have had both behavior and thought-life secrets. We have tried to survive by protecting our secrets that are threatening to us because they make us vulnerable. We tend to go "Rambo" and try to survive on our own. Ultimately, our solo act does not work. Yes, Rambo is big and powerful. Yes, he did not start the "war," but he was willing to settle for merely existing and being left alone. I hope that you are not willing to settle for that. Life is so much more than existing!

In order to experience deep and healthy healing and restoration you will need to be a member of a Pure Desire group. This group will consist of men who are in a similar battle to yours. To be sure, they are imperfect, and some of them are struggling. But, you will learn to love these men, celebrate with them, and value this group. These are the men who will have your back and who will go to war with you as you oppose your sexual bondage that has wounded you and those you love.

Once you identify the change or challenge, you need to understand the Double Bind. Changes and challenges always have a Double Bind. Change is not free; it always costs you something.  Perhaps your Double Bind is that if you act out on the business trip, you will be further hurting your wife and family, while piling on more shame and guilt. However, if you don't act out, you will have to embrace the pain of loneliness and the stress of meeting with clients all day. You will have to find a healthy way to unwind. You have to give up the familiar comfort of using pornography to numb out. Once you have identified the Double Bind, you need to create a specific plan of what you will do. You might choose to leave the TV and Internet off when you get to the hotel. Making your calls while you are at the hotel is also a great way to allow your group to support you. Record your plan and communicate to your group members what question(s) they can ask when you make your calls to know that you are following your Commitment to Change.

## OVERVIEW

Spend at least thirty minutes each day working through the homework, making calls, reading the weekly devotional, evaluating your FASTER Scale, or completing your Group Check-in. Below is an example schedule for completing the work in a typical week.

| | |
|---|---|
| **Tuesday** | Went to group |
| **Wednesday** | Completed the reading for Pillar Two: Lesson Three |
| **Thursday** | Worked through the FASTER Scale, called Joe to talk about the Double Bind related to Speeding Up |
| **Friday** | Read Devotion, completed the SWORD Drill |
| **Saturday** | Worked through the FASTER Scale, called Steve, answered Lesson Three questions |
| **Sunday** | Worked through the FASTER Scale, called Tim, finished Lesson Three homework |
| **Monday** | Filled out the Group Check-in |

## HOMEWORK

In order to truly renew your mind, plan to do homework 30 minutes each day, rather than doing it all at one sitting or at the last minute before group. If you are married, your wife will be looking for change in your behavior. Working on your Pure Desire homework each day will give her hope.

## GROUP STRUCTURE

Each group session is two hours and accommodates the **40-20-60 plan**:

### 40 MINUTES

The first 40 minutes provides time for each person to share their behavior from the previous week. The purpose of the report is to help men become more aware of the addictive cycle and healing processes, and the affect they have in their lives. The tools we use to help quantify and review are the **FASTER Relapse Awareness Scale** and **FASTER Exercise** from *The Genesis Process* by Michael Dye.

### 60 MINUTES

The next 60 minutes are prearranged for discussing the reading portion of the workbook lesson and homework that was assigned the previous week. If you do not have your FASTER Scale and homework completed, you are welcome to attend group as long as incomplete homework does not become a pattern. However, if you do not complete your homework, you may not share.

### 20 MINUTES

The last 20 minutes are used to create a weekly relapse prevention plan. During this time, each man shares his **Commitment to Change** plan and arrangements to **contact three group members** for accountability during the coming week (which should be completed before group), speaking honestly how they are doing with their commitments.

# FASTER RELAPSE AWARENESS SCALE

Adapted from the Genesis Process by Michael Dye (www.genesisprocess.org)

Find the worksheet in the *Seven Pillars of Freedom Journal* or at puredesire.org > About > Resources.

**RESTORATION – (Accepting life on God's terms, with trust, grace, mercy, vulnerability and gratitude)** No current secrets; working to resolve problems; identifying fears and feelings; keeping commitments to meetings, prayer, family, church, people, goals, and self; being open and honest, making eye contact; increasing in relationships with God and others; true accountability.

**CIRCLE EACH BEHAVIOR IN RESTORATION THAT YOU HAVE EXPERIENCED IN THE LAST WEEK.**
This is where we want to live. This is a place where we all have glimpses, but in our sin nature we only tend to get glimpses of living life where we trust God and not what our internal or external circumstances tell us. Restoration is where we want to live our lives, trusting God and trusting those people who are closest to us. When we are not trusting God and the significant people in our life, this will start us down the FASTER Relapse Awareness Scale.

. . . . . . . . . . . . . . . . . . . . . . . . . . . . . . . . . . . . . . . . . . . . . . . . . . . . . . . . . . . . . . . . . . . . . . . . . . . . . . . . . . . . . . . . . . . . . . . .

**FORGETTING PRIORITIES – (Start believing the present circumstances and moving away from trusting God. Denial; flight; a change in what's important; how you spend your time, energy, and thoughts)** Secrets; less time/energy for God, meetings, church; avoiding support and accountability people; superficial conversations; sarcasm; isolating; changes in goals; obsessed with relationships; breaking promises & commitments; neglecting family; preoccupation with material things, TV, computers, entertainment; procrastination; lying; over confidence; bored; hiding money; image management; seeking to control situations and other people.

**❍ Here in Forgetting Priorities, circle anything that you have experienced in the last seven days.** Here is where we make the big slip; we start trusting what circumstances are saying to us rather than trusting God. Take your time and think back to what has happened over the last week. Forgetting Priorities sets the stage for the entire FASTER Scale. Here "image management" is big. You don't want others to see you as you are, so you seek to convince them by actions and words that you are doing better than you really are. As an example, I tend to procrastinate through watching TV or following my favorite sports teams on the computer. In any case, I have lost my sense of purpose in the moment and I am wanting to avoid the "pit" in the middle of my stomach.

It's important to note that you don't go from one category to another, rather they are like building blocks where you add one block to another. So, here you will add some of the symptoms of Anxiety to Forgetting Priorities. This means that when I am in any of the categories below Forgetting Priorities I will show symptoms of each category I have been in within the last week.

**❓ What does Forgetting Priorities look like for you usually?**

. . . . . . . . . . . . . . . . . . . . . . . . . . . . . . . . . . . . . . . . . . . . . . . . . . . . . . . . . . . . . . . . . . . . . . . . . . . . . . . . . . . . . . . . . . . . . . . .

*Forgetting priorities will lead to the inclusion of:*

**ANXIETY – (A growing background noise of undefined fear; getting energy from emotions)**
Worry, using profanity, being fearful; being resentful; replaying old, negative thoughts; perfectionism; judging other's motives; making goals and lists that you can't complete; mind reading; fantasy, codependent, rescuing; sleep problems, trouble concentrating, seeking/creating drama; gossip; using over-the-counter medication for pain, sleep or weight control; flirting.

Here we are in Anxiety. I haven't been doing what I believe I should be doing, I have started to avoid, and it begins to eat at me because I am not doing what I am supposed to be doing. That is anxiety. Think back over the last week, do you identify with any of these symptoms? Often, I find myself being perfectionistic (image management again!) and in my anxiety, I can be resentful and judgmental.

**❯ Circle what you have experienced this week in Anxiety.**

**❓ What does Anxiety usually look like for you?**

..................................................................................................................................

*When we are in Anxiety, we don't like what we are feeling, so we seek to escape by Speeding Up.*

**SPEEDING UP – (Trying to outrun the anxiety which is usually the first sign of depression)** Super busy and always in a hurry (finding good reason to justify the work); workaholic; can't relax; avoiding slowing down; feeling driven; can't turn off thoughts; skipping meals; binge eating (usually at night); overspending; can't identify own feelings/needs; repetitive negative thoughts; irritable; dramatic mood swings; too much caffeine; over exercising; nervousness; difficulty being alone and/ or with people; difficulty listening to others; making excuses for having to "do it all."

Speeding Up is about avoiding and attempting to make yourself feel better. If you keep yourself busy enough, you hope to avoid the feelings of anxiety. In the end it doesn't work, but we try it anyway.

**❯ Circle the behaviors of the last week in Speeding Up that you can identify with.**

This is a good spot to say two things:

1. Some weeks you won't go far down the FASTER Scale. The issue is just learning to be honest. The first person you deceive will always be yourself. If you are honest—you can accept where you are on the scale and take steps to get back to Restoration.

2. Remember that you have used these behaviors for years to protect yourself. Don't beat yourself up. Offer the same grace to yourself that you might offer to someone else who is struggling.

**❓ What does Speeding Up usually look like for you?**

..................................................................................................................................

**TICKED OFF – (Getting adrenaline high on anger and aggression)** Procrastination causing crisis in money, work, and relationships; increased sarcasm; black and white (all or nothing) thinking; feeling alone; nobody understands; overreacting, road rage; constant resentments; pushing others away; increasing isolation; blaming; arguing; irrational thinking; can't take criticism; defensive; people avoiding you; needing to be right; digestive problems; headaches; obsessive (stuck) thoughts; can't forgive; feeling superior; using intimidation.

This is one we probably all know, being Ticked Off. Do you tend to be angry at circumstances? Others? Yourself? Maybe you are like me and, at times, it is all of the above.

**❯ Circle what you have experienced this week in Ticked Off.**

**❓ What does Ticked Off most often look like for you?**

..................................................................................................................................

**EXHAUSTED – (Loss of physical and emotional energy; coming off the adrenaline high, and the onset of depression)** Depressed; panicked; confused; hopelessness; sleeping too much or too little; can't cope; overwhelmed; crying for "no reason;" can't think; forgetful; pessimistic; helpless; tired; numb; wanting to run; constant cravings for old coping behaviors; thinking of using sex, drugs, or alcohol; seeking old unhealthy people & places; really isolating; people angry with you; self abuse; suicidal thoughts; spontaneous crying; no goals; survival mode; not returning phone calls; missing work; irritability; no appetite.

Does Exhaustion feel familiar? Here, our ability to resist the urges to be angry are compromised. After all, we are carrying a heavy load of nearly every category of the FASTER Scale: Forgetting Priorities, Anxiety, Speeding Up, Ticked Off, and now Exhausted.

➲ **Circle what you have experienced this week in Exhausted.**

❷ **What does Exhaustion usually look like for you?**

..........................................................................................................................

**RELAPSE – (Returning to the place you swore you would never go again. Coping with life on your terms. You sitting in the driver's seat instead of God.)** Giving up and giving in; out of control; lost in your addiction; lying to yourself and others; feeling you just can't manage without your coping behaviors, at least for now. The result is the reinforcement of shame, guilt and condemnation; and feelings of abandonment and being alone.

Relapse is that place you promised yourself and others that you would never go to again. We feel defeated, guilty, ashamed, discouraged, powerless, and fed up.

➲ **Circle what you have experienced this week in Relapse.**

❷ **What does Relapse usually look like for you?**

..........................................................................................................................

Let's talk about getting off the FASTER Scale. First, let's get this right; you can't climb back up the scale. Each category drives you down the scale. The solution is simple in concept, but not so simple to implement. Getting off the FASTER Scale requires you to start doing the behaviors and expressing the attitudes reflected in Restoration. Choosing to do this will often require you to go against the emotions and feelings of the moment.

We will teach you how to use the Double Bind as a way to move toward restoration and God. It's about choosing to do what is right and bringing yourself to a place where you are willing to risk trusting God. It will also require you to be vulnerable with your loved ones and members of your Pure Desire Group. You can't do this by yourself. I know this goes against the pattern of how you have sought to win this battle, but take it from thousands of other men who have battled and finally won the victory: Embrace God and trust the men in your group!

## USING THE FASTER SCALE

You will use the FASTER Scale tool every week. I encourage you to fill it out, based on the reality of your last week, and do it on the evening before your group or on the morning your group meets. Give it some time, not a five minute "same ol' same ol'!" Choose to process what you have experienced in the last week and this will be a great tool for you and your Flight Helmet for many years to come.

# COMMITMENT TO CHANGE WEEKLY WORKSHEET

Complete within 24 hours of your next group meeting.

1. What area do you need to change or what challenge are you facing next week?

2. What will it cost you emotionally if you do change? What fear will you have to face?

3. What will it cost you if you don't change?

4. What is your plan to maintain your restoration regarding these changes?

5. Who will keep you accountable to this commitment?

6. What are the details of your accountability for this week? What questions should they ask you?

# SAFETY PLAN/RELAPSE PREVENTION

Just as the G suit is indispensable in combat when flying against the enemy's maneuvers, a Safety Plan is paramount in winning the battle of sexual addiction.

**If you are married:** within the crucible of domestic difficulties called marriage, daily pressures, stressors, and conflicts are a part of life. Before joining a Pure Desire group, sexual acting out was a way of medicating these stressors. But now, as you learn to walk in sobriety, the Safety Plan will give you and your spouse a new tool that will help transform the addictive and codependent (requiring the approval of another for their self-worth, identity, and fulfillment) lifestyle you have created in your marriage. Group leaders report less relapse and a higher rate of sobriety among men whose wives have graciously developed an approach that encourages her husband—and accommodates her safety—through natural consequences if relapse occurs.

The natural consequences your wife is encouraged to create are not meant to be punitive in any way. Rather, they are designed to 1) help her feel safe and learn to communicate without becoming reactionary and 2) help you understand there are natural consequences if you chose to act out.

**If you are single:** For a married man, it's easy to see the hurt that his wife and family experiences when he confesses a relapse, but for a single guy, it's not that simple. In most cases, single men have little experiential understanding of how their sin affects others. It is crucial that you begin to associate your sin with natural consequences.

This describes our Heavenly Father's loving relationship with us, His children:

> 5 *"My son, do not regard lightly the discipline of the Lord, Nor faint when you are reproved by Him; 6 For those whom the Lord loves He disciplines, And He scourges every son whom He receives."* 7 *It is for discipline that you endure; God deals with you as with sons; for what son is there whom his father does not discipline? 8 But if you are without discipline, of which all have become partakers, then you are illegitimate children and not sons. 9 Furthermore, we had earthly fathers to discipline us, and we respected them; shall we not much rather be subject to the Father of spirits, and live? 10 For they disciplined us for a short time as seemed best to them, but He disciplines us for our good, so that we may share His holiness. 11 All discipline for the moment seems not to be joyful, but sorrowful; yet to those who have been trained by it, afterwards it yields the peaceful fruit of righteousness.*
> Hebrews 12:5-11 (NASB)

The following are Safety Plan examples—one for a married man and the other for a single man:

# SAFETY PLAN WORKSHEET EXAMPLES
## IF YOU ARE MARRIED

My desired outcome in writing this safety plan is the restoration of my marriage. In order for my wife to feel that her heart is safe with me, I need to be committed to sexual purity in my marriage. My wife needs to see me working on my health and recovery.

### STEP ONE

**Specific actions for my own healing:** Write specific goals or objectives for the actions you will take to work toward your healing. Think carefully and make them specific to your needs.

*Example: I need to focus on my own restoration. I can use some or all of the following strategies:*

Every person's situation is unique when facing the issues surrounding porn/sex addiction. The following list is included only to give you ideas to help you put together your own list; choose the steps and strategies that are most appropriate and helpful to your life and situation.

- Attend a small group for men that understands addiction and healing.
- Commit to the process of identifying and healing root issues in my life (trauma, anger, addictions, helplessness, etc.).
- Commit to daily prayer and scripture reading.
- Fill out the FASTER relapse awareness scale and subsequent accountability card and give it to two people who will support me in the healing process.
- Begin/continue classes or counseling for healing of childhood wounds.
- Commit to sharing with an accountability partner what I've studied and applied, as well as insights gained throughout the week.
- Seek counseling for current personal, sexual addiction, and/or marriage issues if needed.
- Commit to reading healing-oriented literature about shame issues, boundaries, codependency, trauma, etc.
- Commit to personal journaling.
- Arrange for STD testing if infidelity has occurred.
- For my own spiritual growth, I will make a commitment to a local church.
- Undergo a polygraph test.
- I can also _____

### STEP TWO

If your wife is in a Pure Desire Betrayal & Beyond group, she will be developing a Safety Plan—in Pillar Six—that will include goals and objectives she needs to see in you on your road to health and recovery. She will attempt to cover all possibilities, making the list applicable to your situation. Her intention in writing and implementing her Safety Plan is not punitive. In order for your wife to feel safe, she needs to believe that you are committed to sexual purity in your marriage. She is encouraged to use her Safety Plan to help eliminate her temptation to behave like a "sheriff" during your recovery. Yet, she will be direct and transparent about the actions she needs to see in you. This tool provides protection for you, your wife, and your family.

**Keep in Mind:** In step one, you developed a Safety Plan for yourself. When your wife gets to the point in her own recovery where she has created a Safety Plan, you will replace your Safety Plan with hers. You created a Safety Plan up front to provide guard rails and accountability during the initial stage of your recovery. However, when she presents her Safety Plan to you, that will become the Safety Plan for your marriage: the plan for you and your wife. If your wife is not in a Betrayal & Beyond group, the Safety Plan you created for yourself—with your group—will continue to provide parameters and accountability for you.

Every person's situation is unique. The following is provided only to give you an example of what your wife's Safety Plan may include. Her Safety Plan may look like the following example:

***Example of Your Wife's Safety Plan:*** *I (your wife) need to focus on my own restoration. You are responsible for your own healing. I need to see the following actions which will demonstrate to me that you are making a commitment to your own healing and to the healing of our marriage.*

- Attend men's Pure Desire group weekly. The only reason to miss a group is serious illness of yourself or a close family member, or immediate family obligation. Any absence from group needs to be discussed with me prior to missing the group.
- Complete the FASTER relapse awareness scale daily and sharing those results with a male accountability partner.
- Call your accountability partner at least once per week and/or any time you start sliding down the FASTER Scale towards relapse.
- Abstain from masturbation.
- Abstain from viewing pornography in any form.
- Abstain from viewing suggestive material in any form.
- Abstain from going to strip clubs or 'gentlemen's clubs.'
- Abstain from going to massage parlors.
- Have no private communication in any form (phone, text, instant messaging, etc) with any other female, other than immediate family members.
- Allow me access to any email or Facebook accounts at any time.
- Agree to putting Covenant Eyes/OpenDNS on all computers or devices that access the Internet.
- Commitment to daily Bible study together with me.
- Commit to attending church weekly with me.
- Commit to weekly date nights with me.
- Commit to daily prayer time together with me.
- Commit to at least five sessions of marriage counseling with me.
- Commit to attending a marriage workshop with me.
- Undergo a polygraph test.
- Other: _____

If there has been infidelity:

- Agree to not contact the other woman by any method (email, phone, text, Facebook, instant message, postal service, gifts, etc.), accept any contact from her, or respond to any contact from her.
- Arrange for STD testing.

**Actions During a Sexual Addiction Relapse:** Also included in your wife's Safety Plan will be consequences that will be imposed in the event of your relapse. The consequences are designed to have a positive effect on your restoration. They are not effective if they appear to be an empty threat. The goal of this part of the tool is to provide a relevant consequence to your situation and design it to be painful enough to get your attention. The "pain level" is intended to increase. A consequence for viewing porn on the home computer might be that you are required to disconnect/remove any access to the Internet on your home computer. Her Safety Plan, for example, may include the following:

*Example: If you relapse, there will be a consequence. When your relapse is disclosed to me, I may use a variety of strategies in order to protect myself and my children without falling back into codependent behavior. I can use some or all of the following strategies:*

- I will ask you to sleep in another room/ on the couch/ on the floor beside our bed for _____ weeks / months until sexual purity has been obtained.

- I will ask you to move out for _____ weeks / months until sexual purity has been re-established.

- I can call _____ for counseling and/ or prayer support.

- I will ask you to call and make an appointment with your counselor, pastor, or healing group leader for advice and accountability.

- If I choose to leave my home, I will go to _____. If I cannot go to the location above, then I can go to _____.

- I can impose a fine of $_____ that will go into my personal spending fund.

- Other: _____

**Bottom Line:** Your wife may also include a "bottom line" statement in her Safety Plan. For example, she may state that "if you have an affair with another woman, I will initiate separation. In her Betrayal & Beyond group, she will be encouraged to take time to process this part of her Safety Plan and not act emotionally. If a separation is required by her Safety Plan, the purpose of this time would be to allow time to cool down and think carefully, with consideration over what might be the best next steps. Her Safety Plan may include the following:

*Example: If you have an affair with another woman, I will need to take time to process the betrayal.*

*You will need to leave our home for a minimum of three months. At the end of that three months, we will discuss the future of our marriage, which may need to be with the support of a marriage counselor.*

*If you are still involved with another woman at the end of the three months and have not show commitment to the marriage, I will seek counseling advice and initiate divorce proceedings.*

## STATEMENT OF HOPE

The key purpose of your wife's Safety Plan is restoration. Above all, remember that the goal is to rebuild trust and restore your marriage. This is the message she will be hearing throughout the development and implementation of her Safety Plan. She will be encouraged to share this with you as she creates her plan. For example, she may include a statement like this:

*Example: Restoration of our marriage is my desire. I believe God brought us together and that He has a Divine Purpose for our life together. It is my greatest wish that we are able to re-establish trust and intimacy within our marriage. I am hopeful that you have the same desire and that this safety plan will help both of us heal and move forward.*

## SIGN THE CONTRACT

In conclusion, your wife's Safety Plan is designed as a contract. We recommend you both sign and date the agreement. Your spouse needs to agree to follow through with the consequences if needed, and you need to agree to follow through with the commitments. The point of having it all written in contract form is to take a lot of the emotion out of the implementation process. Should relapse occur, you don't have to argue, discuss, or fight. The Safety Plan delineates your next steps. Keep in mind that this is a "living document." It will change and develop as you both change, develop, and find healing.

Your wife's Safety Plan may conclude with the following statement:

**Example:** *By signing this statement, we both agree to uphold the commitments and follow the consequences stated within.*

## IF YOU ARE SINGLE

Before joining a Pure Desire group, sexual acting out was a way of medicating pain and stress in life. But now, as you learn to walk in sobriety, natural consequences will give you a new tool to help in this battle for sexual purity. Implementing consequences is not a way of experiencing punishment for sin or paying penance. Christ bore all of our sin on the cross and there is no wrath of God or condemnation left for us who have surrendered our lives to Christ. Natural consequences are simply a way of experiencing and associating our sin with the natural pain that it causes others and ourselves. You will begin to take your healing more seriously when you know there will be natural consequences if you relapse.

**Desired Outcome:** State what you are trying to accomplish by writing and enforcing the consequences. State it in positive terms.

**Example:** *My desired outcome in writing these consequences and sharing it with my group is complete healing and recovery from my sex addiction.*

## STEP ONE

**Specific actions for my healing:** Write specific goals or objectives for the actions you will take to work toward your healing. Think carefully and make them specific to your needs.

**Example:** *To focus energy on my own restoration, I can use some or all of the following strategies:*

Every person's situation is unique. The following list is included only to give you ideas to help you put together your own list; choose the steps and strategies that are most appropriate and helpful to your life and situation.

- Upgrading accountability software to a filtering software
- Restrict Internet access during specific hours of the day
- Internet use only when accountability person is present
- Discontinue WiFi service at home
- Donate money that I would normally use for entertainment

At this time, many of the consequences for your choices may not be obvious, but they are there. In reality, our sin affects the people around us. If you take advantage of this tool, you will begin to see the consequences associated with your choices, and see your desire for freedom and health outweigh your previous destructive desires.

Your passion to pursue your God-given calling will overpower any former desire. The pain you previously sought to avoid will fall to the background as you see your purpose and participation in God's kingdom enhance and develop.

# GROUP GUIDELINES

These group guidelines were designed to create a safe environment for open and honest conversations during group meetings. Read and discuss the following guidelines as a group, including when anyone new joins the group:

**Confidentiality**—what is said in the group is not shared outside the group.

**Self-focus**—speak only for yourself and avoid giving advice.

**Limit Sharing**—give everyone a chance to share.

**Respect Others**—let everyone find his own answers.

**Regular Attendance**—let your leader or co-leader know if you cannot attend a meeting.

**Commitment to Accountability**—make a minimum of three contacts a week. If you have relapsed in the last week, then a daily contact is recommended.

**Listen Respectfully**—no side conversations.

**Take Ownership and Be Responsible**—if you feel uncomfortable with anything, talk with your leader or co-leader, or your small group.

**Stay on the Subject/Questions**—watch those rabbit trails!

**Homework Completion**—allow 20-30 minutes per day to complete your homework. If you don't do your homework, you won't win your battle with healing, and you will not be able to participate when the group is processing their homework.

**Covenant to Contend (CTC)**—the CTC is an open commitment of accountability which states why you have chosen to join a PD small group and what you are committed to do in order to win your battle with sexual addiction. At the bottom of the page you will notice a place for you and one other person to sign and date. This is a public commitment. Read the CTC and ask a member of your group to sign as a witness to your signature.

**Memo of Understanding**—this document indicates that you have read and understand the purpose and parameters of PD groups and the moral and ethical obligations of leaders.

# MEMO OF UNDERSTANDING

***Pure Desire Group Participants:*** *Please read and sign this Memo of Understanding, indicating that you have read and understand the purpose and parameters of Pure Desire groups and the moral and ethical obligations of leaders.*

I understand that every attempt will be made to guard my anonymity and confidentiality in this group, but that anonymity and confidentiality cannot be absolutely guaranteed in a group setting.

- I realize that the group coordinator or leader cannot control the actions of others in the group.
- I realize that confidentiality is sometimes broken accidentally and without malice.

I understand that the group coordinator or leader is morally and ethically obligated to discuss with me any of the following behaviors, and that this may lead to the breaking of confidentiality and/or possibly intervention:

- I communicate anything that may be interpreted as a threat to self-inflict physical harm.
- I communicate an intention to harm another person.
- I reveal ongoing sexual or physical abuse.
- I exhibit an impaired mental state.

I understand that the Pure Desire group coordinator or leader may be a mandatory reporter to authorities of sexual conduct that includes minor children, the elderly or the disabled.

I have been advised that the consequences for communicating the above types of information may include reports to the proper authorities—the police, suicide units or children's protective agencies, as well as to any potential victims.

I further acknowledge that if I am on probation and/or parole and I engage in wrongful behavior in violation of my parole/probation, part of my healing/recovery may include notifying the appropriate authorities.

I understand that this is a Christ-centered group that integrates recovery tools with the Bible and prayer, and that all members may not be of my particular church background. I realize that the Bible may be discussed more (or less) than I would like it to be.

I understand that this is a support group and not a therapy group and that the coordinator/leader is qualified by "life experience" and not by professional training as a therapist or counselor. The coordinator's or leader's role in this group is to create a climate where healing may occur, to support my personal work towards recovery, and to share his own experience, strength and hope.

**Name** (please print) _Brian E. Vélez_  **Date** _09/2/2019_

**Signature** _Bn E. Véley_

**Witness: Pure Desire Group Leader Name** _____

**Pure Desire Group Leader Signature** _____

> ***Let God work! He will not rest until the work He has started in you is completed!***

# COVENANT TO CONTEND

## THE COURAGEOUS FIGHT FOR HEALTHY SEXUALITY

There is a battle going on within me. As much as it pains me to admit it, that battlefield is my sexuality. I realize the outcome of this battle not only holds my life in its hands, but the lives of those I love and care for. I now choose to participate in the battle for godly character and integrity, not only for my soul but also for my family, friends, brothers and sisters in Christ, and above all else, Almighty God.

I am beginning to understand I cannot win this battle myself. I am coming to see the biblical truth that "we are members one of another." Therefore, I surrender to God's wisdom, turn to the leadership of the church, and submit myself to the process of the renewing of my mind.

### THINGS I CAN DO:

- Attend a small group weekly.
- Complete the Commitment to Change Pure Desire Weekly Group Check-In each week.
- God's values supersede mine; therefore, I will contend to live life on His terms instead of my own or the culture around me.
- Pay close attention to: what I look at; what I listen to; what I set my mind on.
- Take responsibility for my thoughts and actions.
- Verbally describe my feelings.
- Make contact with a group member or members at least three times between small group meetings.

### I CAN ACCEPT:

- Healing is a miraculous process over time.
- Healing requires feeling the pain and learning from it.
- I am very capable of retreating back into the addictive lifestyle.
- A lapse does not stop the healing process, but it will have consequences.
- I have become skilled at lying to others and myself.
- I do not really live in isolation; my choices do affect others.
- My secrecy keeps me in bondage to my sin.

### I WILL COMMIT TO:

- A willingness to change—and following through with my plans.
- Total confidentiality! I discuss only my experiences outside the group.
- Rigorous honesty with God, my small group, myself, and eventually my friends and family.
- Building my knowledge base (books, CD's, DVD's, videos, & seminars).
- Reading Scripture and praying.
- A biblical standard of sexual purity in my life.
- A goal of moving toward sobriety that is living life God's way.

Signature _Bn E. Vélzy_ Date _9/2/2019_

Witness _____

Now you know the structure of the group, the guidelines for group operation, and you have made a commitment to contend for your healing. This is an epic journey of transformation and we are excited for your transformation and healing. Your survival vest is intact and you are ready to go! **Let the journey begin!**

# BREAKING THROUGH DENIAL

# LESSON ONE

## DIRECTION DETERMINES DESTINATION

I climbed into the cockpit and I was pumped. This was my first solo flight in a jet trainer. I would fly much more powerful aircraft later on, true weapons of war, but this was my first experience of high-speed solo flight. Like the first time you make love to a woman, you never forget it. I had been looking forward to this moment for years. Little did I realize the potential disaster that might lie ahead.

The weather was marginal for a solo flight by an inexperienced pilot like me but in my opinion I was invincible! This was a chance for me to prove just how good I was. Shortly after takeoff, I was in the "soup." As I dodged in and out of the cloud layers, it didn't take me long to lose track of where I was headed. No problem, remember I was invincible. And besides that, I was really committed to doing a great job.

I wasn't just committed; I had studied for this flight and I was very sincere about what I was doing. I had also graduated at the top of my basic flight training class.

> ### *Of course all of that doesn't matter when you are headed in the wrong direction.*

Obviously, I am drawing an analogy from the critical lesson that I learned that day many years ago. A lesson that is crystal clear in a physical situation like flying an airplane. Yet we can so easily "miss it" when it comes to our relational, financial, or sexual lives. The lesson: **your direction determines your destination and eventually your destiny in life**.

Your direction—not your commitment or hopes or dreams or eventually your prayers—will determine where you end up in life. That day in the aircraft I eventually suspected I was lost and began to pray. Yet prayer infected with denial doesn't do a bit of good. In this journey of recovery you are beginning you will discover just how deadly denial is and can be in your life. That day years ago, as I wandered through the overcast skies, I had this haunting sense I was headed in the wrong direction. I just wouldn't admit it.

Over the last twenty-five years, I have listened to story after story of men who have crashed and burned in their lives sexually. And all the while because of their love for Christ, there was this growing sense within that something was wrong all the way up to the moment of the crash.

You may have not experienced a horrible crash in your life sexually; instead, it may be more like a sickening sense of never being able to get off the runway of life spiritually. You know you are capable of so much more spiritually. You hunger to soar on the wings of the Spirit to new heights in Christ, but this cycle of masturbation or acting out, shame, and promises to stop continue to keep you chained to the ground. Whether you have gone down in flames or are stuck on the runway of life sexually, this workbook will help you finally get free. I mean really free. Not just six months of sobriety then another repeating of the cycle. I mean really free.

That is not to say it is going to be easy. In fact, it will probably demand more of you emotionally and spiritually than just about anything you have ever done before. For starters, your pain level will probably increase, not decrease. You will finally face the deep pain within that you have been medicating for years. Over 90% of the men I have counseled through the years started their destructive sexual behavior in the early teen years. Therefore, they have been struggling with this issue in their lives for 10, 20, 30 or more years. That is a lot of buried pain.

It takes a courageous man to face the pain he has been running from for so long. The good news is that you will not be alone in facing the pain. The men in your Pure Desire Group will be standing with you as well as facing their own pain. Don't worry about the source of the pain; we will get to that later in the workbook. The one thing you must focus on right now: **it is time to stop denial and face the pain**.

Denial has to stop! It is easy to say but so hard to do. For starters, most men can't see how much denial has clouded their perception of reality through the years. It is like a slow poisoning process. Little by little cover up becomes a way of life. The shame factor is so high as a man of God that it may seem like the only option you have is to lie, and that is a lie from hell.

My flying career would have ended that day if I hadn't done one simple thing—stop my denial. I had to admit to myself that I couldn't figure out where I was. I couldn't just naturally navigate my way back to the airbase. I had to start trusting the instruments right in front of me and stop flying by the seat of my pants. My feelings were lying to me and I needed to face the facts…I was lost! This workbook, in conjunction with the book *Pure Desire,* will become your instrument panel. Between the book and workbook, you will start to see yourself in a whole new way and come to understand the enemy you really have been fighting all these years. And please don't waste any time in making this decision; denial stops today!

I struggled in that plane for a long time. I was too proud to admit I had managed to get myself ridiculously lost despite how brilliant I was. Finally, as the fuel gage began to run down, I admitted the truth of my situation. Time was running out for me. To make a very long and sweat-soaked story short, I ended up landing with only two hundred pounds of fuel. We are talking about a fuel guzzling jet, not your car. That is about enough fuel to taxi to my parking place back on the line and flame out! But even then, denial tried to live on. I didn't tell anyone. The crew refueling the aircraft couldn't believe how empty the tanks were. They informed the commanding officer. I was hunted down and appropriately disciplined. The correction at the time wasn't pleasant, but I grew to treasure the lesson learned.

> *Your direction in life determines your destination and eventually your destiny. Denial can never change that fact no matter how sincere or committed you may be. Remember: Self-control when aroused doesn't come from willpower.*

Your fuel gage in life may be running down because of your sexual behavior. Your marriage may be suffering. Your relationship with Christ may be in the tank. The first step is breaking through denial. Don't wait another moment. You are not getting any younger and your heavenly Father has tremendous blessings ahead for you. However, you will never be able to fully receive those blessings unless you stop trying harder and instead break through denial. Today is the day to drive a stake in the ground and declare to the enemy of your soul that you will not be jerked around any longer! By the grace of God you will break through denial.

Pillar of Freedom One will help you finally get that breakthrough! What are the next steps? Remember this truth, breakthrough doesn't come into your life by some sudden massive change. **Breakthrough comes because you stay headed in the right direction for a sustained period of time.**

# SEXUAL ADDICTION SCREENING TEST (SAST) SAST—R V2.0

Patrick J. Carnes. © 2008, P. J. Carnes, Sexual Addiction Screening Test – Revised. Test & Scoring information used by permission.

Let's find out where you are actually headed in life by checking on your honesty factor. Below, you will find the **Sexual Addiction Screening Test (SAST-R). Complete that evaluation now.** Although the questions are phrased in the present tense, please answer questions based on your entire life experience. Also notice the cut off scores in each of the categories at the end of the test and transfer your scores to the following chart.

*The Sexual Addiction Screening Test (SAST) is designed to assist in the assessment of sexually compulsive or "addictive" behavior. Developed in cooperation with hospitals, treatment programs, private therapists, and community groups, the SAST provides a profile of responses that help to discriminate between addictive and non-addictive behavior. To complete the test, answer each question by placing a check next to the appropriate yes/no column.*

**1.** YES ___ NO ___ Were you sexually abused as a child or adolescent?

**2.** YES ___ NO ___ Did your parents have trouble with sexual behavior?

**3.** YES ___ NO ___ Do you often find yourself preoccupied with sexual thoughts?

**4.** YES ___ NO ___ Do you feel that your sexual behavior is not normal?

**5.** YES ___ NO ___ Do you ever feel bad about your sexual behavior?

**6.** YES ___ NO ___ Has your sexual behavior ever created problems for you and your family?

**7.** YES ___ NO ___ Have you ever sought help for sexual behavior you did not like?

**8.** YES ___ NO ___ Has anyone been hurt emotionally because of your sexual behavior?

**9.** YES ___ NO ___ Are any of your sexual activities against the law?

**10.** YES ___ NO ___ Have you made efforts to quit a type of sexual activity and failed?

**11.** YES ___ NO ___ Do you hide some of your sexual behaviors from others?

**12.** YES ___ NO ___ Have you attempted to stop some parts of your sexual activity?

**13.** YES ___ NO ___ Have you felt degraded by your sexual behaviors?

**14.** YES ___ NO ___ When you have sex, do you feel depressed afterwards?

**15.** YES ___ NO ___ Do you feel controlled by your sexual desire?

**16.** YES ___ NO ___ Have important parts of your life (such as job, family, friends, leisure activities) been neglected because you were spending too much time on sex?

**17.** YES ___ NO ___ Do you ever think your sexual desire is stronger than you are?

**18.** YES ___ NO ___ Is sex almost all you think about?

**19.** YES ___ NO ___ Has sex (or romantic fantasies) been a way for you to escape your problems?

**20.** YES ___ NO ___ Has sex become the most important thing in your life?

**21.** YES ___ NO ___ Are you in crisis over sexual matters?

**22.** YES ___ NO ___ The Internet has created sexual problems for me.

**23.** YES ___ NO ___ I spend too much time online for sexual purposes.

**24.** YES ___ NO ___ I have purchased services online for erotic purposes (sites for dating, pornography, fantasy and friend finder).

**25.** YES ___ NO ___ I have used the Internet to make romantic or erotic connections with people online.

**26.** YES ___ NO ___ People in my life have been upset about my sexual activities online.

**27.** YES ___ NO ___ I have attempted to stop my online sexual behaviors.

**28.** YES ___ NO ___ I have subscribed to or regularly purchased or rented sexually explicit materials (magazines, videos, books or online pornography).

**29.** YES ___ NO ___ I have been sexual with minors.

**30.** YES ___ NO ___ I have spent considerable time/money on strip clubs/adult bookstores/movie houses.

**31.** YES ___ NO ___ I have engaged prostitutes and escorts to satisfy my sexual needs.

**32.** YES ___ NO ___ I have spent considerable time surfing pornography online.

**33.** YES ___ NO ___ I have used magazines, videos or online pornography even when there was considerable risk of being caught by family who would be upset by my behavior.

**34.** YES ___ NO ___ I have regularly purchased romantic novels or sexually explicit magazines.

**35.** YES ___ NO ___ I have stayed in romantic relationships after they became emotionally abusive.

**36.** YES ___ NO ___ I have traded sex for money or gifts.

**37.** YES ___ NO ___ I have maintained multiple romantic or sexual relationships at the same time.

**38.** YES ___ NO ___ After sexually acting out, I sometimes refrain from all sex for a significant period.

**39.** YES ___ NO ___ I have regularly engaged in sadomasochistic behavior.

**40.** YES ___ NO ___ I visit sexual bath-houses, sex clubs or video/bookstores as part of my regular sexual activity.

**41.** YES ___ NO ___ I have engaged in unsafe or "risky" sex even though I knew it could cause me harm.

**42.** YES ___ NO ___ I have cruised public restrooms, rest areas or parks looking for sex with strangers.

**43.** YES ___ NO ___ I believe casual or anonymous sex has kept me from having more long-term intimate relationships.

**44.** YES ___ NO ___ My sexual behavior has put me at risk for arrest for lewd conduct/public indecency.

**45.** YES ___ NO ___ I have been paid for sex.

## SAST (SEXUAL ADDICTION SCREENING TEST) SCORING

| SCALES | ITEM | CUT-OFF (NUMBER OF "YES" RESPONSES) More than the cut-off number indicates a concern in this area. | HOW MANY "YES" RESPONSES DID I HAVE? |
|---|---|---|---|
| Core Item Scale | 1-20 | 6 or more | |

### SUBSCALES

| | | | |
|---|---|---|---|
| Internet Items | 22-27 | 3 or more | |
| Men's Items | 28-33 | 2 or more | |
| Women's Items | 34-39 | 2 or more | |
| Homosexual Men | 40-45 | 3 or more | |

### ADDICTIVE DIMENSIONS

| | | | |
|---|---|---|---|
| Preoccupation | 3, 18, 19, 20 | 2 or more | |
| Loss of Control | 10, 12, 15, 17 | 2 or more | |
| Relationship Disturbance | 6, 8, 16, 26 | 2 or more | |
| Affect Disturbance | 4, 5, 11, 13, 14 | 2 or more | |

### RELATIVE DISTRIBUTIONS OF ADDICT & NON-ADDICT SAST SCORES

This instrument has been based on screenings of tens of thousands of people. This particular version is a developmental stage revision of the instrument, so scoring may be adjusted with more research. Please be aware that clinical decisions must be made conditionally since final scoring protocols may vary.

A score of 6 or more on the Core Item Scale usually indicates that an individual has an addiction, but this must be confirmed by a trained professional for an official diagnosis.

If your totals exceeded the cut-off scores at any point, see if this Scripture passage doesn't sound and feel familiar.

*6-12 As I stood at the window of my house*
*looking out through the shutters,*
*Watching the mindless crowd stroll by,*
*I spotted a young man without any sense*
*Arriving at the corner of the street where she lived,*
*then turning up the path to her house.*
*It was dusk, the evening coming on,*
*the darkness thickening into night.*
*Just then, a woman met him—*
*she'd been lying in wait for him, dressed to seduce him.*
*Brazen and brash she was,*
*restless and roaming, never at home,*
*Walking the streets, loitering in the mall,*
*hanging out at every corner in town.*

*13-20 She threw her arms around him and kissed him,*
*boldly took his arm and said,*
*"I've got all the makings for a feast—*
*today I made my offerings, my vows are all paid,*
*So now I've come to find you,*
*hoping to catch sight of your face—and here you are!*

*I've spread fresh, clean sheets on my bed,*
*colorful imported linens.*
*My bed is aromatic with spices*
*and exotic fragrances.*
*Come, let's make love all night,*
*spend the night in ecstatic lovemaking!*
*My husband's not home; he's away on business,*
*and he won't be back for a month."*

*21-23 Soon she has him eating out of her hand,*
*bewitched by her honeyed speech.*
*Before you know it, he's trotting behind her,*
*like a calf led to the butcher shop,*
*Like a stag lured into ambush*
*and then shot with an arrow,*
*Like a bird flying into a net*
*not knowing that its flying life is over.*

*Now then, my sons, listen to me;*
*pay attention to what I say.*
*Do not let your heart turn to her ways*
*or stray into her paths.*
*Many are the victims she has brought down;*
*her slain are a mighty throng.*
*Her house is a highway to the grave,*
*leading down to the chambers of death.*
Proverbs 7:6-27 (MSG)

We have discovered that **our direction in life will determine our destination.** The young man described in Proverbs 7 is headed down the highway of denial and being dishonest with himself, which will always leads to an emotional and moral cliff!

The scene in Proverbs 7 is being described by the wisest man of his day. Solomon is looking out the window and sees a young man strutting down the street with testosterone squirting out of both ears. The guy is a moving sexual target. And the woman, porn site, strip club and the prostitutes are irresistible to him. And they know it. He is an easy mark. As Solomon watches he can see clearly what is coming. In fact, everyone around the young man clearly sees what is coming!

I remember sitting in traffic headed north while waiting for the light to change. Everyone around me was getting impatient because of the congestion. Out of the corner of my eye I noticed a brand new Camaro at the corner service station. The gleaming burgundy of the custom paint job still sticks in my mind. It was a classic! The driver was trying to cut across two lanes of jammed traffic and then across a turn lane and head south. Once he pulled in front of me, he was totally blocked by the cars ahead of him from seeing the oncoming traffic he was trying to merge into. I looked up and noticed this truck just ripping down the hill, headed straight our way. Instinctively, I cried out to the driver of the Camaro to STOP. He didn't stop, but pulled directly in the path of the speeding truck. The sound of my fading cry was soon drowned out by the sounds of shattering fiberglass, screeching metal, and exploding glass. The Camaro was totaled!

The guy driving the Camaro was **so blinded by the immediate he couldn't see or sense the obvious.** We have all been there. It seems to be part of being a guy at times. Even Solomon, the wisest of men, ended up with 700 wives and 300 "porcupines" or concubines! That is total insanity! Not only would he have to remember two anniversaries every day, he would have to deal with 700 mothers-in-law! The man was out of his mind! As I said, we have all been there. Testosterone can do that to you.

Years ago Scott Peck uttered a classic one-liner that I come back to time after time in the counseling office:

> *Mental health is a commitment to reality at all costs.*[2]

**Sexual addictions and bondages are sicknesses of escape.** Just like the driver of the Camaro who wanted to escape the confines of the traffic congestion, we can try to escape the pain or loneliness of our lives with a sexual high. That is why the most challenging part of the healing process is acknowledging the fact that we have a problem. **Our struggles with sexual issues have blinded our ability to acknowledge what is real in life.** Once he climbed out of the wreck, the driver of the Camaro was vociferously blaming the truck driver for the problem.

Our sexual bondages usually start because reality is just too much to bear. The Camaro driver found it intolerable that he was going to have to wait. He was desperate to escape the reality he faced. In life, when we escape reality for the briefest moments it can bring a sense of relief. But the problem is that it can become habitual or a lifestyle. That is when addiction becomes our deadly friend, leading us down the highway of denial.

A severe avoidance of reality usually begins early in life. It frequently starts in our family of origin. That is not to blame our parents for our problems, but **if we never understand the defects in the "software" that was downloaded into our brains, we will never have a shot at winning the battle.** Over half of sexual addicts come from rigid, disengaged homes.[3] And some of the most rigid disengaged homes I have ever seen are "Christian" homes that focus on performance and not sinning. Life is always black and white for them. Rules far outnumber any form of relationships. There is only one way of doing things—the right way.

Once the child enters the turbulent times of adolescence there are essentially two options to deal with the pain within: Open rebellion and reaction or quiet compliance with a secret life lurking behind the scenes. Either of these paths can become a deadly environment in which sexual bondages can explode in the person's life. The noose of sexual addiction only tightens because he made a commitment to Christ at some point and now finds himself violating the deepest core beliefs of his life. Welcome to insanity of the most painful kind.

There is only one way out. **You must be honest with yourself.** The direction of your life will determine where you end up in life no matter how much you may want to deny reality. Did you notice the total lack of honesty in Proverbs 7?

❶ What observations did you make about Proverbs 7 as you meditated on it this week? Where are you in Proverbs 7?

_The man in Proverbs 7 was smitten. I need to improve._

❷ When have you been blind to reality in your life like the young man? Share with the group one of your "blind spot" moments in life.

_Blind in trying to find a way out and follow the right path._

❸ What were the lessons from such moments that you learned the hard way?

_Yahweh's way is the best path._

Did you notice the depth of "unreality" found in Proverbs 7, especially in verse 15? The young guy was thinking to himself, "I am so special. I am the man of her dreams. This is amazing; she came out to look for me!"

In the process of being certified as a sexual addiction therapist, I had the opportunity to interview an exotic dancer. She readily admitted to using the exact same approach as the woman in Proverbs 7. She had "special customers" a HUGE number of them. Men whom she told were special. These were the guys who made her lavish lifestyle possible.

Men buy sex for two different reasons. One is the issue of power.[4] Prostitutes in the US are subject to a high level of violence. The second is for pseudo intimacy. The prostitute provides a relationship that isn't demanding or exacting. In other words, it isn't an honest relationship. It isn't real. They provide intercourse without the threat of real intimacy at a price.

The Proverbs 7 woman, whether she is in the flesh or on today's XXX porn site, will lead you down the highway of hell. And you will pay a hellacious price. Notice how Solomon tries to break through the young man's denial. The kid is telling himself he is a rock star and this woman can't get enough of him. This is the best thing that has ever happened to him. And Solomon is crying out, "No, no, No—get real! You are a piece of meat headed to the butcher shop. This thing will tear you apart. You are a proud stag caught in a noose and the more you pull the worse it gets. Then you look up and the hunters from hell surround you with arrows aimed at your heart. This is going to wound you deeply. Like a bird caught in a net that realizes flying is over, your dreams are dying."

Now, some who read these words may feel a mounting sense of grief and shame over what has happened in their lives. You may be asking yourself, "How could I have been so stupid!" Well you are in a room with a bunch of guys who have made similar mistakes. Don't let grief and shame control your life right now.

Later on, we will deal with those adversaries, but **right now your job is to make sure you don't repeat the mistakes of the past.** That means we have to break through the denial structures in our brain. Men who are struggling with sexual issues in their lives have developed an incredible ability to make **excuses** for their behavior such *as:*

- My wife is not sexual enough.
- "I have a high sex drive." (In other words, "I am special or unique.")
- "My wife doesn't understand me."
- "I work hard as a teacher, pastor, accountant, salesmen, or _____; I deserve this release."
- "I don't do it all the time."
- "I can't help myself."

## WHAT ARE THE EXCUSES YOU HAVE USED?

- List all the excuses you have used—the reasons you believed or still believe you don't belong in a Pure Desire group.
- Then do the hard part! Break through the denial by listing the painful truth about your excuses and behavior.
- Use the table provided.

# EXCUSE/TRUTH TABLE

| EXCUSE – DENIAL STRUCTURE | THE TRUTH ABOUT THAT EXCUSE AND YOUR BEHAVIOR |
|---|---|
| 1.      6. | I can break free |
| 2. | |
| 3. | |
| 4. | |
| 5. | |
| 6. | |

## ✐ ASSIGNMENTS FOR NEXT TIME

❶ Be ready to share your Excuse/Truth Table with the group.

❷ Continue meditating on Proverbs 7.

❸ Read *Pure Desire* Chapter 1.

❹ **Very Important!** Read "A Sexy Brain" in Appendix One. Be prepared to share your experience with the Family Table exercise.

# LESSON TWO

## POINTS OF POWERLESSNESS

*And now, son, listen to me,*
*pay attention to the words I have to say:*
*do not let your heart stray into her ways,*
*or wander into her paths;*
*she has done so many to death,*
*and the strongest have all been her victims.*
*Her house is the way to Sheol,*
*the descent to the courts of death.*
Proverbs 7:24-27 (NJB)

**❯ Begin this lesson by reading aloud Proverbs 7:24-27**

Ever been in the grip of something you were powerless to control? I remember being caught in an inverted spin in a fighter aircraft. Suddenly the plane departed (pilot lingo for "no longer in control") and flipped upside down. I was slammed into the canopy. Despite the fact I had securely strapped myself into the aircraft, I was now hanging upside down several inches off the ejection seat in which I had been so firmly seated seconds ago. If I ejected I would break my back.

The aircraft was spinning like a competitive ice skater, but totally out of control. The severe negative G load was making it difficult for me to see, but I could discern the altimeter was unwinding like a scared cat! I was trying every trick I could think of…cross controls…full forward stick…full back stick…full rudder input. All of my efforts only seemed to make the spin tighter!

Then the magic moment came…I let go of the stick and suddenly the aircraft pulled out of the spin. I would sport some blood shot eyes from that experience. The negative G load had broken several blood vessels in my eyes. But it became an incredible learning event for me. After the flight I somehow managed to stop my legs from shaking and calmly walk back to the Ready Room.

My wingman and I were trying to develop a maneuver to counter a particular type of Soviet aircraft we had to face. The one thing we knew about the plane we were flying was that it had an awesome roll rate. It could out roll anything in the sky. That day I was experimenting with high roll rates at high speeds and extreme nose attitudes. So I pulled the nose rapidly up into a severe attitude then rolled the aircraft violently. That is when it "went south" on me. In the Ready Room we opened the *NATOPS Manual*[5] that is the "bible" on how to fly the aircraft. After only a few minutes of reading we found the following safety warning.

> **WARNING…**
> The aircraft will become unstable at high angles of attack at high speed when violent aileron input takes place. Under no circumstances should the aircraft be placed in such severe attitudes that an inverted spin will ensue and the pilot may not be able to recover.

There it was in military black and white visible for anyone who would take the time to read it. It was a Homer Simpson moment! My testosterone had gotten the best of me once again.

The young man in Proverbs is in a flat spin from which he will never recover. And many a man, young and old, has gone into the same spin sexually. Solomon's words in Proverbs are so cogent and clear, just like the warning I didn't bother to read, *"She has done so many to death."*

You think you are unique, special or entitled. But wake up, kid; you are headed down an eight-lane freeway where millions of guys have gone before you. Right off a cliff! It is important to understand that Solomon is not castigating women. He is creating a personification of sexual addiction through the Proverbs 7 woman.

After counseling for nearly three decades I have lost count of the number of times I have said to someone, "I bet when that happened she said this? And then you probably said that and she exploded." The guy will look at me in amazement and say, "Yeah, she did. How did you know that?" That is usually when I will lean over and tell him the obvious truth that he can't see. "You are not the first to travel down this highway, my friend. Sexual addiction is a well-worn road. Millions of guys have spun out of control just like you."

The reason we can be so blind to the highway we are on is that there is something in that "high-way" that has a deep emotional appeal to us: The dopamine high of masturbating, the buzz of another conquest or the thrill of doing something that you know is wrong or dangerous. It is all about medicating the pain deep within. We are so fixated on that deep pain that we don't even know we are on the highway. At some point you have to push the "pause" button and ask the question. "Is this the path I really want to be on in life? The path I am on will determine where I ultimately end up in my life. Is this where I really want to go?" Those are hard questions to ask because we can get so caught up in the here and now.

> *Your Pure Desire group will be your lifeline to sanity. New information alone will not help without a new community to get you off the insane highway you are on. Only friends who are fighting the same battle can help you get that noose off your soul!*

So how do we get off this highway to hell?

First of all we underlined the fact that the **denial has to stop**. So how does that happen, you ask? Great question! It starts with admitting where you are powerless to stop your behavior. For most men it takes a totally out-of-control situation for them to finally admit they are powerless over this sexual bondage. The reason this is so tough is that unlike the young man in Proverbs 7, you see clearly you are headed for the butcher shop of hell. But you can't stop yourself from going. Your intentions are great. You have prayed for God to help you. You have read the Bible. You may have joined a men's accountability group. But you are still on the same highway.

Part of the problem is that most churches define an accountability group in such a way that it's essentially a performance group. The group keeps tabs on one another if they have masturbated or watched porn or "whatever." When you are caught you repent and pray more and the cycle just repeats itself. It essentially becomes a binge-purge fellowship.

A true accountability group doesn't focus on your performance. Instead, when you mess up, they help you to find the resources to heal the gap that has been revealed through the relapse. It is an experience of GRACE and TRUTH.

But the first step of stopping denial is counterintuitive. I had to do the one thing that I just couldn't do…admit I was powerless. I had to let go of the stick and stop trying to control the situation. Doing that when my limbic system was screaming at me was HARD! But if I hadn't done that they would still be picking up pieces of me out of a smoking crater. **And the same is true for you spiritually and emotionally unless you face the places of your powerlessness.**

**Points and places of your powerlessness.** Here are some examples of what other men have said to me in the past:

- *I end up in a massage parlor when I promised myself I wouldn't.*
- *I am unable to honor my marriage commitment because of my Internet activity.*
- *I masturbate at work and don't get the work done I need to do.*
- *Whenever I am alone I feel compelled to be sexual.*
- *I sexualize customers on the job.*
- *I stole women's clothing for cross-dressing.*
- *I take risks with prostitutes.*
- *I can't refuse sex with women.*

❂ **List your points of powerlessness in the chart below. Be prepared to share them with the group at the next meeting.**

## POINTS OF POWERLESSNESS

| MY POINTS AND PLACES OF POWERLESSNESS | WAYS I HAVE TRIED TO STOP | HOW IT MAKES ME FEEL WHEN I ACT OUT AGAIN |
|---|---|---|
| 1. Wandering mind | Try harder | Failure |
| 2. | | |
| 3. | | |
| 4. | | |

Now let's take it deeper. I had to do something else about that near death experience I flew myself into. I had to tell my squadron mates. They were struggling with the same enemy challenge that I was facing and they might make the same mistake. **At a deeper level I needed to be honest about what I had done because excellence is found in openness not bravado.**

I have met a number of arrogant pilots, but I have never met a great pilot who wasn't honest about the mistakes he had made. Their honesty reveals a profound commitment to being an ongoing learner. To fly the aircraft to the edge of its capabilities you had to constantly be in a learning mode. Excellence demands an honesty and openness at its highest levels along with a tenacity that comes from the gut.

You know where I am going with this. Excellence in your life operates the same way. There can't be any **secrets** in your soul if you are going to live life to the max! I am not suggesting that you go home today and unload on your wife all the sexual secrets you have kept inside of you for years. We will get to the issue of disclosure with respect to your wife in Pillar Seven.

For real intimacy to take place in your marriage, or if you are single in your future marriage, there can't be secrets. But getting there is a delicate task. The first steps have to take place in your Pure Desire group. At some point you need to find a man you trust and take the courageous step of sharing your secrets.

Courage is not a natural trait but is learned, developed and disciplined into your soul.

> *Few men are born brave;*
> *many become so through training and force of discipline.*
> Flavius Vegetius Renatus, Military Institutions of the Roman Empire, AD 378

Secrets in themselves become problems. First, there is the pressure of trying to remember who you told what so that you aren't discovered. Add to that the constant fear of being discovered and the guilt and shame within of knowing you are being dishonest. You can see why secrets become one of the most deadly forces hell uses against you. You are as sick as your secrets because soon you believe the stories you have told others. Reality becomes distorted and you begin to live the lie. Courage can only be based on reality. You must start with reality and the secrets must be revealed.

❶ **List the secrets in your life**, using the chart that follows. Some may not be sexual, but they can fuel your sexual behavior. Secrets can be cleverly disguised through omissions—what you chose to omit from the story. It is time to begin developing the courage of real honesty.

❷ **Delineate the problems those secrets are creating.** Lack of intimacy with your wife, lack of moral courage and fear of exposure, etc.

❸ **Then identify the people you have kept these secrets from in your life.**

- Bring your completed chart to your next meeting and be ready to share the results with one or more members of the group.

## SECRETS

| THE SECRET | THE PROBLEM THAT THE SECRET CREATES | THE PERSON(S) I AM KEEPING IT FROM |
|---|---|---|
| 1. PG | Shame | None |
| 2. | | |
| 3. | | |
| 4. | | |

## ✎ ASSIGNMENTS FOR NEXT TIME

❶ Complete the charts from Lesson Three and be prepared to discuss your responses in class.

❷ Meditate on Luke 15:11-32. Read the passage at least one time every day for the next week.

❸ Read *Pure Desire* Chapter 2 (read and reread the parable of the dragon).

❹ **Very Important!** Read "Help! Someone Hijacked My Brain!" in Appendix One. Be prepared to share your dream drawing.

## EXITING THE HIGHWAY OF DENIAL

*11 To further illustrate the point, he told them this story: "A man had two sons. 12When the younger told his father, 'I want my share of your estate now, instead of waiting until you die!' his father agreed to divide his wealth between his sons.*

*13 "A few days later this younger son packed all his belongings and took a trip to a distant land, and there wasted all his money on parties and prostitutes. 14 About the time his money was gone a great famine swept over the land, and he began to starve. 15 He persuaded a local farmer to hire him to feed his pigs. 16 The boy became so hungry that even the pods he was feeding the swine looked good to him. And no one gave him anything.*

*17 "When he finally came to his senses, he said to himself, 'At home even the hired men have food enough and to spare, and here I am, dying of hunger! 18 I will go home to my father and say, "Father, I have sinned against both heaven and you, 19 and am no longer worthy of being called your son. Please take me on as a hired man."'*

*20 "So he returned home to his father. And while he was still a long distance away, his father saw him coming, and was filled with loving pity and ran and embraced him and kissed him.*

*21 "His son said to him, 'Father, I have sinned against heaven and you, and am not worthy of being called your son—'*

*22 "But his father said to the slaves, 'Quick! Bring the finest robe in the house and put it on him. And a jeweled ring for his finger; and shoes! 23 And kill the calf we have in the fattening pen. We must celebrate with a feast, 24 for this son of mine was dead and has returned to life. He was lost and is found.' So the party began.*

*25 "Meanwhile, the older son was in the fields working; when he returned home, he heard dance music coming from the house, 26 and he asked one of the servants what was going on.*

*27 " 'Your brother is back,' he was told, 'and your father has killed the calf we were fattening and has prepared a great feast to celebrate his coming home again unharmed.'*

*28 "The older brother was angry and wouldn't go in. His father came out and begged him, 29 but he replied, 'All these years I've worked hard for you and never once refused to do a single thing you told me to; and in all that time you never gave me even one young goat for a feast with my friends. 30 Yet when this son of yours comes back after spending your money on prostitutes, you celebrate by killing the finest calf we have on the place.'*

*31 " 'Look, dear son,' his father said to him, 'you and I are very close, and everything I have is yours. 32 But it is right to celebrate. For he is your brother; and he was dead and has come back to life! He was lost and is found!' "*

Luke 15:11-32 (TLB)

Few stories that Jesus told have become more popular and have touched the human heart so deeply. The language is vivid, emotions raw, and the pictures are unforgettable.

As you read and re-read this story this past week what did you observe about **your life?**

> **With your group, share how the story is a mirror of your life.**

This is **not** a time to talk theological insights or doctrinal truths.

- Allow 3 to 4 minutes per person, with each man participating, to summarize what the Holy Spirit revealed about his own story as a result of reflecting on this story.

You will find yourself becoming more and more at ease in telling your story. In fact, it will become a significant part of your healing experience. That is why getting rid of your secrets is such a critical gateway to freedom. The significant result of telling your story in a Pure Desire group is admitting you have a problem and the listeners are affirming you by acknowledging that they have had the same experience in some form or fashion. This process reduces the shame for everyone involved and empowers everyone to commit themselves to purity at a deeper level.

I used to wonder why Jesus told so many stories, but recent discoveries in neuroscience reveal the genius of His approach. Research has uncovered the fact that narratives require the participation of multiple structures throughout the brain. They require us to bring together in a conscious manner our knowledge, sensations, feelings and behaviors. In this process, multiple functions from diverse neural networks are brought together providing our brain with a tool for both emotional and neural integration.[6]

*Translation:* Telling your story **truthfully** in a **safe environment** heals you! Story telling is incredibly powerful. When you are reading a bedtime story to one of your kids, have you noticed they will not let you skip any part of the story. They want to hear it again and again because storytelling is not about passing on new information; it's all about bonding. The child feels bonded because they are part of the story. And reading stories to your kids always works best when you hold them or sit closely beside them.

This is something you will hear me say numerous times as we walk through this book together: Sexual addiction is about an attachment disorder or intimacy deficiency. **A Pure Desire group, if it is done right, is a place where you begin a bonding process that makes up for the deficits of your past.**

When Amnesty International began helping torture victims, they had little if any positive results.[7] The victims resisted help at every level despite the fact they were miserable. Then the organization discovered that if the torture victims could tell their painful story in a room full of individuals who were also torture victims, they would finally open up and receive healing.

If you scored 6 or more on the SAST-R, more than likely you have experienced trauma at some point in your life. I have learned a healing truth through the years. If you know the man's trauma story then you know his addiction story. I didn't have a clue that I had experienced any real trauma in my life. I mean come on. I'm a fighter pilot kind of guy, "Stop your whining and get on with life!" But your brain keeps score and the wound usually is inflicted early on in life before you get your tough exterior. Underneath all that muscle and bravado can lay some real pain you have been medicating for years.

Telling your story isn't just about telling how bad things are. Usually that is the starting point if you have been driving down the highway of denial for a while. You have to start with how desperate things really are. You have to let go of the controls in your life or you will stay stuck in a flat spin of pain, right into the ground.

But once the secrets are finally pulled out of the closets you can start telling your story of how things can be. Telling your story is not just about rehearsing how bad things are but telling how they will be with God's help and power! Story telling under the grace of God is about change. Not religious denial or Christian ignorance but looking with brutal honesty at your present condition; and at the same time, seeing the power of the Holy Spirit at work in your life.

We are talking about a realistic application of James 5:16, as presented here in the God's Word translation:

*So admit your sins to each other, and pray for each other so that you will be healed. Prayers offered by those who have God's approval are effective.*

Once you get off the highway of denial, you can emotionally receive the approval God the Father has given us in His Son. It will flow to your kids as well. The blessing of honesty before God will flow to your kids and grandkids. In fact, Scripture declares it will flow to the thousandth generation (Deuteronomy 5:8-10).

Dr. Mary Main discovered the phenomena of the "coherent narrative."[8] Now stick with me on this one. It has huge implications for your family. Dr. Main and her associates devised an instrument called the Adult Attachment Interview to ask the parents questions about their childhood. Here is the amazing part. The way the parents retold their story, in other words how they did or didn't make sense of their past lives, was the most powerful indicator of whether or not their children would grow up with a sense of attachment or security in their lives.

If the parent could share a coherent, reflective and emotionally engaged narrative about their childhood the more likely it was the children would have a good relationship with them. The next discovery they made is huge! It didn't matter how inadequate or abusive the parent's family of origin may have been. It didn't matter what may have happened to them. The determining factor was how they made sense out of what happened to them. That was the significant factor in how emotionally healthy they were and the type of parents they became.

That tells us, **if you can make sense of your story you can change its impact on your life**. It doesn't have to control you. Your destiny is not determined by your past. Your destiny is determined by how you see the sovereign hand of God at work in all of your life. Your past may have been horrific like mine, but once the Holy Spirit raises your vision to see a holy and gracious Father at work in your life, literally everything changes including your brain!

The old church tradition of someone standing up and sharing their "testimony" was incredibly wise. When they described the pit they may have come from and then began declaring where the Holy Spirit has brought them to today, they were literally renewing their minds in accordance with Paul's admonition in Romans 12:2 (NLT):

*Don't copy the behavior and customs of this world, but let God transform you into a new person by changing the way you think. Then you will know what God wants you to do, and you will know how good and pleasing and perfect his will really is.*

One of the most vivid indicators of an individual who has been traumatized by life is their inability to present a coherent story of their past. Asking them to describe what happened to them as children can be a challenge for them. They can become especially mean, angry or incoherent, and/or unable to remember major events of their past. Their deep limbic system has been traumatized in the past. (Refer to the introductory chapters on the brain.) The trauma has shut off their hippocampus. The painful sensations and experiences flooded the amygdala and were recorded as implicit memories blocking them from becoming explicit memories.[9] This is precisely why a guy can explode in anger in the here and now; what is happening in the present is triggering wounds from his past. Yet he is not able to remember what actually happened in the past. Instead, he is just reacting in the present and CAN'T FIGURE OUT WHY.

More commonly the man has a deep sense of worthlessness that he can never quite put his finger on. It is like background music playing in his head that "I am a loser!" The vast majority of men I have counseled through the years have that kind of heart-banging music playing in their soul. This lies at the very core of the pain they have been medicating with sex since they were in their teens.

Now here is the good news! **God the Holy Spirit can give us a whole new perspective on our lives despite the pain and problems in our past *if* we learn to walk in faith.** In other words, we don't have to let the emotions of our past hurts control our minds and provoke us to act out. It is then we will discover that a sovereign God has been at work throughout our lives. I love God's words to a confused young man who was deeply struggling with the pain in his life:

> *Before I formed you in the womb I knew you,*
> *before you were born I set you apart;*
> *I appointed you as a prophet to the nations.*
> Jeremiah 1:5

Now please don't tell yourself Jeremiah was a prophet so that word doesn't apply to you. The truth is, you have even greater promises on your life. The Holy Spirit doesn't rest upon you as an Old Testament prophet. You are a New Testament believer. The Holy Spirit **lives inside of you*!* Ephesians tells us we have been chosen by God before the creation of the world—set apart for his purposes (Ephesians 1:4-5).

As you begin to get off the dead end highway of denial, allow God the Holy Spirit to reveal to you what He has had planned for you since before the beginning of time. As you realize that the wounds of your past, especially if they came from your own family, are a result of others responding to the wounds of their pasts, you can stop the insanity and the generational curse stops with you. Why? Beginning to understand the story of grace that God wants to write with your life. And He can write with some of the most beat-up and crooked pens you have ever seen. In fact, those are the very instruments He writes His best stories with. As you come to the place of being able to tell a coherent, no denial-riddled story of your life, your kids will be able to walk in the blessing of God. With your kids secure in God's love and your love for them, you will leave a legacy that makes a difference in their lives. That is precisely why this battle is so important and well worth the price it may involve. **You have to get off the highway of denial no matter what the cost.**

The turning point in the parable that Jesus told in Luke 15 is verse 17, "*When he finally came to his senses.*" In other words, the guy started getting off the highway of denial. It took him a while because he had gone to a "distant land." Sexual bondages are always a distant land. Therefore, it will take you awhile to get home as well.

The average recovery time runs from two to five years.[10] This is not about a quick fix. This is about finally coming all the way home to Father God. That is why this will be one of the deepest transformation processes in your life. The prodigal son heads home—and please don't miss this—his motives are mixed at best. He is essentially stumbling home to survive and that may be where you are. Don't let the confusion of your motives distract you. Like the prodigal, just keep putting one foot in front of the other and the grace of God will get you there!

Along the way the prodigal is taking a critical step. He is beginning to face the issue of emotional restitution, "Father, I have sinned against you."

Who has been hurt by your behavior? In what ways have they been hurt? I know this is going to be tough! But you will never get out of the pigpen of sexual bondage until you come to grips with the fact that sexual addiction is **never a victimless act.**

In the chart that follows, write down the individuals that you have wounded and betrayed, and the ways in which you hurt them or lied to them.

## VICTIMS OF MY SEXUAL ADDICTION

| THE INDIVIDUAL I WOUNDED AND/OR BETRAYED | THE WAYS IN WHICH I HURT THE PERSON AND OR LIED TO THEM |
|---|---|
| *Example:* <br> • *My wife* <br> • *Friend (name)—if I am single* | • *I constantly tried to confuse her and explain things away* <br> • *I made her feel responsible for my moodiness* <br> • *All the while I was viewing porn…or flirting with other women…or visiting strip clubs* |
| **1.** | |
| **2.** | |
| **3.** | |
| **4.** | |
| **5.** | |

If you are married, let's take it deeper. The prodigal said he had sinned against heaven as well. In other words, God had created the prodigal's father a certain way and the prodigal took advantage of him. List below your mate's God given-gifts and how you used her gifts against her to justify or feed your addiction.

| WIFE'S GIFTEDNESS | YOUR MISUSE OF THOSE GIFTS |
|---|---|
| *Example:*<br><br>• *Your trusting love of me... you believed in me* | *Example:*<br><br>• *I used your trust of me to hide my behavior...and my anger over my shame to blame you frequently* |
| *Example:*<br><br>• *Her financial ability to save money.* | *Example:*<br><br>• *I used our savings to meet my sexual needs.* |
| **1.** | |
| **2.** | |
| **3.** | |

## ✐ ASSIGNMENTS FOR NEXT TIME

❶ Re-read and meditate again on Luke 15:11-32. This time focus on the actions of the Father toward the son. How has your heavenly Father treated you in the same way?

❷ Be ready to share your observations about the Father in Luke 15 with your group.

❸ Be prepared to share your responses to the charts in this lesson with your Pure Desire group.

## THE ROAD TO RECOVERY

*20 So he got up and came to his father. But while he was still a long way off, his father saw him and felt compassion for him, and ran and embraced him and kissed him. 21 And the son said to him, 'Father, I have sinned against heaven and in your sight; I am no longer worthy to be called your son.' 22 But the father said to his slaves, 'Quickly bring out the best robe and put it on him, and put a ring on his hand and sandals on his feet; 23 and bring the fattened calf, kill it, and let us eat and celebrate; 24 for this son of mine was dead and has come to life again; he was lost and has been found.' And they began to celebrate.*

*25 "Now his older son was in the field, and when he came and approached the house, he heard music and dancing. 26 And he summoned one of the servants and began inquiring what these things could be. 27 And he said to him, 'Your brother has come, and your father has killed the fattened calf because he has received him back safe and sound.' 28 But he became angry and was not willing to go in; and his father came out and began pleading with him. 29 But he answered and said to his father, 'Look! For so many years I have been serving you and I have never neglected a command of yours; and yet you have never given me a young goat, so that I might celebrate with my friends; 30 but when this son of yours came, who has devoured your wealth with prostitutes, you killed the fattened calf for him.' 31 And he said to him, 'Son, you have always been with me, and all that is mine is yours. 32 But we had to celebrate and rejoice, for this brother of yours was dead and has begun to live, and was lost and has been found.'"*

Luke 15:20-32 (NASB)

You can't just read this parable with your head; you have to "see it" with your heart. You have to hear it with your right brain. Volumes of research have documented the specialization of function in the two hemispheres of the brain. Some pop psychology fads have drawn absurd conclusions from the research. Yet this fact is indisputable. If you are going to experience a "renewing" of your mind as Paul challenges you to walk in Romans 12, both sides of your brain need to get involved in the process. The left side of your brain is the seat of logic, language, analysis and mathematics. It is the analytical part of your brain. The questions we have been asking in the lessons to this point have mostly required using the left side of your brain.

In this lesson we will be accessing the right side of your brain. The right side of your brain is the seat of the nonverbal processes, visual pattern recognition, auditory discrimination and spatial skills. The left brain is used more when examining details, the right considering the big picture.[11]

❯ **Have someone read Luke 15:20-32 out loud as everyone closes their eyes and attempts to visualize what the person is reading.**

Relax! This is not some New Age exercise! We are simply trying to get the right side of our brain engaged in the healing process. For example, if you have be viewing porn, you have thousands of images embedded in the right side of your brain that can overpower logical arguments when those images are triggered. In this exercise we are attempting to implant some supernatural healing images in the right side of your brain!

The first thing that should grab your imagination is the picture of this incredible father. He is wealthy. He has land, servants, rings and fatted calves. Today we would say he is a multi-billionaire. But he is wealthy in a much deeper way. He is emotionally and spiritually big and incredibly gracious. One of the most significant transitions we go through in life is realizing our physical dad may be great, but there are some things he can't handle. He is a man with limitations and as a teenager we can't believe how limited he is! But that is just the first part of the transition. The second part is when we come out of the craziness of our teenage years and young adulthood to discover just how limited we are as well. Most men get stuck in life right here. The pain of their past and the ever-pressing pain of their current limitations frustrate them. They become angry or isolated. They become frozen in emotional immaturity, deepening the intimacy disorder that lies at the core of sexual addiction.

I am frequently challenged with statements like, "Dr. Roberts I don't find addiction in the Bible. I think it is a creation of modern psychobabble!" I just smile and say, "Apparently you have never heard of the parable of the prodigal son." The guy is a quintessential picture of an addict. Within the space of a few weeks or months the boy went through hundreds of thousands of dollars, possibly millions. Remember, the unbelievably gracious father gave him half of his wealth. We are talking about an insane amount of money. In the span of an incredibly short period of time he blew right through his inheritance.

It still amazes me how much money a man can go through in his sexual addiction. I will ask men I am clinically counseling to give me a financial record of how much money they wasted in feeding their addiction. A million dollars is not an unusual amount when you start computing in the cost of a divorce, child support, and/or loss of a job and career.

I love the picture that comes to mind when I read verse 20: *"While the son was a long way off the father saw him and had compassion for him."* There were several things this father didn't do. First, he didn't go get the kid out of the pigpen. The dad was well connected. He could have discovered where the young man was and driven out there and drug him home. He didn't do that because he knew the son had only one crucial thing left in his life—the **dignity of choice.**

*Pure Desire* and this workbook are based on the fact that God the Father loves you so much that He gives you the dignity of choice. The one who created the entire cosmos with just His words waits patiently for you. Notice that the father didn't wash his hands of the whole thing. He didn't declare that he had given up on his son because the son had fallen so far off the cliff morally.

Hell may have screamed in your head innumerable times that your sexual sin has separated you from the love of God. That is a lie; the devil is a liar! Mark this down…carve it in your brain today! **God your heavenly Father will never give up on you.** In fact, He waits expectedly for you to come home. That is precisely what this entire book is about—you will discover how scandalously loved of God you are!

You have to see the scene. You have to picture what is happening. The prodigal son was forced to walk through the outlying fields and village to get to his father's house. The word would have gotten out, "This worthless son who has betrayed his father is coming come." There are only two options here. The father can let his son walk through the village and crowd of people with his head down and filled with shame, or he can run to the son essentially taking the shame on himself. God our heavenly Father faces the same decision about our lives. He could tell us, "You take the shame walk. You do the religious low crawl." A number of churches have taken that approach towards sexual immorality, but it is never God's choice.

Instead, the father ran toward his son taking the shame upon himself. Hebrews 12 tells us how our heavenly Father did the exact same thing for us through the Son.

*We must focus on Jesus, the source and goal of our faith. He saw the joy ahead of him, so he endured death on the cross and ignored the disgrace it brought him.*
Hebrews 12:2 (GW)

God became a man and wasn't just crucified for your sins; He was publicly humiliated, spit upon and viciously mocked. Ever ask yourself the question: Why did Jesus have to go through such shame? I mean, couldn't He have just died on a cross to atone for our sins? Why did He have to do the "shame walk?" The answer is awesome—so you wouldn't have to!

Forgiveness is given to us before we even repent perfectly. The prodigal is standing before his father giving his rehearsed spiel about being sorry with totally mixed motives. But as soon as the words come out of his mouth the father is releasing blessing on the son. When we think or feel that we have to get this repentance and recovery process perfectly before we are forgiven, we will continue to hide and live in denial.

At some point, for you to totally stop denial in your life you have to realize…

> **Repentance is not something we do in order to earn forgiveness.**
> **Instead it is something we do when we realize we are forgiven.**

The church leader may cry, "But with that definition of repentance men will just go out and sin and tell themselves it is okay because God will forgive them!" I have been counseling struggling men for twenty plus years and nothing could be further from the truth. Once a man truly meets the grace of God the Father, he always ends up in one place—flat on his face in adoration, lost in the wonder of God's grace toward him.

A young man came up after my time of sharing at a men's conference. He told me he had heard me share the concept of God's forgiveness before, but couldn't get his mind around it. That is until something happened in his life. He was at the computer at home doing some work for his business. Suddenly the old urges came back with ferocious intensity. He had struggled with an addiction to Internet porn for several years. It wasn't very long before he found himself back at the old XXX sites and looking for even raunchier ones. He knew it would show up on his accountability partner's read out, but he didn't care because he was lost in the neurochemical rush of the moment. As he found himself going down the old trail of bondage he knew so well, suddenly it happened.

At this point tears were welling up in his eyes as he told me the story. "Dr. Roberts, right at the moment when I was totally out of control I felt these arms wrapping around me as I sat there look-ing at those images. I realized it was God the Father embracing me even when I was tumbling back into the sin that I hated so deeply. That moment completely changed my life. I have been clean ever since. That was over a year ago and now I am helping other men get free. There are still occasional times of struggle, but they don't have the mental power they used to have in my life."

I have never heard a clearer illustration of the power of engaging the right side of your brain in this battle. That young man saw and felt the grace of God. It wasn't about him understanding the theology of forgiveness. It was about experiencing the forgiveness of God. It wasn't an analytical experience, but a holistic experience.

We don't have to wait for such a supernatural encounter in our lives before we can have that type of experience. **God the Father has given us the dignity of choice. We can choose to engage the right side of our brain in the healing and recovery process right now.**

## MY ROAD TO ADDICTION

**❯ In the picture frame that follows draw a detailed picture of your road to the "distant land" that the prodigal traveled. What did your road to sexual addiction look like?**

Take some time and think about the images that used to dominate your mind. Visualize the pictures, images and thoughts that lead you off the cliff. Then draw them.

Engage the right side of your brain. You don't have to be an artist. Use stick figures, whatever! **Spend at least an hour on the drawing, thinking it through and drawing it out.**

Be prepared to share it with your group. Make sure you listen to the stories of the other men in your group. When the addiction process is expressed graphically, entirely new doors of understanding can be opened up.

**MY ROAD TO ADDICTION**

Now let's look at the **road to recovery**. In the picture frame below depict the path you are presently on: the challenges you face, the friends that accompany you, and the joys that lie ahead. There may be a bit of the elder brother in you that has looked down on folks who struggle with addictive behavior.

**⟴ How has the picture changed once you have faced denial within yourself?**

## MY ROAD TO SEXUAL HEALTH

<br>
<br>
<br>
<br>
<br>
<br>
<br>
<br>
<br>
<br>
<br>
<br>
<br>

## ✑ ASSIGNMENTS FOR NEXT TIME

❶ Read *Pure Desire* Chapters 3 and 4.

❷ Complete the two drawings: My Road to Addiction and My Road to Sexual Health. Be ready to share them with the group.

# ✔ PILLAR OF FREEDOM ONE COMMITMENT

The goal in this journey of restoration is not simply to walk through a book, but for transformation to take place in our lives. Therefore, it is of utmost importance that you actually incorporate into your life this information you have studied.

At the end of each of the Seven Pillars you will be challenged to sign off on the fact that you have not only faithfully completed the exercises, but also that you are making a commitment to integrate these truths into your life.

And since we live our lives in community, two individuals will need to sign off on the fact that this process is actually taking place in your life. We were wounded in relationship usually earlier on in life and we are healed in relationship.

Denial is impossible to remove from our lives without the help of others. The two witnesses who sign **Pillar of Freedom One** are affirming the fact of your progress toward health and integrity.

*Note:* Do not ask your wife to sign as one of the affirming witnesses. She will be asked to sign the Pillar Seven Commitment.

..................................................................................................................................

*I have, to the best of my ability, completed all the exercises found in Pillar One. By God's grace I will do everything I can to live these truths out in my life on a daily basis. Denial has stopped in my life!*

My Name _____

Signature _____ Date _____

..................................................................................................................................

## AFFIRMING WITNESSES

❶ *I affirm the fact that* _____ *has grown in integrity and honesty in his life by the grace of God. Denial is no longer part of his life.*

My Name _____

Signature _____ Date _____

❷ *I affirm the fact that* _____ *has grown in integrity and honesty in his life by the grace of God. Denial is no longer part of his life.*

My Name _____

Signature _____ Date _____

..................................................................................................................................

# UNDERSTANDING THE NATURE OF SEXUAL ADDICTION

# LESSON ONE

## HOPE IN THE MIDST OF HOPELESSNESS

By Harry Flanagan

**❯ Please read Pure Desire Chapters 5 through 9 prior to working Pillars Two and Three.**

How many times have you said to yourself concerning your addictive behavior, "This is the last time, I will never do it again." Be honest—all of us who battle with sexual addiction have made this promise only to break it again and again. We understand the desire of the addictive behavior, but we don't understand the internal processes of the addiction. But the Apostle Paul understood the torment.

*What I don't understand about myself is that I decide one way,*
*but then I act another, doing things I absolutely despise.*
Romans 7:15 (MSG)

Yes, Paul speaks to the problem. Sexual addiction will harm you and every person who is significantly connected to you. You and I want to do what is right; we love God and we want to love those around us, especially those closest to us. But in the end we find ourselves doing the very thing we know will hurt all who love us. That is my story.

I wounded every person who loved and/or trusted in me. I lived the life of the hypocrite. The damage from my addiction was nothing less than horrific. I injured every member of the church I pastored, my wife and children, my pastoral friends and peers, my family of origin. And worst of all I tried for a decade to stop the addiction, all to no avail because I tried to stop it on my terms. I was at my wits end, and had no hope of being set free. I was trapped in the addiction and I led a secret life (much like the prince in the parable of the dragon in Chapter 2 starting on page 29 of the 3rd edition/2014 of *Pure Desire* by Ted Roberts).

I had three long-term affairs with women in the church, and I also occasionally read pornographic novels and looked at pornographic magazines; I had an active fantasy life. Yet I still loved God. I was so confused. How could I truly love God and be involved with such horrendous behavior? I feared, above everything else, being exposed. So, I kept the secret. Control became my lifeline. "If I could keep the secret maybe I could resolve this on my own," I thought.

This went on for years, and the truth, which is so obvious now, was that I was losing my family by the slow death of intimacy in my marriage and with my children. I had no friends with whom I would share my secrets. I felt like I was doomed. I feared that one day the secret would get out. Fear and dread became the emotional driving forces in my life. I was doing more existing than living, yet I put on the mask of being the loving, caring senior pastor at work, and a loving husband and father. What a sham, and what a shameful life that wounded the people I love.

I was alone. It felt like God was a zillion miles away. I had not asked the critical question, "Who moved?" I thought God, at best, tolerated me and at worst, hated me. I was stuck and I dreaded contact with everyone. I did not want to answer the phone or even the door. I became a couch potato, and was an emotionally absent member of the family. Life became drudgery. The truth was that

I did not trust God, so I was the one who had created this island of isolation and had moved away from God and loved ones. I thought that I might have a nervous breakdown or go insane; I didn't know how much longer I could go on, something had to give, and it did.

The date is etched into my mind: Monday September 20, 1993. It was a very painful day, yet it was the day that started me on the road to freedom, the path that would bring me my freedom. This was the day that my son was leaving for college. Late in the morning he overheard a conversation with one of the women and he realized that I had been having an affair. Shortly thereafter he left for school, but stopped by the business where my wife was working and faithfully told her what he had overheard. My wife was rightly angered and humiliated. She soon divorced me, sold our home, and she and the kids moved to a community where she felt safe.

I made a phone call to my parents where I confessed to them and then asked if I could eventually move back in with them. I was 43 years old. How humiliating it was to be so needy that I had to move back in with Mom and Dad. Self-pity, shame, and despondency accurately described my state of mind.

During a life-changing phone call to my friend and mentor Morris who was also a pastor, I confessed my sin and basically just cried. But Morris had some startling things to say to me. First he said, "Harry, you are in a hellish place right now, but you haven't been in such a good place in a long time." He told me that three days prior (September 17, 1993) he was in intercessory prayer for a list of people, and I was on that list; when he came to my name and started to pray for me, God interrupted his prayers. God told him that I was trapped in sin, I couldn't find my way out and that I couldn't handle it anymore. God also said, "I am going to expose him and when I do he will call you." Morris stayed by a phone for three days until the night of September 20th waiting for my phone call. Talk about a loyal friend.

It took several days for that phone call to sink in. In fact, the more I thought about it I began to realize that God, for some reason, was working on my restoration even **before** I was. He still had some sort of love or value for me! What a shocker! It was my first glimmer of hope. There was a possibility that I was going to survive this. I have clung to that phone call with Morris throughout my journey down the healing path God has given me. I have learned to trust His love for me. To quote one of my young friends: GIGATT (translated meaning: **G**od **I**s **G**ood **A**ll **T**he **T**ime.)

God is already working on your restoration, I know because otherwise you wouldn't be reading this. You may not be aware of it, but it is the truth and therefore there is hope. He promises that He will not rest until He has finished what He started in us. In our shame and pain we deceive ourselves. We tell lies of commission and also have lies of omission, all to protect the secret addictive lifestyle, but God is in the business of restoration. His desire is that you be set free!

> *And I am certain that God, who began the good work within you, will continue His work until it is finally finished on the day when Christ Jesus returns.*
> Philippians 1:6 (NLT)

It's time to put aside your lies and deceptions and begin to tell the real story of who you are; begin the process of discovering how all of this came to pass in your life. Just remember: He is on your side, and wants to partner with you in your healing. But that can't happen fully until you own your **true** story.

## ✐ ASSIGNMENTS FOR NEXT TIME

❶ Your first assignment in this lesson is to make a simple, but comprehensive list of **significant elements** of your secret life.

*Here are a few examples out of my life:*

- I became addicted to pornographic novels at the age of 9.

- I also have looked at hundreds of pornographic pictures.

- I had an affair with _____ that lasted three years.

❯ **Now begin to list the significant elements of your addictive life:**

❷ Write a **first draft** of your addictive story, including those significant elements of your addictive life that are listed above.

- *Note:* As you get healthier your testimonial story will grow into more detail and self-awareness, but this assignment is a good starting point.

_____

_____

_____

_____

_____

_____

_____

_____

_____

_____

_____

_____

_____

_____

_____

_____

_____

_____

_____

❸ Read *Pure Desire* Chapter 5.

# LESSON TWO

## SECRECY

By Harry Flanagan

In Pillar Two: Lesson One we began the process of opening up and telling our stories. This is so important because all addicts tend to keep secrets. When we seek to protect secrets we establish a pattern of life. The result? Protecting those secrets becomes lord to us. (See Pure Desire Chapter 6 titled, "When Sex Becomes Lord") One of the strongest unhealthy bonds that results in this "Lordship" is created through protecting the secret.

The lie that we buy into is that we have the ability to keep the secret. We think something like, "Nobody will ever know." We might throw up a prayer such as, "I will do this again Lord, please don't let me be caught." Does that sound familiar? It sure does from my past. But the love letters of God speak clearly on this matter.

*Whatever you have said in the dark will be heard in the light, and what you have whispered behind closed doors will be shouted from the housetops for all to hear!*
Luke 12:3 (NLT)

*Take no part in the worthless deeds of evil and darkness; instead, expose them. It is shameful even to talk about the things that ungodly people do in secret. But their evil intentions will be exposed when the light shines on them.*
Ephesians 5:11-13 (NLT)

*So don't make judgments about anyone ahead of time—before the Lord returns. For He will bring our darkest secrets to light and will reveal our private motives. Then God will give to each one whatever praise is due.*
1 Corinthians 4:5 (NLT)

Yes, we are deceiving ourselves if we believe our secrets aren't going to be exposed to the very people we are trying to hide them from. It's you vs. the Hand of God, and I have a suspicion that you don't have a chance.

I know from my own experience described in Pillar Two: Lesson One. I kept the secret of my addiction from the time I was a young boy until the exposure of my secret life, especially the last 10 years when I had the affairs. The misery of keeping the secret far outweighed the supposed benefit of keeping the secret. My life, and yours, becomes torturous and debilitating. Life loses its purpose and we feel stuck. Have you been there? For many of you this has been your life for a long time.

I wonder about King David when he sinned so vilely with Uriah and Bathsheba. He certainly was trying to keep his secrets, not wanting people to know that he arranged for Uriah to be killed and that he had been having sexual relations with Uriah's wife. Maybe David thought that because he was king he could get away with it. But how much did he fear the exposure? Whatever was happening internally, his day of reckoning came as the prophet Nathan confronted him with "You are the man!" (2 Samuel 12:1-9) Nathan did this in front of King David's Royal Court. It was not a private intervention; rather it was very public. What a humiliating and painful moment for King David.

I can identify with David. I know what it feels like; I bet you had a similar experience when you were exposed. You know, that feeling deep in your gut when the fear of consequences comes over you. This is a feeling that you never want to have again. It's this fear and shame that drive you to make the promise to your family, friends, and maybe your employer, "I will never do this again." But you know the truth; unless something changes it **is** going to happen again.

So, here you are at the place you promised yourself you would never come back to, yet here you are. What can you do? How can you possibly overcome this tangled web in which you feel trapped? If keeping the secret won't work, what will work?

Healing begins by understanding the nature of addiction. At it's very core, sexual addiction is a self-coping behavior. In other words, when you feel stress, anxiety, fear, or pain you turn to your addiction to cope. As you learned in the Introduction, the neurotransmitters from the brain are very powerful. For example, when the neurotransmitter dopamine is released during arousal it acts as a euphoric and temporarily lowers the pain, stress, anxiety, and fear. Through dopamine you become focused on the addictive experience and the unwanted thoughts and feelings are pushed out of your mind for a short time. During that time you feel better, but you and I know that later you still have to face the problem, and the fears and feelings that are associated with them. So, in the short term it works, but in the long run your addiction doesn't work; in fact it complicates the whole matter, making everything worse.

"Okay, I get what you are saying, Harry, but what does work?"

The answer is very basic in concept, but far more difficult to walk out. Instead of avoiding your problems, you will need to learn how to face them, but not alone. You must allow those who love and care about you to come along side you. Some friends and peers will offer you emotional support; others will become mentors or teachers. These mentors are people who have already walked down this road; they have knowledge and experience to teach and guide you. You will find the hope that they give very encouraging.

Ted has declared, **"We get hurt in relationships and the only place to get healed is in the context of relationships."** Within your Pure Desire group you can find friends to support, encourage and mentor as you walk through the Pillars of Freedom. Your healing will happen over time as you commit to the road that will move you toward integrity, honesty, and sexual purity.

## ✐ ASSIGNMENTS FOR NEXT TIME

**❯ Write responses to the three questions; be prepared for discussion with your Pure Desire group:**

**❶** List the friends and peers who have brought you hope and encouragement recently or in your past. If family has provided this, please remember to include them.

• Next to each name, write a short description of how that person has supported you.

........................................................................................................................

**❷** Who are the people who have been the most influential mentors or teachers in your life? Give a short description of how each one has influenced your life.

........................................................................................................................

**❸** Which of these friends, peers, mentors, and teachers are presently available to you? Please list them.

........................................................................................................................

• As you develop your relapse prevention plan, how can you be purposeful and intentional about involving these people in the healing process and as accountability partners?

........................................................................................................................

# ISOLATION

By Harry Flanagan

This lesson is huge! If you don't break out of isolation, there is literally almost no chance of getting healed. I personally put the odds at 1 out of 100 billion. I know that is just an educated guess, but after being in this ministry for a number of years and working with men all across the United States, I have yet to see someone isolated receive healing.

**Isolation is the first behavioral sign of an addictive personality** and has a foundational place in protecting the secret. Isolation has many forms, but they all have something in common: **All forms of isolation for the addictive personality are present to protect the secret behavior and mental thought life from being discovered.** In fact, most addicts are very comfortable in isolation and think that it is normal. It's all about feeling safe.

Isolation creates a false sense of security. Each addict wants to avoid the shame and humiliation of his addiction being exposed. Early on the pain of exposure feels like it is greater than the pain of living a lie.

Two other behavior patterns, passivity and procrastination, are strongly connected to the addictive personality. I will mention all three and then tie them together:

- **Isolation:** anyone who protects a secret (thought, feeling or behavior) from the significant people in their life is isolated. No true accountability can exist when someone isolates. **You will lie by commission or omission. Isolation is about *avoiding* exposure.**

- **Passivity** (sometimes passive-aggressive, which is a form of anger). Passivity helps the addictive personality to *avoid* and even abdicate responsibilities. Usually they are tired of failing so they pass the buck on to someone else. Then if something goes wrong, they can point the finger at someone else. Passivity enables them to avoid conflict that may result in exposure of the addiction.

- **Procrastination** is all about *avoiding* painful or unwanted tasks or projects. Procrastinating people usually will move toward behaviors that give some positive and immediate gratification. The addictive personality desires immediate gratification, and therefore will avoid behaviors that may lead to pain or even everyday discomfort.

All three of these characteristics are about avoiding. **Isolation is about avoiding relational intimacy. If** someone gets too close, the addict fears exposure. **Intimacy and isolation cannot co-exist.** Biblically we are called to intimacy, to know and be known. Passivity is about avoiding responsibilities. Procrastination is about avoiding painful or unwanted tasks and projects. The important point here is that the primary motive in the addictive personality is to avoid any and all forms of pain such as anxiety, fear, stress, or physical and/or emotional pain.

Our goal with Pure Desire groups is not only that someone merely stops sinful and poor behaviors, but also that each person will have healthy intimacy with their significant loved one and a true intimacy with God. Healthy behavior choices and intimacy go hand in hand.

After the great parables Jesus told in Matthew 25, he talks of people reaching out to feed him when he was hungry, clothe him when he was naked, visit him when he was in prison, etc. The people's response was something like, "When did we do these things for you because we don't remember this?" When he talked of people who did not reach out, his comments were off the page and uncomfortable. He said, *"Whatever you did not do for one of the least of these, you did not do for me."* (Matthew 25: 45)

**You can't isolate from people without isolating from God.** Can you admit that there are those painful or empty moments when you feel the lack of God's presence? It can feel like He is far away. You don't realize that in the midst of your isolation you are trying to keep your distance from God.

People isolate in two significant ways: internally and externally. Both play a major role in addictive isolation. The internal isolation is almost invisible so we will begin by examining internal isolation before looking at external (behavioral) isolation.

**Internal isolation** is based on a lack of self-awareness—areas of our thought life and emotional life that we have not wanted to examine. Emotional pain will result if we bring those areas up to our conscious thought process; therefore, we "stuff" unwanted memories or circumstances to avoid facing unpleasant reality.

Let me give you an example of internal isolation. It was September 29th, 1998. My father had just celebrated his 84th birthday, and he was dying. Everyone knew it including my father. He kept up his daily routine. As friends and family came over, they said their "goodbyes." My Dad knew Jesus and I am so proud of the way he walked through the last moments in this life. Though I was his caretaker, I backed off and merely observed these last tender interactions. My sister had just arrived from the east coast and was grief stricken. I gave her as much time with Dad as possible, as he was her hero. But there was something going on within me that I didn't catch until later. I was stuffing my own sorrow and grief over my father's looming death. I found myself almost detached from the events going on, but I told myself that I had already spent much time with Dad, and now was the time for others to have their moments with him.

On Dad's last night on earth, my sister was in his room and I thought I was giving her space to be with him. In the middle of the night Dad called out, "Where's Harry?" and I heard him. I went in for what turned out to be my last conversation with my father. I assured him I was close by and that I was giving Deb (my sister) and the boys a chance to say their goodbyes. I told him that I was here and that I would remain close by. Physically that was true, but emotionally I was shut down; I just wasn't there. I desperately shoved down the grief and sorrow that tried to express my emotional reality. Dad fell into a sleep, and I gratefully went to bed, not to rest, but hoping to sleep so I wouldn't have to face this painful reality. Dad never woke up; early on the morning of September 30th he passed into eternity with Christ. I stayed busy taking care of the arrangements and the guests who came by, but the one thing I did not take care of was me. Oh, I took care of my body, but I ignored the battle that was raging inside. The grief was trying to express itself and I was trying to keep it away.

It took several months before I emotionally acknowledged my grief, and as I am writing this I have the emotions coming to the surface today that wanted to express themselves on September 29 and 30, 1998. The difference today is that I have learned to allow myself to feel the pain and sorrow. It's as real as if I was back there for my father's last days all over again. Now, I have the chance to process those emotions and I am not afraid of facing the death of a loved one. In Christ I am strong enough to look the death of a loved one in the face and not try to avoid it emotionally.

**With external isolation**, you find ways to separate yourself from others. This separation can take on many forms. Some people will literally move away. My sister and mother butted heads throughout my sister's youth. When my sister moved to Los Angeles in her twenties, she discovered that a thousand miles wasn't enough, because they still had arguments. What was my sister's response? She moved to New York and farther away from Mom; by magic my sister and mother had a relationship that was almost devoid of conflict (except when they visited each other!). For my sis, moving 3000 miles accomplished her goal of isolation.

For others it will look different. For some it will take the form of working jobs that keep them from others; some examples would be cross-country truckers, traveling salesmen, workaholics, and people working odd hour shifts that keep them from deep relationships. For others it may be vegetating in front of the television or the computer. Let's be honest, many of us have found ourselves playing some computer games and we lose track of time—sometimes hours! In those moments we are isolating.

But do you know the most effective way to isolate? Be an angry person. I have yet to meet anyone who likes to hang out with someone who is angry or raging. Anger pushes people away, and therefore allows the person to isolate. People keep their distance, walking on eggshells to avoid conflict. Yes, anger is a great choice for those who wish to isolate.

Ultimately, isolation removes us from God and the people of significance that God has placed in our lives. In isolation we move from living to a form of mere existence where we just go through the motions of living.

My friend, Michael Dye, who created the Genesis Process (one of our curriculum pieces), puts it this way: "**The right thing to do is usually the hard thing to do.**"[12] For those of us who have addictive personalities, breaking the addiction, becoming vulnerable to our own feelings, and vulnerable to the people God has lovingly placed into our lives, is the hard, but right thing to do.

*"Teacher, which command in God's Law is the most important?" Jesus said, "'Love the Lord your God with all your passion and prayer and intelligence.' This is the most important, the first on any list. But there is a second to set alongside it: 'Love others as well as you love yourself.' These two commands are pegs; everything in God's Law and the Prophets hangs from them."*
Matthew 22:36-40 (MSG)

## ✍ ASSIGNMENTS FOR NEXT TIME

**❯ Please write responses to the questions and be prepared for discussion with your group:**

**❶** List the ways you emotionally isolate (internal isolation) from feelings and thoughts that you did not want to face.

...........................................................................................................................................................

**❷** Write a detailed account of one of the times that you isolated from your unwanted thoughts/ feelings.

...........................................................................................................................................................

**❸** Make a list of the ways you physically distance yourself (external isolation) from people.

...........................................................................................................................................................

**❹** Now write out a detailed account of one of the times that you isolated physically from people.

...........................................................................................................................................................

**❺** What do you think the consequence is to you when you isolate?

...........................................................................................................................................................

**❻** What do you think the consequence is for those who love and care about you when you isolate?

...........................................................................................................................................................

❯ Read *Pure Desire* Chapter 6.

## SHAME

By Harry Flanagan

*And Lord I've come to know the weakness I see in me*
*will be stripped away by the power of your love.*
"Power of Your Love" by Hillsong

The song, *Power of Your Love*, became my anthem as I was walking through my healing; it was a real point of encouragement when I was struggling. Amazingly, I discovered that I couldn't win my battle with sexual addiction if I didn't win my battle with shame.

My first year at East Hill Church in Gresham, Oregon, was less than great. I was still very stuck in my addiction and struggles, but I persisted in attending my Pure Desire small group. During one meeting our leader and my counselor, Scot, brought a chapter from the book *Tired of Trying to Measure Up* by Jeff Van Vonderen.[13]

For the first time, I felt that someone had been in my head; the entire chapter was on shame and it was describing me!!! Things finally clicked. I had been driven by shame nearly all my life and I hadn't even realized it. A surge of interest and downright excitement was birthed in me that night. This was a God-orchestrated moment, the turning point in my healing. I know it was a God thing because a year later I re-read that chapter; it was okay, but did not carry the connection or power that I had experienced before.

I read several books on the subject of shame, and took a graduate level class on shame at a local seminary. I was a sponge on the subject. I was finally able to begin shedding the chain of shame that had so entangled and trapped me. I felt like a new man.

After writing a curriculum for a class on shame, I gave it to Pastor Scot who did a very wise thing; he sat on it. Actually, though he has never owned it, I think he used it for a burnt offering! I was making progress, but I still needed to focus on my ongoing healing and not be teaching classes. It was another moment of grace extended toward me even though I didn't know it in the moment.

Scot choosing to sit on my material was an incredible gift. You see, the shame that had been with me since I was a small boy led me to the conclusion that I didn't love or value who I was. I had inadvertently been taught that I was inadequate, and that if I was going to have value it would be based on what I did rather than who I was. My writing the curriculum was another way of gaining value-based on performance. (We will talk about this a little later in the lesson). By Scot not taking action on my curriculum proposal, I had to put my energy into my ongoing healing and growth, rather than gaining validation in the church through teaching a class.

One day, I was reading the account in Genesis 3 about the fall of man. I saw something that shocked me. I thought that the first response of Adam and Eve when God showed up in the garden on the day they had eaten the forbidden fruit was to hide. I think that most people have that perception. As I travel around the country, I often ask that question as I'm teaching. Without exception what I hear from the congregations is, "They hid." It sounds right, but it is not what Adam said as he was talking with God.

*Adam said, "I heard the sound of You in the garden,*
*and I was afraid because I was naked; so I hid myself."*
Genesis 3:10 (NASB)

Before Adam hid he felt afraid. His first response was fear. Some translations use "ashamed" in place of "fear." Either translation is accurate, as the word in the original language means the fear of being exposed, which is also the clinical definition of shame. Clinically, shame means being exposed and feeling diminished by that exposure. Adam hid because he did not want to feel diminished and exposed in the presence of God.

For the first time I saw "it" as I was meditating on Genesis 3. It was a pattern unfamiliar to me, yet it was staring me in the face. It made so much sense.

**Sin** **that has not been dealt with leads to** *shame* **that drives us to** *secrecy* **(hiding). The consequence of this sequence is that secrecy always creates isolation and the isolation always leads to** *separation***.** I believe this is the universal pattern of sin. Shame is the glue that holds this pattern together. Shame keeps you away from truly resolving your sinful choices and away from the very people God has placed in your life to help you.

Let's be honest with ourselves; we have all hid at one time or another. Hiding takes on many forms. You might hide your present reality by wearing a mask that allows you to stuff your feelings. Hiding might mean for you physically separating yourself from people who might discover your truth. Anger also allows you to push people away. These are just a few samples of what hiding could look like.

Sin tied to the power of shame is toxic. You are poisoning the precious gift of life and relationships that God has so graciously given you. Why would anyone do this? What is underneath the shame? Earlier I made reference to it. Where does your validation come from?

Within your humanity you believe value must be earned. You think, "My value is determined by how well I perform." Linking performance to value is where we make our mistake.

The Bible does teach performance. In John 8, Jesus tells the adulterous woman to go and "sin no more." Later in John, Jesus states that if we love him we are to keep his commandments. He also teaches that we have value. John 3:16 tells us that we are so loved that Father God gave the life of His Son that we might live. That is how valuable we are to God.

But here is where the difference comes: **God never ties performance to value**. Our value is determined by who we are—children of the Living God—not by how well we perform. He may hate some of our behaviors, but does not hate us. We think that because there are consequences for our behavior our value to Him has been diminished. Not true!

*…I observed people who followed the rules and missed God, and people who broke*
*the rules and missed God. What burdens me, though, is that group of people who*
*still believe that they missed God because they broke the rules.*
Phillip Yancey[14]

We need not feel shame because we are tempted. Hebrews 4:15 teaches us that Jesus was also tempted. The temptation itself is not the problem; it is our reaction and response to the temptation that can become the problem.

# VALUE BY PERFORMANCE

People use six primary ways to establish value based on performance. Each may initially sound good, but seeking validation by any of these means will move you away from true validation and, in fact, bring you toward exhaustion and the tyranny of, "What have you done for me lately?" People stuck in performance begin to resent God as their work moves them toward obligation and bitterness.

## TITLE

This is when we find validation by having a title. A short list of common titles includes pastor, doctor, owner, missionary, supervisor, captain, leader. The false belief here is that having the title makes the person more valuable because somebody made the choice to put that person in the position. Instant validation—NOT!

## POSITION

This is very much like TITLE, but with a twist. POSITION is about gaining validation by being part of a team. When you are a member of a team that is either famous and/or successful, the assumption is that association brings validation. Examples: sports team, the company you work for, being member of a committee, or maybe part of the worship team at church. Here we try to gain validation by association with this famous/successful team.

## POSSESSIONS

Everyone knows this type of validation by performance. If I drive a new BMW, or if I flaunt my wealth, have an expensive house, or have the newest stylish clothes then I believe that having these possessions will give me a form of validation.

## ASSOCIATION

Have you ever experienced a "name dropper?" This person wants you to think they are valuable by letting you know they have an association with someone who is successful or famous. We think that the association with that other person will bring a greater valuing of who we are. I used to make up stories about my Dad knowing General Eisenhower in World War II. It was actually a lie, but I did it because I believed that people would see my value through that association.

## APPEARANCE

Validation is based on wearing the "right" clothes, or going to the gym to gain the "right" body image, that will increase their attractiveness thereby giving them a new level of value. Maybe you know other variations of this category of performance. This one also works in reverse. If I don't wear the "right" clothes or have the "right" body image then our perception of our value goes down.

## SKILLS

This is especially true within our culture. We value musicians, actors, and athletes because of their skill set, and it usually has little to do with character. We believe that if we are good or great at something that it increases our value. Because we are in a celebrity driven culture, we will seek to win the "big one" by combining appearance and skills so we can be King of the Mountain. This concept of value through skills can also be a dynamic in intelligence or mental giftedness. "If I could only get my boss to see that I have greater mental skills and ideas then I will get a promotion." Here is where perfectionism lives. Mistakes are not OK because they reveal flaws and shame us.

All six of these attempts to gain value through performance are shortcuts that ultimately don't work. Your value can truly be determined by only one thing: That you are a son of the Living God. In Pillar Two: Lesson Five we will explore the answers to our identity being found in who God says we are.

*As for me, it matters very little how I might be evaluated by you or by any human authority. I don't even trust my own judgment on this point. My conscience is clear, but that doesn't prove I'm right. It is the Lord Himself who will examine me and decide.*
1 Corinthians 4:3-4 (NLT)

## ✎ ASSIGNMENTS FOR NEXT TIME

**❯ Please write responses to the questions; be prepared for discussion with your Pure Desire Group:**

The sequence in the universal pattern of sin:

**SIN** ❯ **SHAME** ❯ **SECRECY** ❯ **SEPARATION**

❶ Please write a detailed account of this sequence as it resulted from one of your past circumstances. Please acknowledge in the story the part played by each of these four steps into creating a shame-filled life for you.

_____

_____

_____

_____

_____

_____

_____

_____

_____

_____

_____

_____

_____

_____

_____

_____

_____

_____

❷ Value by performance puts all of the weight of gaining or receiving value onto us; the Bible teaches that our value comes from who God says we are. Following are the six primary ways that we seek to gain value through performance, which ultimately fails because we never measure up, and that leads to feeling shamefully inadequate.

- Please list under each category the different ways you have sought validation by performance. Give at least one detailed example for each category.

*Example:*
**TITLE -** Pastor, supervisor, college graduate, owner.

*I always felt morally bad about who I was so, I tried to gain validation from others by becoming a pastor. I thought to myself, "If I can't find value in who I am, then why would anybody else find value in me?" So, I tried to gain value by what I did. As a Christian, I thought becoming a pastor would give me added value. Boy, was I wrong!*

## NOW IT'S YOUR TURN:
**TITLE**

..................................................................................................................................................

**POSITION**

..................................................................................................................................................

**POSSESSIONS**

..................................................................................................................................................

**ASSOCIATION**

..................................................................................................................................................

**APPEARANCE**

..................................................................................................................................................

**SKILLS**

..................................................................................................................................................

# LESSON FIVE

## WARFARE

By Harry Flanagan

> *When a man is deeply embedded in the wicked web of sexual bondage, he will, at some point feel deserted by God. This is a classic strategy of hell, designed to increase the shame level in our lives, which only tightens the noose of sexual bondage around our souls.*
> Ted Roberts in Pure Desire[15]

We are so surrounded by the products of sin and dysfunction that we take their presence for granted. "That's just the way it is in a fallen world," I have heard more than once in my counseling office. We have learned to take this evil for granted. We have learned to live along side it pretty comfortably. This is a far cry from God's plan as revealed in scripture.

The Apostle John tells us, **"The Son of God came to destroy the works of the devil."** (1 John 3:8 NLT) I don't think God could be clearer on at least one of the main purposes in sending Jesus Christ to earth. In fact, Satan was blinded to God's plan. Remember Paul's statement in 1 Corinthians 2:8? **"None of the rulers of this world understood it, for if they had, they would not have crucified the Lord of Glory."**

If Satan had deciphered the heart and mind of God, then he would have done anything to keep Christ from Calvary. Instead Satan gloated until he encountered the Victorious Christ. In redeeming us from our sins through the cross Jesus destroyed the foundation of Satan's strategies.

> *Satan's methodology is one of accusation, always to increase our sense of shame which increases his control over us.*
> Ted Roberts in *Pure Desire*[16]

Satan's accusations are against us, not just in the secrecy of our thought life, but also in the very presence of God. The great news is that our salvation will be revealed as God casts Satan down. Revelation 12:10 (NLT) says:

> *Then I heard a loud voice shouting across the heavens,*
>
> *"It has come at last—*
> *salvation and power*
> *and the Kingdom of our God,*
> *and the authority of his Christ.*
> *For the accuser of our brothers and sisters*
> *has been thrown down to earth—*
> *the one who accuses them*
> *before our God day and night...."*

Satan's accusations, on the surface, are all about our behaviors and the consequences of those behaviors. Because we have embraced the concept of value by performance, we tend to believe the accusations, but we also will believe ugly outcomes that Satan is whispering in our ears. In the short term, the consequences he is whispering may be true, but the ultimate outcome will be determined by the grace of God, not the hatred of Satan.

> *…but he has told me, "My grace is all you need, for my power is perfected in*
> *weakness." Therefore, I will most happily boast about my weaknesses,*
> *so that the Messiah's power may rest on me.*
> 2 Corinthians 12:9 (ISV)

The enemy's attack sight is set on the main target, your identity. We love based on who we believe we are. If the devil can influence who you perceive yourself to be, then he will influence your motives, which affect your behavioral responses to circumstances.

I believe it was in the late 80's or early 90's that I read Chuck Colson's book *Against the Night: Living in the New Dark Ages*. It was a revelation to me as he explained that we had moved toward postmodern America. He named the two "isms" that were leading us into the decline of our culture: materialism and individualism. Materialism is simply that I believe what I see. Many Americans think that the spiritual realm is fictional or non-exist. Another current thought the media presents us is that supernatural evil is far more powerful than good. This denies the truth out of Isaiah 54:17 (NASB):

> *"No weapon that is formed against you will prosper;*
> *And every tongue that accuses you in judgment you will condemn*
> *This is the heritage of the servants of the LORD,*
> *And their vindication is from Me," declares the LORD.*

Colson's second point on 'isms" was individualism. One definition of Individualism by Dictionary.com is "the pursuit of individual rather than common or collective interests; egoism."[17] In 21st century America the media has been the great advocate for the individual placing his/her needs above all others. Have you experienced this in your own life? I have.

Historically, July 4th is considered the last day of the Civil War battle at Gettysburg. The first time I visited this greatest of all American battlefields was July 4th. I was standing on the edge of the woods on the west side of the battlefield along the line of "Pickett's Charge." On July 3, 1863, early in the afternoon, between 13,000 and 14,000 men lined up in rows of three, covering almost a mile. Those were desperate times. The Confederates had just put on the largest cannonade in US history, but it did not do what was needed—dislodge the Army of the Potomac or eliminate their cannons. That meant that when these men moved onto the open field where most of them had to walk more than a mile to their target, they would be in range of the Union cannons. These 19th century soldiers walked into a bloodbath, and that blood was their own. They knew it was coming yet they went. They were willing to die for something greater than themselves. As I looked out across the grain fields, I cried. I cried because I didn't know if I would have had the courage to go forward with the knowledge that I probably would die or be maimed. The scene reminded me that as a Christian, I battle with putting my needs above the needs of even the dearest people in my life.

In Judges 6, we learn of a man who had lost his God-given identity just like we have. His name was Gideon. The story begins in Judges 6:11 with Gideon's unusual entrance. The angel of the Lord showed up to speak to Gideon who is beating wheat in a winepress because he's hiding from the Midians who had overrun Israel. The Angel said, "The Lord is with you, oh valiant warrior." Here Gideon began to complain: Where is God? How come we haven't seen miracles? If God is with us, why are we suffering? Blah, blah, blah.

Finally he said something to the effect of, "You can't choose me. I am the youngest in my family; in addition, our tribe and community aren't capable of beating the Midianites." You know the rest of the story.

We can't forget that Gideon resisted God because he saw himself as weak. He didn't think that he and his community could handle the enemy whom he perceived to be invincible. God had to train him in who he really was, and Gideon had to realize that God is also a valiant warrior. With God's help, Gideon and his army of 300 finally defeated the Midianites. Gideon's victory began when he started to let the Angel disciple him. He gained a new identity with God and a new identity within himself.

Our spiritual warfare is on a similar front. We must learn who we are in Christ. Right now we are fighting the wrong battles; because of our fears we, like Gideon, are fighting the fight of survival. To survive is not to win. Winning is all about conquering. Leonard Ravenhill said it best:

> ### *Many of us are hunting mice—while lions devour the land.*[18]

We have a battle to fight, and we are going after the lions. Paul declares in Romans 8:37 that we are "more than conquerors." In the original Greek, this wording meant that by the time we finish the battle, it will be as if our enemies had never existed! You, in Christ, are that powerful a warrior. Go get 'em, tiger!

# ✎ ASSIGNMENTS FOR NEXT TIME

These exercises will take courage, the courage to be truthful with yourself. If you are battling with sexual addiction you do have major issues with your perceived identity.

➲ Read *Pure Desire* Chapter 7.

➲ **Be prepared to share your responses with your Pure Desire group at the next meeting.**

❶ **How do you feel about yourself?** Write several paragraphs.

- Don't hide behind theology; rather, put on paper your doubts, fears, and self-judgments that you carry against yourself. If you don't face these feelings you are going to remain stuck in your addiction.

❷ **Now take a look at Romans 8:29-39.**

- This passage printed here is the NLT. Compare it to another translation that you value.

- Your assignment is to **list positive thoughts concerning your identity and your destiny** that are found within this passage.

- You will discover that you are a warrior who is invincible in Christ! Your battle begins as you rediscover who you are in Christ.

| ROMANS 8:29-39 (NLT) | MY IDENTITY & MY DESTINY |
|---|---|
| *29 For God knew his people in advance, and he chose them to become like his Son, so that his Son would be the firstborn among many brothers and sisters. 30 And having chosen them, he called them to come to him. And having called them, he gave them right standing with himself. And having given them right standing, he gave them his glory.* | |
| *31 What shall we say about such wonderful things as these? If God is for us, who can ever be against us? 32 Since he did not spare even his own Son but gave him up for us all, won't he also give us everything else? 33 Who dares accuse us whom God has chosen for his own? No one—for God himself has given us right standing with himself. 34 Who then will condemn us? No one—for Christ Jesus died for us and was raised to life for us, and he is sitting in the place of honor at God's right hand, pleading for us.* | |
| *35 Can anything ever separate us from Christ's love? Does it mean he no longer loves us if we have trouble or calamity, or are persecuted, or hungry, or destitute, or in danger, or threatened with death? 36 (As the Scriptures say, "For your sake we are killed every day; we are being slaughtered like sheep.") 37 No, despite all these things, overwhelming victory is ours through Christ, who loved us.* | |
| *38 And I am convinced that nothing can ever separate us from God's love. Neither death nor life, neither angels nor demons, neither our fears for today nor our worries about tomorrow—not even the powers of hell can separate us from God's love. 39 No power in the sky above or in the earth below—indeed, nothing in all creation will ever be able to separate us from the love of God that is revealed in Christ Jesus our Lord.* | |

# ✔ PILLAR OF FREEDOM TWO COMMITMENT

The goal in this journey of restoration is not simply to walk through a book, but for transformation to take place in our lives. Therefore, it is of utmost importance that you actually incorporate into your life this information you have studied.

My Name _____

Signature _____ Date _____

## AFFIRMING WITNESSES

❶ *I affirm the fact that* _____ *has faced his addictive mindset by the grace of God. I see that he is battling to dismantle that addictive mindset.*

My Name _____

Signature _____ Date _____

❷ *I affirm the fact that* _____ *has faced his addictive mindset by the grace of God. I see that he is battling to dismantle that addictive mindset.*

My Name _____

Signature _____ Date _____

# SURRENDERING TO THE PROCESS

# LESSON ONE

## LEARNING TO FACE THE PAIN

By Harry Flanagan

This critical pillar will require you to face your addictive attitudes and behaviors. This cannot and should not be done alone. In Pillar Two we talked about the damaging role that choosing isolation plays. It's not that you don't have times to yourself; rather, you can't go into your cave and hope to be fixed.

In other pillars we will talk about some significant aspects of participating in a healing community, but now we will focus on the practical process of taking the beginning steps on the healing path.

> *Share each other's burdens, and in this way obey the law of Christ.*
> *...For we are each responsible for our own conduct.*
> Galatians 6:2, 5 (NLT)

The healing that you desire will come as you participate in the Pure Desire healing community. It is here that you will process and face your pain, and put the Seven Pillars into practice in your life. The Apostle Paul got it right. In a healing community we share each other's struggles, but ultimately we alone are responsible for our own conduct. Paul in Romans 12:15 tells us to cry with those who are crying and to celebrate with those who are celebrating. In the healing process you will be in both camps before you are finished.

We must learn that there are people and circumstances that we can't control. We must also learn that within our addictive triggers there are places where we have no ability to stop the rituals in the moment. **If we don't break down the addictive mindset we will be doomed to a lifestyle of addiction.**

Grief is a great example. You can try to stuff it, run from it, or bitterly embrace it. But it is beyond our human capacity to control. We have no real say about the timing when loved ones die, and we can't control the actions of other people in a multitude of ways. Decisions by other people will have an impact on our lives whether we like it or not.

Let me tell you the story of a person who encounters horrific pain and how he learned to deal with it. His story is remarkable and I believe we can learn from his experience.

Gerald Sittser and his family were traveling home from a mission trip in the spring of 1996 when their car was hit head-on by a drunken driver. The crash changed Gerald's life. He lost his wife, mother, and daughter. He was severely injured and still had the responsibility for his three other children.

After he came home from the hospital, he did not do well, even though he knew there was life before the trauma and there would be life after the trauma. Please hear his words:

> *If normal, natural, reversible loss is like a broken limb, then catastrophic loss*
> *is like an amputation. The results are permanent, the impact incalculable, the*
> *consequences cumulative. Each new day forces one to face some devastating*
> *dimension of the loss. It creates a whole new context for one's life.*
> Gerald L. Sittser[19]

Gerald began to have a recurring nightmare. In this nightmare, he would be on an endless beach with the sun low in the early evening sky. Darkness seemed to be gathering in the eastern sky and he feared being swallowed up in the darkness. Gerald began to run as hard as he could toward the setting sun hoping that he would be able to stay in the daylight. His nightmare ended in stark terror just as the sun set below the horizon and he was immersed in the darkness. Gerald would be exhausted and drenched in perspiration after these nightmares because he had actually threshed in bed as he "ran" toward the setting sun.

He had this horrible dream every night for several weeks. This nightmare was consuming him in almost every way whether he was awake or asleep. After several weeks, Gerald made a great choice. He called his sister and told her of the dream. She responded with an incredible and insightful comment. She told her brother that nobody could catch the setting sun; she told him to turn, face the darkness, even run into the darkness, for in doing so he would catch the rising sun.

Gerald would not have broken the strangle hold of this nightmare if he hadn't shared with his sister. Her prophetic words apply to all of us. **We must turn and face whatever we fear the most and run into the darkness.**

(*Note:* I highly recommend that you read Gerald Sittser's monumental book, *A Grace Disguised*.)

What does working through the grief and sorrow look like? Grief has many stages. We must learn our location in the process and be willing to experience that which we can't control.

Michael Dye in his *Genesis Process*[20] describes the five stages of grief. Freedom from grief comes from allowing the process to work its course. The key is to neither embrace nor deny the grief; rather it is about allowing the pain to wash over you. Think of grief as the ocean tide. You can't control its comings or goings; it is what it is and each wave that washes up on the beach is unique. So, also, will grief be unique to every one of us. Grief can come with any kind of loss. It can be death such as Gerald Sittser experienced because of a tragic auto accident. Or it can be the loss of relationship, loss of a job, loss of freedom or mobility, or even loss of self-respect.

## STAGES OF GRIEF

**Anger**
Blaming someone
or something, feeling
injustice and rage

**Shock/Denial**
Numbness, blanking
out, avoiding thinking
about "it."

**Bargaining**
Thinking "If I'd only..." and
dealing with guilt, vain regrets of
the past, and fear of the future.

**Acceptance**
Embracing reality, forgiving and
moving forward, forming new
friendships while trusting God.

**Depression**
Feeling hopeless, helpless,
disappointed, isolated, and lonely.
Inability to enjoy anything.

© Genesis Process - Dye/Fancher

*Remember:* Unless you allow THE PAIN AND GRIEF to work through you, you will end up becoming stuck in whatever part of the grief process YOU HAPPEN TO BE IN. This is especially true with denial and anger. If you become stuck in either of these stages, the pain or the desire to avoid pain will drive you back into addictions and bitterness. I am hard pressed to think of a worse place to become stuck!

- **Shock/Denial** is all about avoiding the reality of the situation. After a family member had a severe accident that paralyzed him, the doctor came in and told him the bad news; my relative promptly went to sleep. After sleeping for almost a day, he woke up and I asked if he remembered what the doctor had said. His reply was "no." So I had to re-tell him about his new disabilities.

Sexual addicts can live in this phase, denying the severity of the addiction and how it impacts themselves and those that they love.

- **Anger** is really the blame game. We have to blame someone for all of this pain, and so we find the "scapegoat" who might be a friend or an enemy, or it could be God. You will be having an adrenaline cocktail as you rage. One of the properties of adrenaline is its ability to numb or medicate pain. If you are a sports fan then you will understand that most football players play under a controlled rage, especially the linemen. But look at them four hours after the game; they walk around like old men! Anger is just another tool of avoidance.

- **Bargaining** is moving to a coping skill that helps us deal with the guilt of the past. It is thinking, *If only I had done ____, this would never have happened.* But this is also the start of the healing because you are seeking to admit your feelings—no matter how negative—and you are seeking to take responsibility for the event.

Sometimes out of both guilt and shame you will take on responsibility that is not yours. After the exposure of my sin, I saw how painfully my family was reacting to my betrayal. I tried to take on their pain, rightly so. But when they made poor choices, I took responsibility for *their* choices. God spoke to me in one of my prayer times and said something like this, "Harry, you and you only are responsible for wounding your wife and children, but they are responsible for how they deal with their wounds." **I had to find that healthy boundary of not minimizing or denying my sin, yet giving others the opportunity to make their own choices, good or bad.**

- **Depression.** Once we move past bargaining we experience depression. It's unfamiliar territory for some of us. We are beginning to feel pain without the help of our addictions medicating the pain. It's both disheartening and discouraging. But it also is where there is a glimmer of light as we learn to process the pain. We begin to see a different aspect of the reality, though we can't enjoy much of anything. Depression is like a regulator that limits how much you can feel. It won't last forever; there is hope.

- **Acceptance.** Finally we move through the grief to its conclusion. We begin to accept the new reality with both its pains and joys. We make great strides to enter back into old relationships as well as new ones. **In acceptance, we learn to accept life on God's terms instead of ours.**

Grief is like an onion; as you slice an onion you discover that there are many layers. Grief also can have many layers. In especially heavy grief, you may go through the five-stage cycle several times until you have fully accepted the reality of your losses. Just remember that it will end. Paul once again says it best:

> *For our present troubles are small and won't last very long. Yet they produce for us a glory that vastly outweighs them and will last forever! So we don't look at the troubles we can see now; rather, we fix our gaze on things that cannot be seen. For the things we see now will soon be gone, but the things we cannot see will last forever.*
> 2 Corinthians 4:17-18 (NLT)

Your situation may not seem so light, but Paul is letting us know that if we stay the course, the rewards will far outweigh the negatives. Hang in there! There is true hope for you as you work through the grief.

## ✎ ASSIGNMENTS FOR NEXT TIME

➲ Read *Pure Desire* Chapter 8.

➲ **Complete the homework and prepared to share your results next week with your group.**

❶ **List the top ten most painful times in your life.** Rank them with the most painful being #1.

❷ Next, answer the following questions for each of these painful memories:

    **A.** What part of the pain are you responsible for, and what part of the pain do you need to let go? During the debrief at the next Pure Desire meeting, allow the guys in the group to call you out in a loving way if they feel you are blaming others for your choices.

    **B.** How did this event affect the important people of your life?

    **C.** How has that event affected life for you today?

➲ **Write your responses in the spaces provided below and on the following pages.**

## THE 10 MOST PAINFUL TIMES/EVENTS IN MY LIFE

After you have completed listing each event, rank these events from #1 most painful to #10 least painful.

___ **(RANK) PAINFUL EVENT** _____

**A.** What part of the pain am I responsible for, and what part of the pain do I need to let go?


**B.** How did this event affect the important people of my life?


**C.** How has this event affected life for me today?


..........................................................................................................

___ **(RANK) PAINFUL EVENT** _____

**A.** What part of the pain am I responsible for, and what part of the pain do I need to let go?


**B.** How did this event affect the important people of my life?


**C.** How has this event affected life for me today?


..........................................................................................................

## ___ (RANK) PAINFUL EVENT _____

**A.** What part of the pain am I responsible for, and what part of the pain do I need to let go?


**B.** How did this event affect the important people of my life?


**C.** How has this event affected life for me today?


.............................................................................................................

## ___ (RANK) PAINFUL EVENT _____

**A.** What part of the pain am I responsible for, and what part of the pain do I need to let go?


**B.** How did this event affect the important people of my life?


**C.** How has this event affected life for me today?


.............................................................................................................

## ___ (RANK) PAINFUL EVENT _____

**A.** What part of the pain am I responsible for, and what part of the pain do I need to let go?


**B.** How did this event affect the important people of my life?


**C.** How has this event affected life for me today?


.............................................................................................................

## ___ (RANK) PAINFUL EVENT _____

**A.** What part of the pain am I responsible for, and what part of the pain do I need to let go?


**B.** How did this event affect the important people of my life?


**C.** How has this event affected life for me today?


.............................................................................................................

## ___ (RANK) PAINFUL EVENT _____

**A.** What part of the pain am I responsible for, and what part of the pain do I need to let go?

**B.** How did this event affect the important people of my life?

**C.** How has this event affected life for me today?

...............................................................................................................................

## ___ (RANK) PAINFUL EVENT _____

**A.** What part of the pain am I responsible for, and what part of the pain do I need to let go?

**B.** How did this event affect the important people of my life?

**C.** How has this event affected life for me today?

...............................................................................................................................

## ___ (RANK) PAINFUL EVENT _____

**A.** What part of the pain am I responsible for, and what part of the pain do I need to let go?

**B.** How did this event affect the important people of my life?

**C.** How has this event affected life for me today?

...............................................................................................................................

## ___ (RANK) PAINFUL EVENT _____

**A.** What part of the pain am I responsible for, and what part of the pain do I need to let go?

**B.** How did this event affect the important people of my life?

**C.** How has this event affected life for me today?

...............................................................................................................................

# LESSON TWO

## BEING YOUR TRUE SELF

By Harry Flanagan

*Jesus replied, "'You must love the Lord your God with all your heart, all your soul, and all your mind.' This is the first and greatest commandment. A second is equally important: 'Love your neighbor as yourself.' The entire law and all the demands of the prophets are based on these two commandments."*
Matthew 22:37-40 (NLT)

Every person on the planet has been or will be wounded because we live in a fallen world full of broken people. We don't want to be wounded or made vulnerable again. It is at this point we either move toward health or we go into some form of isolation.

Isolation has two purposes: First, its job is to protect the secret, whether that secret is about your thought life or hidden behaviors. The second reason for Isolation is to keep you from unwanted vulnerability in relationships.

Here is our paradox:

> **We are wounded in relationships, but we heal only in the context of relationships.**
> Dr. Ted Roberts

The way we avoid true vulnerability in relationships is through seeking to control the people who potentially threaten us. Control has two major categories: Overt Control (openly aggressive) or Covert Control (passive or passive-aggressive). Control in either category has two major primary core beliefs. Each belief is about self-protection and safety.

The first core belief: I only feel safe when I am in (overt) control. If we can control the circumstances, we protect our secrets. But protecting the secrets means that we view others as threats to our safety. This belief will manifest itself in three sub-categories:

1. **Position of Power and Authority (Boss, Sarge, Commander, The Big Guy):** "It's my way or the highway," "Because I said so," "I am the decision maker," or "My word is the final word." These folks tend to make decisions on their own with no or little input from others.

2. **The Persuasive Preacher:** Talking over the top of others or talking loudest and being convinced they are morally right. Literally, there is no room for disagreement. Often they will quote scriptures and/or claim the moral high ground. "How could you disagree with me?"

3. **The Enforcer (anger, rage, or calculated payback if someone disagrees):** Choosing to be the final authority on decisions. This person may consult with others, but ultimately makes the final decision even though it affects other people.

Other people will feel disenfranchised, minimized, not heard, or not valued; yet the perceived benefit is safety for the addict because they believe they have the ability to control circumstances and, therefore, other people.

**❷ Do any of those sub-categories resonate with you? Are there times that you find yourself in any of those roles? Explain:**

*None. I try to treat others how I want to be treated.*

The second core belief is about the fear of failing played out as covert control (passivity or passive-aggressive behaviors). You quietly manipulate others to be the decision makers, thus avoiding responsibility. Based on past painful circumstances, its message is, "I can't fail again." In this core belief rooted in shame, we presume our value is based on how well we perform. We fear failing, but it becomes about our identity instead of our behaviors. Shame tells us that if we fail at a task, then we become the failure. This belief also has three sub-categories:

1. **Route of Least Resistance**, going with the flow and allowing others to take the lead. Now you will not be responsible for any outcome: "Whatever you want, honey," or "I don't care," or "Whatever!"

2. **"Caught You!" also called "The Ambush."** This is passive-aggressive and you have data that the other person(s) are not aware of. You will use that advantage by revealing you know what they are saying is a lie or by telling them you already know what they have been doing. In either case, it puts the person in a position of control.

3. **Route of Silence.** This can be passive and associated with Route of Least Resistance or can be passive-aggressive by punishing people for their choices related to you. Here you let others make the decision and then you choose to be critical of the decision.

**❷ Do any of those sub categories resonate with you? Are there times you find yourself in any of those roles? If so, explain:**

*No, I try to be assertive.*

## THE MASKS WE WEAR[21]

Numerous subsets of these categories of control, sometimes called masks, describe ways we self-protect. Michael Dye, in *The Genesis Process*, calls these masks "Protective Personalities." These masks are not just a covering over the face; rather, we take on the personality related to the masks. Instead of being yourself, you hide behind these masks that protect you.

### PROTECTIVE PERSONALITIES

| | | | | |
|---|---|---|---|---|
| Clown | Contempt | Car Salesman | Hostess | Doormat |
| Actor | Control | Rescuer | Protector | Victim |
| Anger | Needy | Victimizer | Perfectionist | CEO |
| Spiritualist | Obnoxious | Overachiever | Hard Worker | Uninvolved |
| Pharisee | Dunce | Underachiever | Right | Lazy Loser |
| Bully | Judge | Timid | Black Sheep | Martyr |
| Bouncer | Drama King | Pleaser | Lost Sheep | I'm Okay |
| Hero | Drama Queen | Wannabe | Critic | Bureaucrat |
| Nice | Caustic | Guru | Gentleman | |
| Confusion | Overwhelmed | Professor | Lady | |

❶ Circle or underline those masks that you have worn for self-protection.

❷ Name the three most emotionally powerful masks for you.

_____, _____, and _____

❸ How do these masks protect you? What would happen if you couldn't wear them?

*None. I try to be myself at all times*

....................................................................................................

❹ How and when did they become a part of your life?

....................................................................................................

❺ What would happen if you couldn't wear your masks? How would you solve your problems/issues?

....................................................................................................

**Assertiveness** can be defined as the quality of being self-assured and confident without being aggressive.[22] We want men to learn the concept of being assertive. Control seeks to manipulate another person's choices. Assertiveness simply allows others to hear your point of view, while they retain the right to think or interpret the facts as they see fit.

Being assertive in your relationships allows the significant people in your life—such as your friends, family, and/or coworkers—to know your needs, hopes, and fears without requiring them to do anything to resolve or complete any tasks for you.

The struggles or pain of being passive or passive-aggressive are many; but the rewards of being assertive are worthwhile. When we are passive we often allow others to lead, but feel resentment when our unspoken needs, desires, and feelings aren't being considered. This could lead to conflict or some form of exacting revenge. When we become assertive, others can now consider our thoughts, feelings, and positions as they make their decisions. This will reduce both resentments and conflicts in our relationships.

Being passive or passive-aggressive can leave people feeling like victims or martyrs. This can draw people into situations where they take on the unhealthy roles of victim, rescuer, and prosecutor, which can create a downward spiral in their relationships. Being assertive allows you to express your feelings and allows others to freely respond to your needs and circumstances, and removes you from the role of victim or the martyr.

Keeping your hopes, fears, needs, and desires to yourself will tend to increase stress, which will affect your health emotionally, physically, and spiritually. Being able to communicate hopes, fears, desires, and needs will go a long way in helping to release the stress and to participate with those whom you love and value. And this approach gives them the freedom to support you.

Robert Alberti and Michael Emmons, authors of *Your Perfect Right*, provide a few questions to consider before choosing to be assertive:[23]

- How much does it matter to you?
- Are you looking for a specific outcome or just to express yourself?
- Are you looking for a positive outcome? Might asserting yourself make things worse?
- Will you kick yourself if you don't take action?
- What are the probable consequences and realistic risks from your possible assertion?

**❯ Now let's put these great questions to use as you consider becoming assertive.**

❶ Name a present or past set of resentments. What or who are you resenting? Why do you think this situation caused feelings of resentment?

❷ What will be the consequence if you choose not to be assertive (thereby keeping your resentments to yourself)?

..................................................................................................................................

❸ What will be the potential consequences if you choose to be assertive and allow the appropriate person or people to know about your feelings and resentments?

..................................................................................................................................

❹ What are the realistic hopes of an outcome if you choose to be assertive?

..................................................................................................................................

❺ Share with your group the difficulties and struggles with being assertive in this situation. Allow them to support you in your decision.

## ✐ ASSIGNMENTS FOR NEXT TIME

❯ **Review the Covenant to Contend and prepare written responses to all the exercises and questions included in this lesson.**

## LOVING, ACCEPTING & FORGIVING

By Harry Flanagan

*How much we know and understand ourselves is critically important, but there is something that is even more essential to a wholehearted life: loving ourselves.*
Brené Brown[24]

Healing from addiction requires more than stopping bad or difficult behaviors. Rather, it requires embracing a whole new way of living and redefining who we really are.

As a young Christian in the late 1970's, I found myself transported to a new, more eloquent view of Christianity when I read Jerry Cook's seminal work *Love, Acceptance, and Forgiveness*. It was my first venture into the concept of the church as a force through learning to love, accept, and forgive people right where they are. This simple book changed my view of life and eventually became a foundational piece in my healing. While the book focused on how to love, accept, and forgive others, it did not fully address being able to love, accept, and receive forgiveness for yourself. This caused a gap in my own healing. This is also an essential step for you in your endeavor to experience true healing.

Below are listed some truths related to loving, accepting, and forgiving. After each truth is stated, you will have an opportunity to identify how it plays out in your life.

**Truth: Loving**—If you are truly finding value in yourself, you will become someone who is learning healthy self-care; that is, healthy ways of coping with the stress and strains of life.

*And Jesus said to him, "'You shall love the LORD your God with all your heart, and with all your soul, and with all your mind.' This is the great and foremost commandment. The second is like it, 'You shall love your neighbor as yourself.'"*
Matthew 22:37-39 (NASB)

**❷ What are the healthy ways you cope and nurture (love) yourself?**

.......................................................................................................................................................

**❷ One of the great battles in learning to value and care for yourself is over self judgments. How do you justify being critical, having contempt, or even self-hatred? Please list below those judgments you have held against yourself.**

.......................................................................................................................................................

**Truth: Accepting**—Accepting your circumstances is part of the grieving process. It is important to come to the place of accepting the reality you have an addiction. It includes accepting the reality that you can't heal by yourself.

*Therefore, accept each other just as Christ has accepted you so that God will be given glory.*
Romans 15:7 (NLT)

➲ **Below please share a brief story of how you came to the understanding that you have an addictive personality and why you chose to join a Pure Desire group. Choose to be a grace-filled truth-teller.**

**Truth: Forgiving**—As long as you hold yourself and others in judgment you will never experience true freedom from your addiction. A perverse form of arrogance is associated with addicts; though God and often others have forgiven them, they cling to their lack of being able to accept forgiveness. They continue to live with their judgments and self-abuse. Healing can only come when you allow God, others, and yourself to give you a fresh start. This always begins with God. Take a few minutes and do some business with God. This Bible verse can guide you:

*If we claim we have no sin, we are only fooling ourselves and not living in the truth. But if we confess our sins to him, he is faithful and just to forgive us our sins and to cleanse us from all wickedness.*
1 John 1:8-9 (NLT)

➲ **We are gifted a fresh beginning! List below the sins for which you have been forgiven.**

➲ **Write a short prayer about believing God for His forgiveness; be specific about the sins for which you are now receiving His forgiveness.**

## ASSIGNMENTS FOR NEXT TIME

❶ Be prepared to share with your group what you discovered in this lesson about yourself and love, acceptance, and forgiveness.

## SELF-CARE

By Harry Flanagan

People with addictions establish protective personalities. These personalities act like masks or defensive mannerisms. They have become vigilant in keeping the secret. This vigilance will dominate and control our lives.

One of the casualties of investing in our protective personalities has been our lack of self-care. I have yet to meet a person in bondage or addiction who started the healing process with a clear sense of self-care. They may be doing something in one of the areas, but never have I seen anyone who easily embraces self-care, even after years of trying to work through their healing.

This is a daily battle for me. I still have areas where I'm not naturally good with self-care. It seldom is on the top of my list of priorities, although it needs to be. God has called us His temple. The word temple has two choices in the Greek. One is about a building used for religious functions. The second is the place where God's presence dwells. It is the second definition that Paul intended in his words to the Christians at Corinth.

> *Do you not know that you are a temple of God and that the Spirit of God dwells in you? If any man destroys the temple of God, God will destroy him, for the temple of God is holy, and that is what you are.*
> 1 Corinthians 3:16-17 (NASB)

This verse is at once both comforting and convicting. It's comforting because God is saying that you and I are so valuable that "If anyone harms you I will destroy them." It reveals not only that we have value to Him, but also that He desires to protect us. For people who have lived in isolation it is awkward and even uncomfortable to have God be so loving and intimate with us. Yet, in our heart of hearts this is what we have longed for.

1 Corinthians 3:16-17 is also very convicting. Paul uses the phrase "if any man" destroys the temple (us) then He will destroy that person. When I look back on my life, or even evaluate it now, I am the one person who has done the most damage and neglect to the temple that is my body.

Oops, now I have done it; God wants to love and protect me and I mess it up; now in my heart I fear I am back in a place of opposition to Him. Even now, I can hear the enemy using scripture to accuse us, just as he used scripture to accuse Jesus. Yes, I can almost hear an audible voice saying, "*Anyone who isn't with me opposes me.*" (Matthew 12:30) The Message translation of the verse is even starker in its comment:

> *This is war, and there is no neutral ground. If you're not on my side, you're the enemy; if you're not helping, you're making things worse.*
> Matthew 12:30 (MSG)

We do need to heed this verse, but I do not think that our Father is just waiting for us to fail Him so that He can nail us. He is not the mythical Viking god Thor, with his hammer and lightning bolt ready to take us out because we are His enemies. We are His children who are broken and in need of His grace and power. I am reminded of another verse penned by the Apostle Paul:

*And then he told me, My grace is enough; it's all you need.*
*My strength comes into its own in your weakness.*
2 Corinthians 12:9a (MSG)

That's clear enough for me! I know that I am weak spiritually and I believe that God's grace is ultimately all I need. His strength will be revealed in the acknowledgment of my weakness and my dependence on Him. Remember that we are moving toward accepting life on His terms. Therefore, we need to risk learning to lean on Him. He won't let you and me down; we're His kids and He is the perfect Father who is on our side.

### FOUR AREAS OF SELF-CARE WILL BE THE FOCUS FOR THE REMAINDER OF THIS LESSON:

- Nurturing Ourselves Spiritually
- Nurturing Ourselves Mentally
- Nurturing Ourselves Physically
- Nurturing Ourselves Relationally

## NURTURING OURSELVES SPIRITUALLY

Although we seem inept in this arena, we are deep spiritual beings. Paul tells us in 2 Corinthians 5 that to be absent from the body is to be present with Christ. Think about that; my body is only a vessel that allows me to move around and through this world. My body is a part of my being but it is not the totality of who I am. In fact, my eternity is tied to my spirituality, not how much I know or how much I do. It is the state of being in relationship with Him.

For almost the entirety of my Christian walk, I have been amazed at a few things in Revelation 2 where John becomes the scribe for Jesus. John tells us that Jesus can't find fault with the behaviors of the people of the church in Ephesus. Now that is incredible. The King of Kings couldn't find fault with any of their behaviors. What a marvelous church! As a young Christian, I thought I could go into any church and find fault with something they were doing. I didn't realize that just pointed out my own battle with self-righteousness!

But Jesus does expose their area of need. He tells the church at Ephesus that they have abandoned their first love. Unless they repent (turn around) and do the things that they did at first, this church would lose its authority and influence within the Christian community. Paraphrased, Jesus was telling them, "You have been so busy doing things for me, that you have stopped spending time with Me."

Now that gets my attention! I know that I have been guilty of that periodically through my walk with Christ. How about you? I am guessing that many of you, like me, get caught up in the hustle and bustle of both life in general and life in the church. None of that is bad, but it's not our ultimate calling.

Martha complained that Mary wasn't helping, and Jesus said, **"Martha, Martha, you are worried and bothered about so many things; but only one thing is necessary, for Mary has chosen the good part, which shall not be taken away from her."** (Luke 10:39 NASB) The good part is spending time in the presence of God. How are you doing with that?

## TWO SIMPLE STEPS WILL MOVE YOU TOWARD INTIMACY WITH GOD.

**First, purposely choose to dedicate 15 minutes to an hour, not to devotions in the classical sense, but to be quiet in His presence.** Only read as the Holy Spirit leads you; keep paper and pen close by so that you can write down the promptings that comes from being in His presence.

**The second step is to journal.** I know, I know. I have yet to find someone who easily embraced journaling. But please give me a chance to state my case. In this fast-paced world we need some regulators, something to slow us down. That is the role of journaling. It slows us down, allows us to think and gives us a chance to become more self-aware. Journal notes chart our progress over time and allow us a wonderful map of the journey of life.

## SWORD DRILL: LEARN TO JOURNAL IN RESPONSE TO THE WORD OF GOD[25]

Practicing the SWORD Drill will help you tie to Scripture the truths you discover. In other words, you will be touched but unchanged if journaling God's Word is not part of your experience. This process involves some of the most significant renewing of your mind you have ever experienced and that only happens when you encounter the supernatural power of God's Word in your heart and not just in your head.

The term **SWORD (Scripture. Wait. Observe. Request. Dedicate)** can be helpful in the journaling process. It reminds us that this is about spiritual warfare. This isn't just about some clinical process; this is WAR. We must approach each day of the rest of our lives with the weapon of the Word of God in our hearts and on my mouths.

More information about using the SWORD Drill is included in the *Seven Pillars of Freedom Journal*.

# NURTURING OURSELVES MENTALLY

How do you think outside of your box? Scientists tell us that the quality of our life and the strength of our brains are partially tied to keeping our brains stimulated with new mental experiences.

Ted amazes me; he consumes books at a rate beyond any other friend or acquaintance. He loves knowledge and embraces the practical aspects of applying the new knowledge into his life.

Mentally are you in a rut? Do you study or have interest in only one or two areas or do you have some variety? Even when it comes to reading my Bible, I love to switch to other translations regularly because the new phraseology allows me a fresh look at familiar passages.

I do love to read. I read many books and articles for my work at PDMI (Pure Desire Ministries International). I also love history, and always keep one or two history books handy. I enjoy an occasional novel or humorous book.

Mental self-care isn't just about books; many other choices also stimulate, such as browsing art galleries, museums, and other types of exhibits. My wife and I explore some of these on our date nights. Consider other positive ways to break out of your ruts.

## NURTURING OURSELVES PHYSICALLY

Nurturing ourselves physically is not just about exercise and dieting. Though they play a major role, there is much more. Do you regularly go to the doctor and dentist for both preventative and restorative checkups? Do you regularly get enough sleep nightly? How do you work through stress in healthy ways?

Stress is behind a vast majority of the obstacles that keep you from living a healthy life. The busyness of life also adds to stress and we need to learn to separate the urgent from the important. Many things that seem urgent in the moment are not really very important. Slowing down and learning to relax in your faith and lifestyle will bring you to a place where you have the opportunity to be renewed.

When I worked in the mortgage business I would tell people, "You want to own the house, and not let the house own you." In that same way, God has given you stewardship over your life. Does the life you live own you or do you own the life that you are living?

Breaking out of isolation, passivity, and procrastination will set you free of having circumstances owning your life. Instead you can begin to take ownership, with the guidance of God, and begin to live life the way He is teaching us. If you don't take responsibility then you will always have those people around who are more than happy to run your life for you. In that case, self-care will not be of any true value to you.

This area is the one that gives me the most trouble. I have been so consumed with my healing from sexual addition that I didn't take care of my whole being. As I am maturing, or as I am fond of saying, I get more and more "extinguished" every day, I am finding limitations that have resulted from the lack of self-care in my life. I am overweight and have Type 2 diabetes directly tied to poor self-care management. The good news is that it is never too late to get started! I am feeling better about self-care as I become more disciplined.

## NURTURING OURSELVES RELATIONALLY

During World War II when the Nazi's bombed England, both the elderly and the young had high death rates as families were being torn apart by death and war. Then someone had the big idea that the elderly should take care of the young. People began to watch a miracle as the young ones felt love and affection (they were not abandoned and alone) and the elderly felt valued and useful (they had something to contribute). The death rate in both groups rapidly and significantly diminished.

We were made for relationships. If we don't give ourselves permission to develop great friendships we miss out on a sense of belonging and knowing we are truly loved. Life will merely be about existing, which is not what God has called us to.

> *The thief comes only to steal and kill and destroy;*
> *I came that they may have life, and have it abundantly.*
> John 10:10

The word "abundantly" in the original language of the New Testament is very powerful. It means both quantity and quality. Now take that definition and put it in the verse. *"I came that you may have true life and that life will be both abundant and the quality of your life will also be increased."*

This truth sure sounds good to me. How about you? What is your priority to develop friendships? I know that if it weren't for the friends that God sent my way during my healing time at East Hill Church I would not have made it.

My friendships are a priority in my life. I have friends who I go to the coffee shops with and we simply enjoy and invest in each other. My wife, Debby, and I have a small group that we attend weekly. These people are not just members of the church; they are the core and most important piece of my church experience. They are wonderful friends, and, truth be said, they are a part of my clan!

Your healing depends on how well you embrace self-care, which should be incorporated into your relapse prevention plan. If you have good and godly friends, be sure to maintain them through the healing process.

## ✎ ASSIGNMENTS FOR NEXT TIME

❶ **Self-care goals. Write down at least one goal and one or two action steps for each of the four self-care areas:** Spiritual, Mental, Physical, and Relational. Develop these goals and action steps in a one or two page paper on self-care.

- Be prepared to read your paper to the group and discuss your ideas at the next meeting of your Pure Desire group.

. . . . . . . . . . . . . . . . . . . . . . . . . . . . . . . . . . . . . . . . . . . . . . . . . . . . . . . . . . . . . . . . . . . . . . . . . . . . . . . . . . . . . . . . . . .

❷ **Review the Pillar Three Commitment and be ready to sign it at the next meeting.** What are some of your "take-aways" from Pillar Three?

. . . . . . . . . . . . . . . . . . . . . . . . . . . . . . . . . . . . . . . . . . . . . . . . . . . . . . . . . . . . . . . . . . . . . . . . . . . . . . . . . . . . . . . . . . .

❸ Read *Pure Desire* Chapter 9.

# ✔ PILLAR OF FREEDOM THREE COMMITMENT

I have, to the best of my ability, completed all the exercises found in Pillar of Freedom Three. By God's grace I will do everything I can to live out these truths in my life on a daily basis. I know that healing does not come while I am alone. I am choosing to surrender to the process by participating in the life of this healing community as it has been outlined in Pillar Three.

My Name _____

Signature _____ Date _____

## AFFIRMING WITNESSES

❶ *I affirm the fact that* _____ *has complied with Pillar Three by using the tools presented, and participating in the life of the group as outlined in Pillar Three.*

My Name _____

Signature _____ Date _____

❷ *I affirm the fact that* _____ *has complied with Pillar Three by using the tools presented, and participating in the life of the group as outlined in Pillar Three.*

My Name _____

Signature _____ Date _____

PILLAR OF FREEDOM FOUR

# LIMITING DAMAGE

## YOU NEED A DAMAGE CONTROL PLAN

It is amazing how student pilots can get themselves into such difficult situations. As a flight instructor in the military, I had students trying to kill me in some very creative ways. But when left in the airplane alone, they can really get inventive!

I remember one student's incredible dilemma. At the time, we were pushing pilots through the training process as fast as we could because we were in the middle of war. We were even using "retread" aircraft from the fleet. These were aircraft types that hadn't proved that useful because of some design limitations, but were more than adequate for the training process. One model in particular was a joy to fly. It was a single seat high performance aircraft that could turn on a dime. One problem: it had a propensity to develop corrosion in the saltwater environment of carrier operations. So instead of expending a staggering number of man-hours in preventative maintenance to fight the corrosion, the aircraft would be sent back to the training command.

The fledgling pilot must have thought he had "died and gone to heaven" to have an opportunity to fly such a high performance aircraft in the final stages of the training process. He was in the midst of air-to-air gunnery, flying what was called the "squirrel cage pattern." This is where four planes take turns making runs on a banner that is being towed through the air by another aircraft. It is an intense experience as four aircraft twist and turn through a circular pattern around the rapidly moving banner.

At the top of the pattern the young pilot rolled into the target and simultaneously looked down into the cockpit to arm his guns. Now this aircraft could really accelerate once you pointed its nose earthward. It began rocketing toward terra firma at a frightening speed. The student pilot raised his head out of the cockpit to the sight of the ground exploding upwards toward him. In a total state of panic, he yanked back on the stick for everything he was worth. Remember, I told you this aircraft had corrosion problems. Well deep within the wing structure of that bird there was some serious deterioration.

This is where the story starts to get *very interesting*! The sudden and violent loading of the plane caused the outer left wing section to **snap right off!** The terrified student is now thrown into an extreme left bank as the right wing rises. Then the severed left wing slams into the right wing breaking it off as well! The plane is now dropping like a brick with just two stubs for wings. The cockpit is so far forward and the wings are so swept back it is hard for the pilot to see the wings. This young man is scared out of his wits. He is applying every ounce of throttle he can find. He doesn't have a clue what has happened. His entire focus is on damage control and staying alive. He can barely control the attitude of the aircraft and has to use full power just to stay airborne, but soon full power will mean no power…he will run out of fuel. Fighter aircraft are notoriously thirsty beasts and at this power setting his life can be measured in moments not lengthy minutes.

Then he makes a wise decision. He gets on the radio and starts crying out for help. The policy was to always have an instructor at home base for panicked student pilots to call for help and advice. And this guy was screaming out for help at the top of his lungs. It took awhile before the instructor could get the young man to calm down and speak clearly.

After listening to the young man's frantic plea for help, the instructor asked him to fly by the tower to see what the problem was. It was obvious the kid had lost his cool. It was probably nothing more than a minor problem. There must have been stunned silence in the control tower as the young aviator came roaring by with the plane cocked up in an exaggerated nose-high attitude. He was literally standing it on its tailpipe. He had no idea he was flying on nothing more than the stubby remnants of what had once been wings. Somewhat shaken, the control tower suggested the student fly to a nearby, uninhabited area and get out of the thing. He needed a damage control plan that would save his life!

Just like this pilot, you need a damage control plan as well my friend, because sexual addiction can kill you. You need to face the fact that you choose your behavior in the past, but reality chooses your consequences in the present. You have sown some weeds in your life through your addictive behavior. Yes, you have just completed Pillars Two and Three. You have come to understand the nature of sexual addiction and bondage. More importantly: You have surrendered to the process. In other words you are making *great choices*! But—the crop of your past thorny choices, may just now be coming to fruition in your life. That can be an incredibly frustrating experience. You are doing all the right things, however nothing but bad stuff seems to be hitting you.

The reality for most guys is the unmanageability of their lives. You may feel like it has continued long after you have chosen to come clean and get right with God. You don't have any control over the consequences from past choices that may be impacting your life right now! That can make you angry and feel like you have been betrayed. At this stage in the process it is so easy to say, "This thing isn't working!" It can feel like everything is spinning out of control, especially when your wife is so wounded she can't even speak to you and you may be experiencing deep financial problems. Things from your past can draw extreme levels of compound interest in the present. The enemy of your soul is doing everything he can right now to discourage you and draw you back into the old patterns of behavior.

Yet the **negative consequences you may be facing right now are gifts in disguise.** As you choose to stand your ground and face the pain within instead of medicating it, your brain literally gets reprogrammed. You realize the truth that there really aren't any secrets. Sooner or later the truth always comes out. You honestly face the fact you are powerless to change your behavior on your own. You need others and you start coming out of isolation.

One of the worst things about your past double life is it worked for a while. In the acting out, the sin was hidden from view and you could function fairly well. Maybe you were even successful in some areas of your life. The problem is, you ended up paying a horrific price. It set you up to become grandiose in your thinking, believing you could somehow pull it off. "I can fly this thing even if both wings are ripped off." All the while chaos was closing in on you. You were running out of gas and options and God loved you enough to let you go there.

In order for health to truly take root in your life you must develop a damage control plan. You may not have problems ripping off your wings right now, but in the days ahead, those moments may come from severe relationship difficulties or battling with the public shame of having your true story told through the process of disclosure. **So hold on to the truth that your addiction was a form of insanity in which you were deluded about reality.**

Therefore, in the present **you must pursue reality at all costs**. And that means you must deal with the problems you are currently facing. You may feel like you have tumbled out of the sky and are barely able to stay airborne, but God has an answer for every one of your problems. If you will face them with the help of others then the sanity of God's blessing on your life will give you new wings.

> *But those who wait on the Lord will find new strength.*
> *They will fly high on wings like eagles.*
> Isaiah 40:31a (NLT)

❶ What are the major problems you are facing right now that are the result of past choices?

- Describe them in detail in the space below making sure you note the origin of the problem.
- It may take you a while to see the connection. Take your time to think through the relationship.
- Once you see the connection then your anger level will be greatly reduced.

| A SIGNIFICANT PROBLEM I AM FACING | THE ORIGIN OF THE PROBLEM I CREATED OR ALLOWED TO EXIST |
|---|---|
| *Example:* *My wife's anger towards me* | *I lied to her to cover up the deep sense of inadequacy I struggle with.* |
| 1. | |
| 2. | |
| 3. | |
| 4. | |
| 5. | |

❷ Simply acknowledging that you have a problem and identifying the origin of that problem doesn't solve it. The question is: **Do you have a damage control plan? What are some possible solutions to the problem?**

➥ **Select one significant problem from your list** _____

- Make sure you get input from others.
- Be creative and have your support system help you "think outside the box" of the problem.

❯ **Possible solutions: list as many as you can think of!**

..........................................................................................................................

❯ **What might be some positive results of the best solution?**

..........................................................................................................................

❯ **What action steps do you need to take so it can happen?**

1. _____

2. _____

3. _____

4. _____

5. _____

❯ **What kind of support do you need and from whom?**

..........................................................................................................................

## ✎ ASSIGNMENTS FOR NEXT TIME

❶ Work through at least **two** other significant problems you are facing in life using the process described in this lesson. Be prepared to share with the group during the next meeting.

❷ Read *Pure Desire* Chapter 10. Take the **Spiritual Altitude Test** at the end of the chapter. Be ready to share about your "spiritual altitude" with the group.

# THE MATRIX OF ADDICTION

As I walked out of my office, I heard that distinctive sound you never forget—the firing of an aircraft ejection seat. Through my office window that overlooked the runway, I saw a plane only hundreds of feet above the ground with the instructor's ejection seat blasting out of the stricken plane. A micro second later the student's seat exploded him out of the front cockpit as well. The question: Would his chute open before he impacted the ground? With only about fifty feet to spare the student's chute inflated and swung him to the ground. The crippled jet continued on its deadly path slamming into the ground in a searing ball of jet fuel and flying wreckage. Amazingly, the stunned pilots were totally unscathed as they disconnected themselves from their chutes.

The instructor was my newly acquired friend Chuck Scott. I had the pleasure of sharing Christ with him. However, our first meeting was not all that encouraging. He had openly attacked me about my faith in front of other instructor pilots. After he responded to Christ I asked, "Chuck, why did you assail my walk with Christ when we first met?" I will never forget his response, "Ted, I wanted to see if you honestly lived out your faith. I was looking for answers in my life." I was so thankful I hadn't punched the guy's lights out when he verbally attacked me.

The process of sharing my faith with Chuck was not an easy one. Shortly after our initial confrontation, the Lord told me to put a Christian book in his mailbox at the squadron. I said, "No way, Lord. You saw how the man demeaned me!" I don't know why I argue with the Lord. He is so relentlessly gracious and He always wins. I think God gets a kick out of all my protestations because we both know I am eventually going to do what He says. So, with maximum stealth, I quietly put the book in his mailbox.

The next day as I walked into the squadron, Chuck unloaded a verbal blast my way with both barrels. "Roberts if you ever leave Christian garbage like that in my mailbox again I will knock your &*#** head off!" That settled it. The guy was a nut case. I would have nothing to do with him.

Of course, that is precisely when the Lord told me to put the book *back* in his mailbox! There was absolutely no way I would ever do that. Yet once again, I found myself surreptitiously placing it back in his mailbox. This is where the story gets very interesting. The next day, Chuck grabbed his mail as he rushed out to the aircraft carrier. We were in the process of training students about the exciting and terrifying intricacies of landing aboard the carrier. He was part of the advanced party for this training cycle. The carrier got fogged in and he was stuck on board with nothing to read but this book that God had demanded I put in his mailbox. It turned out to be exactly the thing he needed. In the crowded confines of his office aboard the carrier he opened his heart wide to an infinite and gracious Savior.

When he returned, he shared his newfound faith with me. I was stunned to say the least. It is interesting how, at times, I can pray for miracles and when they happen I have a hard time believing them. I don't think I am the only one who struggles with just how good God is to us. Soon I began to mentor my new friend.

I shared with him how to read God's Word, not as a theological textbook, but instead how to let it read him. You are learning to do exactly the same thing in the meditation exercises in this workbook. Chuck was an eager student and soon learned how to hear God speaking to *him* personally through the Word.

At the time we had lost a number of planes and pilots in accidents. Most of them involved the pilot waiting too long before they ejected when the aircraft was out of control or malfunctioning.

Early one morning as Chuck read the Bible, he sensed the Lord telling him to check out the NATOPS (Naval Air Training and Operating Procedures Standardization) manual; this is the Bible on how to fly the plane. Specifically, the Lord led him to the section dealing with the low altitude ejection sequence. He spent about half-an-hour figuring out at what altitude he would have to make an instant decision to get out of the plane if it was in trouble. Those thirty minutes of obedient investment would save not only his life, but his student's as well.

It was nearing the end of the flight and they were in the landing pattern. The high speed of the aircraft was challenging the reaction times of the student. He was "behind the aircraft." The fighter plane was flying faster than he could think; which is a common occurrence for a student. Chuck ordered the student to apply full power and come around again for another approach for landing. They were at a very low altitude and as power was applied the plane initially began to climb. Then, suddenly, all the instruments went blank; radio communication was lost and the aircraft began to falter. Unbeknown to Chuck, the sudden acceleration of the engine triggered a catastrophic failure of some of the turbine blades. They disintegrated, cutting through the engine housing, electrical wiring and hydraulic lines. The plane essentially died in midair and the two pilots were destined to be part of the carnage soon to occur below, unless someone responded instantly. The student pilot didn't have a clue. He was still trying to get his flight helmet on and stay pointed in the right direction. However, Chuck's early morning investment in the Lord would pay huge dividends as he instinctively triggered the ejection sequence.

I was a part of the accident investigation team for the crash. Once we were able to determine that the cause wasn't pilot error, but faulty turbine blades, we began checking other aircraft in the squadron. We were horrified to discover that several other planes were set up to have the same problem. There were hairline cracks in the turbine blades. When these blades were initially cast, mistakes had been made and as a result, a number of the engines were ticking time bombs. It was only a matter of time until the disaster would be repeated. By carefully tracing the steps backwards we were able to understand exactly why the failure had occurred.

Now here is where I am headed with this story. It is a parable of your life sexually. You have crashed in your life sexually otherwise you wouldn't be interested in this workbook. You can tell yourself things like:

- *"Well my problem is not as bad as that guy's!"*
- *"Since I haven't acted out in six months, I must be healed!"*
- *"I can handle the problem."*
- *"I have prayed and promised God, my wife, myself, or whoever that I will never do it again."*

**But if you don't understand what set the crash up in the first place, you are destined to repeat it!** And repeat it! And repeat it! You get the picture. You need to clearly understand the matrix of the addictive process in your life. The damage will only deepen until you do.

Your shame and embarrassment will try to keep you from looking carefully at the sequence of the crash. But if you don't, it's only a matter of time before you will act out again. At the bare minimum you will be living a double life. Denying what caused the crash in the past will make you duplicitous in the present. You will not be able to understand how your spiritual adversary is leveraging your weaknesses against you. You will be a stranger to certain parts of your soul.

## PERSONALIZING THE MATRIX OF ADDICTION

Most of the addictive thoughts that drive you into the ground occur at the limbic level. Your prefrontal cortex or higher reasoning power is not primarily involved. If either of those were involved, you would have stopped your behavior long ago because of your commitment to Christ. Instead, you are reacting at an instinctive level. If you draw a blank, ask the Holy Spirit to reveal the sequence to you.

*Remember:* Relapses don't just happen in your life; relapses are *always preceded* by certain types of thoughts and actions. I have not depicted the relapse as a steady downward progress for the simple reason it doesn't feel that way. If it did, you wouldn't go there. It starts out feeling good, and then suddenly it curves down. The rapid downward progress is triggered once you get to the point of "no return." This is a limbic decision point so you are frequently not even aware that a transition has taken place; thus the curved line versus a sharp turning point. This is precisely why it is so important you draw out a picture of several of your addiction sequences so you can understand your thought process prior to the crash. Understanding the sequence will enable you to catch yourself in the future and hopefully bail out or prevent the crash.

I have depicted a typical matrix of addiction compiled from what I have heard from thousands of men. The critical factor in doing this exercise is for men to hear what they say to themselves along the way. These are excuses that we use, the rationalizations we tell ourselves to feed the addiction. Once we have acted out, the lies we have told ourselves along the way seem ridiculous, but then it is too late. We have to learn to pick up on the excuses during the process and refute them!

> ***If you don't understand what set the crash up in the first place,
> you are destined to repeat it!***

## TYPICAL MATRIX OF SEXUAL ADDICTION

A=Action | E=Excuse

**A:** Look up the porn site and feel sexual arousal
**E:** *I can handle it; I can stop anytime I want.*

**A:** Notice a sexual picture, site, or pop-up
**E:** *This is interesting!*

**A:** Spend extended time online masturbating
**E:** *Consumed in the pleasure, but feeling deep guilt*

**A:** Cruising the Internet
**E:** *I am just checking my email.*

**A:** Look at other sites and stimulate self
**E:** *I am not hurting anyone.*

**A:** Feelings of deep shame and frustration
**E:** *Hide the behavior and/or pray and promise God I will stop*

In the space below, describe your "**matrix of addiction**" or trajectory of relapse. What are your "**broken turbine blade thoughts**" that precede you crashing into the ground sexually? If you have never taken the time to do this type of exercise this *can really challenge you*!

## MY MATRIX OF ADDICTION

A=Action | E=Excuse

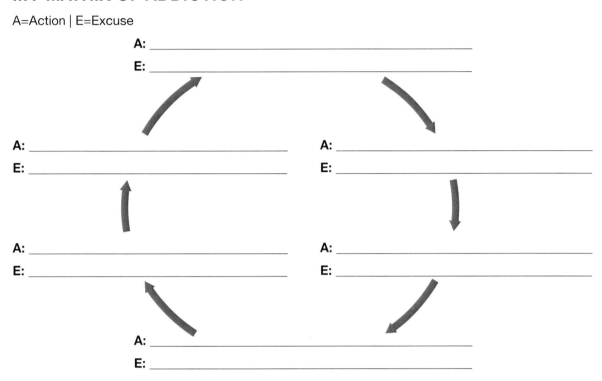

A: _____

E: _____

A: _____

E: _____

A: _____

E: _____

A: _____

E: _____

A: _____

E: _____

A: _____

E: _____

❷ **Now let's take it deeper. Remember back to the last time you acted out? What were the preconditions? Identify your moods or things that had or had not occurred in your life that day.**

1. _____

2. _____

3. _____

4. _____

If you do this exercise thoughtfully, you will probably discover there were some very common preconditions. Your addiction is primarily a process whereby you medicate your pain within. It could be that something in the present reminds you of the pain of something from your past. It could be boredom or a haunting sense of worthlessness, despite all your achievements.

**The sequence is almost always triggered by some inner emotional discomfort.** Once you have "crashed" sexually enough times, your brain changes the way it actually functions. You end up operating on "autopilot" and it's flying you into the ground again and again. This difficult exercise helps you to finally identify the destructive autopilot switch so you can begin to turn it off.

Finally, look in *Pure Desire*, Chapter 3, at the **noose of addiction**. What we have has helped you identify *your addictive lifestyle*.

**❯ Now identify the following in your life:**

**❶** Your sexual fantasies that are part of the preconditions.

...........................................................................................................................................

**❷** Your rituals that set you up for the relapse (cruising the Internet, watching sexual videos, flirting on the job, etc.)

...........................................................................................................................................

**❸** Your attempts of trying to "keep the lid on" include:

...........................................................................................................................................

**❹** Stop and look back over what you have written down. What are your observations concerning the battle that you have been fighting?

A. _____

B. _____

C. _____

D. _____

## ✍ ASSIGNMENTS FOR NEXT TIME

**❶** Mediate on **2 Samuel 9:1-13**. Read the passage through at least five times and find yourself in story.

**❷** Be prepared to share with your group all that you have discovered about your **Matrix of Addiction**.

# LESSON THREE 📄

## YOUR GRIEVANCE STORY

➡ **Read 2 Samuel 9:1-13 (MSG) out loud at the next group meeting.**

*One day David asked, "Is there anyone left of Saul's family?
If so, I'd like to show him some kindness in honor of Jonathan."*

*2 It happened that a servant from Saul's household named Ziba was there. They
called him into David's presence. The king asked him, "Are you Ziba?"*

*"Yes sir," he replied.*

*3 The king asked, "Is there anyone left from the family of Saul
to whom I can show some godly kindness?"*

*Ziba told the king, "Yes, there is Jonathan's son, lame in both feet."*

*4 "Where is he?"*

*"He's living at the home of Makir son of Ammiel in Lo Debar."*

*5 King David didn't lose a minute.
He sent and got him from the home of Makir son of Ammiel in Lo Debar.*

*6 When Mephibosheth son of Jonathan (who was the son of Saul),
came before David, he bowed deeply, abasing himself, honoring David.*

*David spoke his name: "Mephibosheth."*

*"Yes sir?"*

*7 "Don't be frightened," said David. "I'd like to do something special for you in memory
of your father Jonathan. To begin with, I'm returning to you all the properties of your
grandfather Saul. Furthermore, from now on you'll take all your meals at my table."*

*8 Shuffling and stammering, not looking him in the eye, Mephibosheth said, "Who
am I that you pay attention to a stray dog like me?"*

*9-10 David then called in Ziba, Saul's right-hand man, and told him, "Everything that
belonged to Saul and his family, I've handed over to your master's grandson. You and
your sons and your servants will work his land and bring in the produce, provisions
for your master's grandson. Mephibosheth himself, your master's grandson, from
now on will take all his meals at my table." Ziba had fifteen sons and twenty servants.*

*11-12 "All that my master the king has ordered his servant,"
answered Ziba, "your servant will surely do."*

*And Mephibosheth ate at David's table, just like one of the royal family.
Mephibosheth also had a small son named Mica. All who were part of Ziba's
household were now the servants of Mephibosheth.*

*13 Mephibosheth lived in Jerusalem,
taking all his meals at the king's table. He was lame in both feet.*

There was a man named Mephibosheth who was in line to be the next king of Israel. His father Jonathan was killed in combat against the Philistines and God did something only God could do; He reached right over Mephibosheth without violating him in the process and put a relative unknown on the throne.

We don't see David as an unknown, but his own father saw him as essentially worthless. When Samuel the prophet looked closely at the seven sons Jesse had lined up before him to choose from, he was puzzled. The Lord would not let him anoint any of them to be king. "Do you have any other sons?" Samuel asked. This was a crazy question because a Hebrew father would obviously present each of his sons to Samuel for selection as king. But amazingly enough Jesse replies, "Yes there is the youngest one." The NIV politely uses the word "youngest." The Hebrew term is "*kaw-tawn*" which could easily be translated the "worthless one."

David was not highly rated by his family of origin. It makes me suspect that, like me, he might have been an illegitimate child. I can't prove, it but the bottom line is that he wasn't a favored son. Yet he was favored in God's eyes. You see that in the Lord's comments to Samuel prior to sending him to Jesse's home.

> GOD addressed Samuel: "So, how long are you going to mope over Saul? You know I've rejected him as king over Israel. Fill your flask with anointing oil and get going. I'm sending you to Jesse of Bethlehem. I've spotted the very king I want among his sons."
> 1 Samuel 16:1 (MSG)

*Translation:* Samuel, I have found a man after my own heart. I found a little shepherd boy out in the hill country of Judea. He is dancing before me, writing me love songs and blowing me kisses. This is the man I will make the next king of Israel.

It is fascinating to watch God call out someone who isn't even supposed to be in an exalted position. He can take them from the gutter and bring them to a place of grace and power. God took David from the gutter-most to the uttermost!

You can always tell when a man realizes this reality in his life. His worship isn't plastic or mechanical, but profoundly from the soul. The first book I read in the Bible was the book of Psalms. I used to carry a small New Testament and Psalms in the pant leg of my flight suit. Whenever I got a spare moment between flights as an instructor, I would pull out the Psalms and begin reading. I was amazed at David's passion and power. He grabbed life by the throat and wrestled deeply with the vicissitudes of daily existence in a fallen world. Yet somehow he always seemed to hold on to God's love for him and his love for God! Yes, the guy was a sex addict as well. David was this amazing amalgamation of contradictions just like many of us!

David could be stunningly gracious and you see that in his question: "Is there anyone from the household of Saul left that I can bless?" That is a mind-boggling question because Saul had hunted him down like a dog for over a decade. The man sought every means possible to kill David. Yet, David is now responding with such graciousness in seeking to bless someone from the household of Saul. What a powerful picture of a man who knows that everything he has is a gift from God. The servant, Ziba, informs him there is one grandson left. Mephibosheth is living down in Lo Debar. I absolutely love how the King James Version expressed David's response.

*Then king David sent, and fetched him out of the house of Machir,*
*the son of Ammiel, from Lo-debar.*
2 Samuel 9:5 (KJV)

Sounds rather strange, doesn't it—"fetching" someone out of a place. The old English word refers to a pulling or jerking of someone out of something. But that is a graphic description of what God's grace has done in your life, isn't it? Maybe you grew up in the "perfect Christian" home and gave your heart to Christ as a preschooler. Yet, God pulled you out of the pit of hell. For guys like myself that don't have a background like that, "fetching" is an easy concept to grasp. I met Christ in the middle of having to kill men at close range.

But it doesn't matter if you meet Christ in the middle of a war or in the middle of a Sunday School class; we were all pulled out of the pit by the grace of God. You didn't decide to receive Christ on your own. God gave you the ability and the desire to make that decision in the first place. And He will give you the grace to defeat the sexual bondages that now plague your soul! But it doesn't happen with just more prayer or effort on your part. It only takes place as you come face to face with the deep healing and restoration that God wants to bring about in your soul.

Mephibosheth was down in a place called Lo Debar that means "pastureless," a place of desolation and aloneness. Isolation lies at the core of sexual addiction. It is an intimacy or attachment disorder. I have never counseled a man struggling with sexual issues in his life who hasn't spent some time in Lo Debar. It is not that they want to live in Lo Debar; the problem is that they got stuck there like Mephibosheth. They all have a Grievance Story.

## WHAT IS A GRIEVANCE STORY?

It is the story line we have within our soul. It's about those times when we were wounded and betrayed. It's a dark thread of hurt we can all have within. It's the price of growing up in a fallen world. The problem is, the story line is usually laid down very early in our life. Like David, we can carry profound wounds from our family of origin. The wounds have been there so long that we no longer notice them. Yet, they can control our thought processes at the limbic level.

That's not to say our addictive choices are caused by the actions of others. We made the choices. **But if we don't understand the pain of our past, we can't reclaim the blessing and destiny God has set aside for us in the future.** Blessings God has ordained for us before the beginning of time. The enemy of our soul further complicates the issue by making sure to reinforce the theme of our past pain, thus grievances begin piling up in our soul. Soon entitlement can become part of our thought process. We can quietly tell ourselves, "I am so hurt; therefore this type of activity is an acceptable way to medicate my pain within."

Our prefrontal cortex isn't telling us that, but our limbic brain is screaming that refrain deep within when we are in pain. Soon, to justify the destructive choices we are making, we will make an alliance with self-deceptive thoughts. We will find a way to justify our behavior. We will live in the denial that we looked at in Pillar One.

When Ziba knocked on Mephibosheth's door down in Lo Debar he probably told Ziba to go away. But I am sure Ziba kept knocking until Mephibosheth heard the message, "The King has need of you!" At that point Mephibosheth had to deal with his Grievance Story. He could continue on a path of negative intimacy by retelling himself the story of how he got a raw deal in life. Had he rehearsed the story over and over he would have never gotten out of Lo Debar. Instead, at great personal risk to himself, he came to the palace and discovered the goodness of God in a way he never dreamed possible.

## GRIEVANCE STORY EXERCISE

The following exercise will challenge you like Ziba's arrival challenged Mephibosheth. It will feel risky and uncomfortable to respond to the questions. Please don't rush through this exercise. In fact, it might work best if you initially read through the questions and take a first pass at filling in the blanks. Then set it aside, pray about your responses, and ask the Holy Spirit to enable you to see down to the depths of your soul. Notice the patterns of pain; more importantly, discover what God has been up to throughout your life despite the pain.

## MY GRIEVANCE STORY

| GRIEVANCE LIST Where & when have you been betrayed & wounded in life? Who was involved in the betrayal? | WHAT HAPPENED? Describe the event. What happened? Who was involved? | WHAT WERE YOU FEELING? What were your emotions? What were you thinking and feeling? What was being said about you? | THERE IS A STORY HERE.... What are some common elements in these events? |
|---|---|---|---|
| Ted's example: Alcoholic mom | Not there for me | Abandonment & rage | Authority figures will betray you |
| Ted's example: 7 step-dads | Humiliation & abuse | Fear & rage | Authority figures will betray you |
| 1. | | | |
| 2. | | | |
| 3. | | | |

| GRIEVANCE LIST<br>Where & when have you been betrayed & wounded in life? Who was involved in the betrayal? | WHAT HAPPENED?<br>Describe the event. What happened? Who was involved? | WHAT WERE YOU FEELING?<br>What were your emotions? What were you thinking and feeling? What was being said about you? | THERE IS A STORY HERE....<br>What are some common elements in these events? |
|---|---|---|---|
| 4. | | | |
| 5. | | | |
| 6. | | | |
| 7. | | | |

**❯ Now let's put the pieces together. Look at what you have written in the chart and answer the following questions.**

**❶** What are the core (limbic) beliefs that were communicated to you through these grievances?

A. _____

B. _____

C. _____

D. _____

E. _____

**❷** In light of this analysis, with what life issues do you struggle? Anger? Trusting authority figures? Sense of worthlessness at times? Or _____?

A. _____

B. _____

C. _____

D. _____

E. _____

❸ What is God saying to you through your grievance story and the struggles of your life? God always desires to **replace the negative with a positive**. As I looked closely at my core beliefs and the life issues that I struggle with, it became apparent that I was ultimately battling with a HUGE FATHER WOUND!

As I finally came to grips with that fact in my life, I waited on the Lord to see what He would say to me. I was stunned with what I heard. The Holy Spirit strongly spoke to my soul and declared, "**Ted, I would make you a father to the fatherless!**"

◗ **Take some time and listen to what God would say to you about your deep wounds and struggles.** What positive would he speak over you to redefine the deepest negatives you have experienced in your life? Write down what your heavenly Father speaks over you.

...................................................................................................................................

## ✎ ASSIGNMENTS FOR NEXT TIME

❶ Read and reread 2 Samuel 9:1-13.

- Where are you in the story?

...................................................................................................................................

- How are you like Mephibosheth?

...................................................................................................................................

- How are you different than Mephibosheth?

...................................................................................................................................

- Have you found your place at the table yet in life?

...................................................................................................................................

❷ Be ready to share the vision God has given you for the future. What does your place at the table look like in the days ahead?

# LESSON FOUR 📄

## IDENTIFYING YOUR CRIPPLED-NESS

It is one thing to be fighting a crippled aircraft as the student pilot did in the first lesson of this Pillar. It is another thing entirely when you realize that **you** are the crippled one. This was precisely Mephibosheth's struggle and yours as well.

How did he end up crippled?

> *Another descendant of Saul was Jonathan's son Mephibosheth, who was five years old when Saul and Jonathan were killed. When the news about their death came from the city of Jezreel, his nurse picked him up and fled; but she was in such a hurry that she dropped him, and he became crippled.*
> 2 Samuel 4:4 (GNT)

The news that David had become the new king spread like a violent shock wave throughout Israel. It was terrifying news to the household of Saul for this reason: If you became king and your father had not been the king before you, that always lead to major trouble. It was "Standard Operating Procedure" for a new unknown king to hunt down and butcher every member of the previous king's family. If he didn't, they could rise up against him and reclaim the throne.

Mephibosheth's nurse didn't know David's heart, so she ran for her life in panic. In her haste to save herself she dropped the child and as a result he was crippled in both feet. Therefore, the reason Mephibosheth is struggling now is because someone dropped him in the past.

If you struggle with sexual issues in your life and it has been a battle since your teen years, more than likely someone dropped you along the way. Someone you were counting on, someone who should have been responsible or supportive.

You survived it. You have gone on with life. Yet it has affected your "walk." It hinders the way you deal with others. It affects your ability to love, trust and relate. Remember, we are not saying others are to blame for our problems. That is a total waste of time. We are not blaming, instead we are *reclaiming*! **You can't deal with the present unless you understand how you were dropped in the past.**

Mephibosheth had been delivered by the goodness of God to David's palace. He is delivered, but he is damaged. It is difficult for him to do normal things. **When you have been dropped in life, you praise God for things other folks can't even relate to because their normal is your miracle.**

Now here is where I am headed. **You can identify your crippled-ness when you begin to see your "reactive-ness."** I used the phrase "begin to see" for an important reason. You have hobbled along for so long that you have a tough time even noticing you are crippled. You think your relational gait is totally normal. The challenge is that your crippled-ness is internal not external. Therefore, you can be totally oblivious to it. That is one of the reasons marriage is such a gift to you. (You might want to fasten your safety belt before you read the next sentence.)

**Your wife is usually right...right about your hang-ups and hurts. She sees your inner woundedness like no one else can!**

Marriage is the most challenging relationship outside of your walk with God. Your wife can develop this ability to read you like a book after a couple years. Once the honeymoon haze wears off and she realizes she can't change you as quickly as she initially thought, she can really get frustrated. Out of the frustration come incredible challenges for you. She points out incidents that provoke you to overreact. You may get defensive because what is obvious to her is not obvious to you.

Sure, she has her own issues as we all do, but marriage is designed by God to heal both of you. Focusing on her stuff in reaction to the truth she is speaking into your life will get you both absolutely NOWHERE. Of course, it could put you on a path to divorce and it frequently does. But that is NO-WHERE. You just end up paying a bunch of lawyers lots of money!

If you are single, the crippled-ness is more difficult to see, but it will come out in stressful relationships.

## CRIPPLED-NESS IN MY LIFE

Where are you noticing some crippled-ness in your life? Chose one or several of the categories below and make some observations about **your** struggles.

❶ Dealing with conflicts and differences in close relationships

..................................................................................................................

❷ Dealing with money and budgeting in family relationships

..................................................................................................................

❸ Dealing with children and how to discipline them

..................................................................................................................

❹ Discussing sexual frustrations and expectations

..................................................................................................................

❺ Dealing with personal hurts and wounds in the relationship

..................................................................................................................

Because I grew up with deep inner wounds, I learned to live in isolation despite the fact I was very outgoing and enjoyed relating to others. My relationships, however, were shallow and functional. I could lead and relate to others to get the job done, but I didn't really understand their world.

Marriage forced me to face my lack of depth and empathy. My wife is the ultimate problem-solver. She is constantly thinking of ways to deal with problems. I am the ultimate visionary. I am constantly thinking of the way things could work! It didn't take long for our worlds to collide. Add to that the wounds from an alcoholic mom in my life and things became very explosive.

The source of my frustration finally dawned on me one day as my wife asked me a million questions about how something I had dreamed up was going to work. I realized it felt as if she was pointing to the fact I was crippled in both legs, while I was frantically gesturing to the mountaintop of adventure I envisioned ahead for us. I reacted angrily and deeply wounded her. But I finally "got it!" She was just being the problem-solver that God designed her to be and I was being a jerk.

Once I faced my "jerkiness," I realized I was reacting from the past. As I had hit the teen years, my alcoholic mom hung on to me for dear life as I attempted to discover who I was as a young man. With all her ups and downs, as she married and divorced several times, I had become an emotional support to her. I had become her reason for living, but needed to pull away. She smothered me with a million questions out of her fear. I don't blame her for her response. She was battling the bottle. But it deeply wounded me at a level I had never understood until I got married. I began to see that when Diane would ask me a flood of questions, limbic reactions deep within would rise to the surface. It felt like I was being smothered once again. I felt that she was questioning me as a husband and as a man.

There were other reactions that would trouble my soul in marriage. When children arrived, I was scared stiff at the prospects of being a dad. The only fathers I had known were angry and abusive. I reacted in hurtful ways toward my kids when they were just being kids.

Those were crazy moments in my life as I struggled with my over-reactions. The deepest agony came from the fact I had said "Yes" to Christ. I had been delivered. Why was I feeling like this? The guy up front on Sunday morning talked about freedom and victory in Christ and I wasn't experiencing it. The "how-to points" didn't seem to work for me; trying harder only made matters worse. There is a loneliness of the soul that is born in those times that makes your sense of isolation grow only deeper. I found myself putting on a mask to make things work. I would cry out, "If I'm ever going to experience in-ti-ma-cy then there needs to be someone who 'sees-into-me'!"

As Mephibosheth sat down in Lo Debar, he was convinced no one even realized he was alive, let alone cared about him. That is always the limbic lie that hell loves to trigger in our brain. The truth, however, was something so good, so inconceivable it would blow his mind and transform his crippled-ness. King David all the while was preparing a place at his table for him. Let me point out the obvious.

*I am going there to prepare a place for you? And if I go and prepare a place for you, I will come back and take you to be with me that you also may be where I am.*
John 14:2b-3

Jesus Christ is preparing a place at the table just for you. I remember when I first read that passage and heard someone speak about the celebration feast. One day I will be with Christ. I pictured this table, miles long with all these place settings and mine would be at the opposite end of the table from Christ. You know—way out there in the "cheap seats." Then the Holy Spirit whispered to my soul, "No, it is a table set for just you and your Savior." Jesus is God Almighty! He is omnipresent. Therefore, he will have a table set individually for each of us! This is a difficult reality to get a handle on when you are wrestling with your own crippled-ness. In fact, if you are like most guys, you will have a negative reaction towards that truth.

Harry Flanagan, who wrote Pillars Two and Three, has become a deeply trusted friend through the years. I still remember the day I first noticed Harry sitting in the back of the church as I talked up front. He had been removed from the pastorate for having multiple affairs with women in his church. He was totally broken and filled with shame. He sat in the back and cried nearly every service. I waited until the Lord gave me permission to approach him.

Finally, that day came and I headed to the back of the sanctuary after the service. I had to move quickly before Harry ran out the door. I maneuvered myself so he couldn't escape. I walked up to him and extended my hand and said, "How are you doing Pastor Harry?" His face blanched and I could tell he was struggling. Later, I asked him what he was feeling that day. He told me, "It felt like you stuck a knife in me when you called me Pastor." The shame was so deep in his soul that a blessing felt like a curse to him. He couldn't believe that God hadn't given up on him. He was convinced he would forever be worthless in God's eyes. He thought he would never be a pastor again. Yet now he is a pastor to so many hurting men through Pure Desire Ministries.

We can have the same reaction when we are violently struggling with our crippled-ness. This Pillar is about learning how to control the damage that hell would inflict upon us. One of the most important skills is learning how to stop shaming and attacking yourself. It's a very difficult skill to develop. Yet once you do, then you can finally take that long difficult look within at your crippled-ness and not be overwhelmed with shame. You have to clearly see the patterns within if you are ever going to change them.

One of the classic examples of just how crazy we can get is the true story of Bill Wilson. He was the cofounder of Alcoholics Anonymous. He struggled with sexual issues all his life. Nan Robertson describes his life this way:

> *"Bill Wilson was a compulsive womanizer. His flirtations and his adulterous behavior filled him with guilt, according to old-timers close to him, but he continued to stray off the reservation. His last and most serious love affair, with a woman at AA headquarters in New York, began when he was in his sixties."*[26]

**When we don't look deep within, we end up with the problem James so bluntly described.**

> *For if you listen to the word and don't obey, it is like glancing at your face in a mirror. You see yourself, walk away, and forget what you look like. But if you look carefully into the perfect law that sets you free, and if you do what it says and don't forget what you heard, then God will bless you for doing it.*
> James 1:23-25 (NLT)

Bill W. could describe in detail how he won his battle with alcohol, but he never looked deep enough to see reality. Remember, **maturity is a commitment to reality at all costs**. We can't just glance at ourselves in the mirror of reality. We have to see our actions from the perspective of the lives of others.

Our initial reaction is to pull away because we feel the guilt over what we have done. That is why denial became such a big part of our lives. We feel the shame of not being perfect and not fulfilling the Law. Like Bill W, we feel the pain of not doing what is right. But James tells us to keep looking steadily at the "law that sets you free." The actual word James uses is the Greek word "*eleutheria*" which literally means freedom.

**If you will honestly and deeply look at your behaviors, holding on to the fact that Christ will never give up on you, then at some point you will break through to freedom.** By God's grace you will be able to see the patterns within that have controlled your life for years. When that takes place, THEN and only THEN can you reach a turning point in the healing process. **It is critical you realize that you can never win the battle until you fully see the battlefield you face.**

In the chart that follows, list your sexual behaviors that have had direct impact on others. Go beyond people you directly know. Pay close attention to behaviors that you might initially consider "victimless." You might delude yourself into thinking that pornography and prostitution is harmless, telling yourself that the gal got paid for her services. But as a committed follower of Christ you know in your heart the truth. You were supporting the exploitation of another person. The next column asks you to stand off to the side of the mirror of your life and **observe** your actions. How would others describe your actions? In the final column list your nonsexual behaviors that have harmed others.

## MY SEXUAL BEHAVIOR & ITS IMPACT ON OTHERS

| MY SEXUAL BEHAVIORS THAT HARMED OTHERS | WHAT WOULD OTHERS SAY ABOUT MY ACTIONS? | MY NONSEXUAL BEHAVIORS THAT HAVE HARMED OTHERS |
|---|---|---|
|  |  |  |
|  |  |  |
|  |  |  |
|  |  |  |
|  |  |  |

As I always say, "Let's take it deeper, much deeper!" Let's look in the mirror of your nonsexual behaviors.

## MY NONSEXUAL BEHAVIORS THAT HAVE HARMED OTHERS

| PEOPLE I HAVE HARMED BY MY BEHAVIOR THAT I KNOW WELL (LIST THE PERSON & THE BEHAVIOR) | PEOPLE I DON'T KNOW WELL THAT I HAVE HARMED BY MY BEHAVIOR (LIST THE PERSON & THE BEHAVIOR) |
|---|---|
| *Example:* <br> *Wife—Lying to her about money* | *Co-workers—letting them take blame for a problem I created on the job.* |
| | |
| | |
| | |

❯ **Look back carefully at your responses to clearly see the battlefield that faces you.**

❯ **Next, identify the patterns and challenges you see.**

## MY PATTERNS & CHALLENGES

| THE PATTERNS I SEE | THE CHALLENGES I FACE |
|---|---|
| *Examples:* <br> *A pattern of dishonesty* <br> *An inability to be vulnerable and open* | *Examples:* <br> *Being totally honest about my life* <br> *Being open and able to deeply connect with others* |
| | |
| | |
| | |

*So Mephibosheth, who was crippled in both feet, lived in Jerusalem,*
*eating all his meals at the king's table.*
2 Samuel 9:13 (GNT)

What was the greatest challenge Mephibosheth faced and what is yours? Obviously, it is a loaded question. I am hoping you would come to the realization that you both face the exact same challenge.

What is the challenge? You both have experienced a damaging blow in life, either through your moral failures or the addiction that grew out of an instinctive response to medicate the pain within. You may differ in the fact that your crippled-ness is internal, not external. But you don't differ in the fact that it affects how you operate in life. **Your relationship with others, with your wife, even with your children is affected by your sexual bondage.** And like Mephibosheth, you have been lifted up by the grace of God and brought to a place of blessing.

Mephibosheth didn't deserve what he received from David and you don't deserve what you have received from God either. It is called **GRACE**! He has given you a second chance, a third chance and a four millionth chance!

You are reading this workbook and are part of this unique clan of men in your Pure Desire group thanks to the grace of God. At times my life is probably like yours, so hectic that it's hard for me to even realize all the things that are driving me. And despite my craziness, God is good to me.

But it is in times of silence before the Lord I realize that all the fears and anxiety that can propel me through life is a mask. And in the presence of Christ's love for me I can slowly let go of the mask. I come to see those destructive emotions boil up in me at times for what they are—manifestations of a false self. But those destructive emotions lose their power in the embrace of God's love.

My times of silence before the Lord, which is a practice I challenge you to develop in your times of meditation in the scripture, are moments of conversion for me. I am gradually led by the Holy Spirit to see who God has made me to be. It is a conversion experience for me, not in the sense of being saved but of being released from the insanity of showing others what I can do or what I have done.

Instead, I am learning to lift up open and empty hands to God in recognition of the fact that all I have is a free gift from Him. It is in silence that I think we encounter not only God, but also our true self. In fact, **I am convinced it is only in those times of meditation and silence before God we can take our rightful place at his table.** We come to see who we really are, crippled legs and all. Yet there is a divine paradox here that you clearly see in Mephibosheth's life. In the paradox you discover his greatest challenge and yours as well.

> ### Mephibosheth has got to get up off the floor—and so do you!!!!

I can't express that truth strongly enough. Now listen very carefully. I am not talking about trying harder out of your own strength. You have probably tried that for years and it definitely hasn't worked when it comes to dealing with your sexual bondage.

Change can happen, however, once you begin to understand how scandalous God's love is for you and that He will never give up on you, despite how many times you have given up on yourself. God's grace can give you the courage to look at your crippled-ness within, which you have done in a number of the workbook exercises so far. It is then that **you can have the chutzpah to GET UP OFF THE FLOOR**!

Yes, it is going to be hard to do what other people do so easily because of your brokenness within. You are not broken everywhere, just at those strategic points where hell uses it against you sexually. Years ago, I was deeply troubled by guys in the ministry who would have an absolute aversion to sexual temptations. They would immediately turn from things that I would have to battle myself out of. I wasn't upset at them. I was upset at myself. "Why does it take so much effort on my part to walk clean?" I would constantly ask myself that question.

Then I realized it was a waste of time to keep asking why I had to fight to stay on my feet all the time. "Stop whining, Ted, and get up off the floor!" Over time I came to see that what once seemed like such a battle, soon became a natural response.

Purity became a natural response once my mind was renewed. The renewal process does not happen overnight. For the numerous men I have counseled through the years, it usually takes two to five years with a miracle from God every day. Clinical research has verified the fact that it takes that long.[27]

God will not just pull your brain out and put a new one in when you pray for sexual healing. He respects your freedom of choice; a love relationship is always characterized by a commitment from both parties. I even grew to appreciate the battle I had to fight because it gave me tremendous empathy for the men who came to me with their sexual struggles. Above all, the battle deepened my sense of gratitude to the Lord for his patience and grace towards me. BUT **I HAD TO GET UP OFF THE FLOOR IN MY LIFE**!

Getting up off the floor is not easy, but you can't stay down there because God has a place set for you. He has a place of blessing and destiny at his table. Therefore, whatever it takes, you need to get up. Even if you have to crawl hand over hand. These lesson assignments at times will feel like you are crawling to get there.

One of the reasons this can be such a frustrating experience is a common misunderstanding of the term "deliverance." So many men are praying for God to cast out of them things that are not demons. They are trying to get something out of them that is, frankly, not coming out. That part of their life has to be **discipled**, not delivered. The flesh is the flesh and no man's flesh is totally saved this side of heaven. If your body was totally saved you wouldn't need deodorant and your breath wouldn't stink.

*My point:* Sooner or later every man of God has to decide to become a disciple. **A disciple is simply someone with a disciplined life.** God doesn't take away your flesh and He will not deliver you from your flesh. For freedom to grip your life you will have to deal with your own devils. **You will have to choose to renew your mind, to marinate your mind in the truth of God's love and His call on your life.**

When you are almost at the place of freedom God has set aside for you, I guarantee something will happen. When you are so close to your place at Christ's banquet table, so close you can smell the food, is when hell will unleash its most devastating attack. He knows you are "this close" to a total breakthrough and he is terrified of you ever getting free. This is why so many men get right to the gates of freedom then violently relapse back into old patterns of behavior. We will discuss how to avoid that trap in Pillar Five. **But no relapse prevention plan will work unless you make a decision before you get there to keep moving forward no matter what it costs.**

You will finally take your place at Christ's table and become convinced of His love for you and your personal worth. When that happens, you will look back over your life and realize something you have never understood before.

- *You should have died in that car wreck.*
- *You should have lost your mind in the middle of that financial crisis.*
- *You could have become totally cynical over that betrayal.*

For me, it would be, *That antiaircraft fire should have hit me. There is no way I should have made it through all of that.*

Once we have a seat in the place God has prepared for us, we realize the awesome sovereignty of our God. He has been at work all the way through your life! And because God has a place for you, there is no devil in hell that can keep you from it—*if you just get up off the floor*!

Can you picture Mephibosheth seated at the king's table with distinguished guests and rulers beside him? You would never know there was anything wrong with him. Of course, if you pulled back the tablecloth, you would see he is still crippled in both feet despite all the blessings he is now enjoying. He is seated at the table as if nothing had ever happened to him. Not pretending or denying his brokenness, but letting the King cover him and bless him. Despite his limitations, he belongs there and he knows it.

**Your miracle is that you get to sit at the table of God's blessing right now as if you had never been dropped.** There is a place at the table for you. The amazing thing about walking with God is that it doesn't matter who you are or how you have been dropped or how you may have messed up in life. If you get up off the floor and come fully to Christ without any masks or hidden areas in your life, He will carry you in such a way that He will make it up to you and He will never, ever drop you.

Sometimes it is very difficult for us to realize the areas in which our lives are crippled. We have become so good at hiding our weaknesses, hobbling effectively through life that we have lost sight of our brokenness within. But we serve a gracious Savior who can get our attention in spectacular ways.

I looked at my counseling schedule and noticed (I will call his name) Joe was on at seven o'clock in the morning. He was struggling with cocaine and not doing well. I sighed, anticipating a difficult dialogue ahead. As I pulled up to my office I noticed Joe was already there. He had a huge smile on his face and declared, "Dr. Roberts I am doing great. I don't have any questions; in fact, I have come to bless you this morning."

I thought that was novel. "So how do you want to bless me Joe?" I asked.

"I want to wash your feet." He shot back

"Oh come on, Joe, we live in Oregon. It is cold and rainy this morning."

"I know pastor I have heated the water for you," he responded.

Inside my office as Joe started taking my shoes and socks off, I was really uncomfortable. I was literally squirming in the chair. The Lord gently asked me why I was so anxious. The Lord never asks me a question for information. Instead, He is hoping I will pick up on something. I hesitated and quietly responded, "Because I am not in control, Lord. When I am ministering or counseling others I have a sense of control. I guess my deep wounds of the past have made me very protective in the present."

That was when I sensed the Lord asking me to open up and let Him love me. He wanted me to drop my protective pastoral walls and just have a seat at His table as Joe washed my feet. That is when Joe looked up at me and said, "Pastor I think I heard the Lord say something about how He feels about you."

"Go ahead, Joe, I would love to hear it, " I cautiously responded.

"The Lord told me to tell you that when you were in your mother's womb he saw how you fought for life and He loved your warrior's heart."

I totally lost it. I was truly seated at the Lord's Table. I have a scar down the left side of my chest caused by my mother strapping her stomach down so her pregnancy wouldn't show. I was an illegitimate child and she was terrified of what people would say. There was no way Joe could have ever known about that scar. It was a setup from God. He was telling me to get up off the floor.

Sometimes we think we are standing, but instead we are curled up in a fetal position protecting ourselves in life. We have not stood boldly in the full "Son-light" of God's grace. We have not taken our place at the table of God's divine purposes because we have been quietly hiding our brokenness with a false bravado. We can even do it in ministry in the name of God! Go figure!

## WHERE DO YOU NEED TO GET UP OFF THE FLOOR IN LIFE?

In answering that question let's start with a review of the past places of victories in your life.

- Think back over your history and identify those times where you made good decisions, where you got up and helped yourself by the grace of God.

- Remember those commitments you made and followed through and how they affected your life?

- List in the following chart: the decision; the time or circumstance; action steps you took; resulting in long-term change. Most important of all, note what you discovered or learned in the process.

## PAST "GET UP OFF THE FLOOR" VICTORIES IN MY LIFE

| "GET UP OFF THE FLOOR" DECISIONS | THE TIME OR CIRCUMSTANCE | SPECIFIC STEPS TAKEN | RESULTING CHANGE | WHAT I DISCOVERED OR LEARNED |
|---|---|---|---|---|
| 1. | | | | |
| 2. | | | | |
| 3. | | | | |
| 4. | | | | |
| 5. | | | | |

You know the drill! Let's take it deeper!

**Where do you need to get up off the floor in your life *right now*!** What decisions do you need to make today, this month, this year? What decisions **must you make** to get you to the place God has set aside for you?

*Reminder:* There is a place at God's banquet table for you.

❶ List the decisions you must make to get up off the floor and move forward.

❷ List the steps you need to take to get going.

❸ What will be the results in your life if you get up?

❹ How much chutzpa (meaning audacity or nerve) is it going to take? Use a rating scale from 1 (not much) to 10 (nerves of steel!).

❺ Finally, rank the places where you need to get up off the floor in order of importance. Use a rating scale for 1 (not that important) to 10 (absolutely necessary).

## "GET UP OFF THE FLOOR" DECISIONS FOR ME RIGHT NOW

| GET UP OFF THE FLOOR DECISIONS | STEPS I NEED TO TAKE | THE RESULTS IF I GET UP? | CHUTZPA FACTOR! | IMPORTANCE OF THE DECISION |
|---|---|---|---|---|
| 1. | | | | |
| 2. | | | | |
| 3. | | | | |
| 4. | | | | |
| 5. | | | | |

❶ Now look back over your responses in both charts.

- What is true about your relationship with YOU?

........................................................................................................

- How do you tend to view yourself, especially under pressure?

........................................................................................................

❷ Look at the times in the past where you decided to get up off the floor.

- Did you get further than you ever thought possible?
- Was God faithful to you?
- Was the change positive?
- What does this say to you with respect to the tough decisions you listed in the "right now" get up off the floor decisions, those with high chutzpa and importance factors?

........................................................................................................

❸ What patterns do you see in your life from these charts? Be specific.

A. _____

B. _____

C. _____

D. _____

E. _____

## ✒ ASSIGNMENTS FOR NEXT TIME

❶ Complete all the charts in this lesson and respond to the accompanying questions.

- It may take a couple of meetings for everyone in the group to respond, but group time will be used so that each person can share responses to the charts and life patterns that emerge from the chart exercises.

❷ How does your greatest challenge correlate with your God-given vision?

_____

_____

_____

_____

_____

_____

_____

_____

_____

_____

_____

_____

_____

_____

_____

_____

_____

_____

_____

_____

❸ Read *Pure Desire* Chapter 11.

❹ Review and sign the Commitment for Pillar Four.

# ✔ PILLAR OF FREEDOM FOUR COMMITMENT

I have, to the best of my ability, completed all the exercises found in Pillar of Freedom Four. By God's grace I will do everything I can to live these truths out in my life on a daily basis.

My Name _____

Signature _____ Date _____

## AFFIRMING WITNESSES

**1.** *I affirm the fact that* _____ *has grown in integrity and honesty in his life by the grace of God. Denial is no longer part of his life.*

My Name _____

Signature _____ Date _____

**2.** *I affirm the fact that* _____ *has grown in integrity and honesty in his life by the grace of God. Denial is no longer part of his life.*

My Name _____

Signature _____ Date _____

# ESTABLISHING SOBRIETY

# LESSON ONE

## UNDERSTANDING FANTASIES

Recently, I was watching one of our granddaughters dance in the family room. She was doing all these ballet moves. It was enchanting. I asked her, "Are you a ballerina?" She looked at me as if I didn't have a clue and said, "I am a *prima* ballerina!" I am thinking to myself, "Come on grandpa get with the program." The fantasies of children are awesome.

But let me ask you an intriguing question, "What are your fantasies in life?" Do you picture yourself crossing the finish line at the Ironman in Kona, Hawaii? That is mine! Or maybe you are shooting a game of golf with Tiger Woods and giving him a run for his money. Or launching the game-winning three-pointer from "downtown" to win the NBA finals. Maybe it's catching the winning touchdown at the Super Bowl. What are your sport fantasies?

### LIST SEVERAL OF YOUR SPORT FANTASIES:

1. _____
2. _____
3. _____
4. _____

A lot of guys have financial fantasies. What are yours? If God allows you to win the lottery, of course, you will tithe to the church—that is part of the bargain you make with God. Maybe your financial fantasies have an altruistic nature and you become so financially secure you can lavishly give to people in need.

### WHAT ARE YOUR FINANCIAL FANTASIES?

1. _____
2. _____
3. _____
4. _____

We could go on with this all day, but now focus on your achievement fantasies. Is it about you getting that incredible promotion, or a front office, or speaking before thousands (for Christ, of course).

### WHAT ARE YOUR ACHIEVEMENT FANTASIES?
### LIST A FEW OF THEM BELOW.

1. _____
2. _____
3. _____
4. _____

Where am I headed with this? I want us to look deeply at an intriguing window of your soul—your fantasies in life. When you are under pressure some of your deepest fantasies can bubble to the surface. The journey of the people of Israel across the Sinai wilderness is a classic example of what I am talking about. God had delivered them from over 400 years of captivity in Egypt. It was a bumpy ride, but real deliverances are always a challenge. In fact, that's what you probably have been experiencing as you plow your way through this workbook.

First off, Israel ran out of water—not a pleasant event in the middle of a searing desert. But no problem, God led them to the waters of Marah. The name "Marah" means bitter, which was a very accurate description of the place. The bitterness was caused by a very high concentration of magnesium and calcium in the water. And what happened next was not a pretty sight. Over a million people gulped down bitter water because of their intense thirst, but calcium and magnesium at these levels becomes a powerful laxative! Suddenly a million folks are saying to themselves, "Where is the bathroom?" And there is not a tree insight.

> **Sometimes God has to get something out of us before he can take us to the next level.**

Why would God allow that to happen? You may have asked that question at times in your healing process. The answer is intriguing to say the least. It turns out that the irrigation canals of Goshen where Israel lived for four centuries were loaded with water-born parasites. It is even true of the region today.[28] **A sovereign God was healing them for the journey that lay ahead.** Sometimes the promises of our heavenly Father are wrapped in problems. At times we deal with one problem only to discover another one confronting us.

> *In the desert the whole community grumbled against Moses and Aaron. The*
> *Israelites said to them, "If only we had died by the Lord's hand in Egypt! There we*
> *sat around pots of meat and ate all the food we wanted, but you have brought us out*
> *into this desert to starve this entire assembly to death."*
> Exodus 16:2-3

The next thing they know they are out of food. As I said, tough times bring our greatest fantasies to the surface. That doesn't mean they are reasonable thoughts. At times, our fantasies are not harmless, but deadly. They reveal some of our most distorted thinking processes. For example, is what Israel whines about really true? Did they really sit around all day having fondue with the Pharaoh? Hardly! They were working night and day for the man, getting their backs ripped open by vicious taskmasters for 400+ years. How could their thoughts have gotten so distorted?

An even deeper question: How do we deal with the distorted thinking that lies at the root of our sexual struggles? At the foundation of all addictions will be cognitive distortions. Translation: garbled thinking!

The Apostle Paul challenges us to take every thought captive (2 Corinthians 10:5). So, what does that mean? In today's world there are a number of self-help options touted as being the solution.

# 1. "THE THREE-SECOND RULE"

You are told that if you have a destructive fantasy hit your thought process you have three seconds to get rid of it. There is one huge problem; that approach doesn't work for the simple reason that the more you try to get rid of the fantasy, the more you are thinking about **it**. Also, recent discoveries in neuroscience reveal you don't have three seconds; instead you have about three tenths of a second to get rid of it. So, the trick is not to think of it in the first place.

## 2. "THE RUBBER BAND APPROACH"

I have heard a lot of Christian speakers use this approach. You are supposed to snap the rubber band on your wrist every time you have a negative fantasy. Of course, this is a behavioral conditioning approach. And guess what? You are not a Pavlovian dog. This approach has been tried in sex offender programs and it clearly doesn't work. The cattle prod approach will never bring you to real freedom.

## SO WHAT DOES WORK?

For starters, it is realizing your thoughts are not your enemy. The enemy is the enemy. Our thoughts can be messengers of the deepest longings of our soul. If you understand the messenger and his message concerning your longings, then the stage is set for real healing to begin.

## IT IS CRITICAL THAT WE UNDERSTAND THAT OUR FANTASIES ARE TELLING US THREE THINGS.

❶ Some fantasies replay a past event expecting or at least hoping for a different outcome. For example, I have counseled a large number of individuals who really struggle with procrastination. It is fascinating, but they are usually not ignoring the task at hand. In fact, quite frequently they are saddled with a sense of perfectionism. They are spending huge amounts of time fantasizing about how they will get it perfect this time. Their fantasies are trying to reveal to them the wound in their soul that has engendered such perfectionism. They deeply fear failure and fantasize about getting things just right.

❷ Other fantasies are about a desire that has never been fulfilled. My deepest sport/achievement fantasy is not winning the Hawaiian Ironman. Instead it is to be fighter pilot ace. You know—the Tom Cruise "Top Gun" scene where he buzzes the carrier, then lands and all his macho squadron mates surround him celebrating his victory. I still have that dream occasionally. That fantasy points to the father wound I have deep within. But thank God, I realize that now. So when it comes to mind, I know it is just telling me I am feeling some pressure in my life right now and my mind wants to escape.

❸ The fantasy repeats an event that happened early in the individual's life that was nurturing and the person continues to return to it. A pastor was removed from his pastorate because it was revealed he was having sex with other men. For most people, this was so shocking they reacted with open hostility toward the individual. "How could he do such a thing?" they exclaim. He was a father of two small children, deeply loved his wife and initially couldn't explain his behavior. But as I listened to him, I helped him understand the origin of this fantasy. What had driven him into such paradoxical behavior? As a small child his parents went through a vicious divorce; in the chaos of the family environment his own sister sexually assaulted him. The only friend he had was a gentle and kind little boy down the street who would listen to him as he poured out his hurt. The various clinical instruments that I used to initially evaluate him clearly indicated that he wasn't homosexual. His trigger point was when he felt like a failure or was under pressure. The demeaning voice of his father would echo in his soul. Then he would go back to that fantasy place in his head where his friend would bring comfort to his soul. There was nothing sexual about the initial relationship, but the fantasy in his head had been so distorted by hell it became a deadly trap. That is precisely why he would find himself acting out with other men and yet was deeply in love with his wife.

## LOOKING INTO THE MIRROR OF YOUR FANTASY...

I don't recommend the Harry Potter series for general reading because of the heavy demonic tone at times. But there is one scene in *The Sorcerer's Stone* that presents the power of fantasy with gripping insight. It deals with the Mirror of Erised. The dean of Hogwarts (the school Harry attends) learns that Harry and a friend have been staring into the mirror; he warns the boys of the disastrous potential of such an act. He tells them the power of the mirror is found in the fact that it reflects your deepest desires. For Harry, it was gazing on his murdered parents, with them looking back on him with approval and affirmation. Harry's friend looked in the mirror and saw himself as successful and out from under the shadow of his brothers. The dean's warning to the two boys carried a unique insight into our deepest addictions. He tells them people have literally been captured by the mirror and are unable to leave. The name Erised is "Desire" spelled backwards! [29]

The dean's point is that fantasy is a way to avoid the reality of our situation. Harry is never going to bring his parents back. He instead needs to grieve the loss and find his affirmation from a present source. Harry's friend is better served by creating his own place of significance rather than living in a fantasy.

Maturity and healing take place in our lives when we pursue reality at all costs. The mirror of Erised in today's world is so frequently Internet pornography. With a simple click of the mouse a guy can enter a dream world where his every fantasy is fulfilled by a willing and ever-ready woman. The sexual images constantly promise to meet our deepest sexual cravings.

But fantasies are actually mirrors of our deepest wounds, hurts and disappointments in life. The mirror of Erised can become a powerful tool for our healing if we don't let it pull us in. Instead, we need to look in the mirror of our deepest sexual desire with total honesty by the grace of God.

## SO WHAT IS YOUR DEEPEST, DARKEST SEXUAL DESIRE?

Usually when I ask that question in the counseling office all the air gets sucked right out of the room. The man either looks at the carpet or tells me he doesn't have sexual fantasies. I smile and say, "We all have them and just because you have said 'Yes' to Christ doesn't mean that God drained all the hormones out of your body. Christians have deep, dark sexual fantasies. They only become dangerous and damaging when we don't acknowledge them."

**◉ So here we go! List your ideal sexual fantasies. These are the ones that can easily have a real grip on your life. What are the sexual pictures in your mirror of Erised?**[29]

**Your responses may be too embarrassing for you to share in the group openly.** *But it is critical that you find at least one other man with whom to share your responses.* Hopefully the leader of your Pure Desire Group will be someone with whom you can share your responses.

1. _____

2. _____

3. _____

4. _____

Now back up and review your previous responses concerning sports, financial and achievement fantasies at the beginning of this lesson. Compare them with your sexual fantasies.

❓ **What are the common patterns you see in all these lists?** Trust me! Patterns are there; seeing them helps you begin to uncover the reason you have struggled so deeply with sexual issues in your life.

1. _____

2. _____

3. _____

4. _____

Next is the payoff for all this difficult work that you have done so far.

⊗ **Look at the patterns you've discovered.**

**What does all of this tell you about your deepest desires? Where do they come from?** Possibly it is something very painful that occurred early in your life, like Harry Potter's friend who was always demeaned by his older brothers. Or maybe it is a truth about yourself that you have been avoiding. **Behind our deepest, dark desires always lies a wound that has yet to be touched by the grace of God.** What are they for you?

**For this portion of the lesson it is critical that you share your responses with the entire group. Yes, it is going to be tough, but at some point you need to realize you can't get healed on your own or healed by trying harder. Pause for a moment and think of the cost of not fully acknowledging these wounds so far in your life.**

## THE SOURCES OF MY "ERISED" DESIRE

1. _____

2. _____

3. _____

4. _____

5. _____

## ✐ ASSIGNMENTS FOR NEXT TIME

❶ Be prepared at the next meeting to share the results of your Erised Mirror exercises.

❷ Read *Pure Desire* Chapter 12.

❸ Meditate on Luke 22:14-34.

## TRUSTING GOD IN THE MOMENT

**⊃ Read Luke 22:24-34 (GNT) aloud in the group the next time you meet.**

*24 An argument broke out among the disciples as to which one of them should be thought of as the greatest. 25 Jesus said to them, "The kings of the pagans have power over their people, and the rulers claim the title 'Friends of the People.' 26 But this is not the way it is with you; rather, the greatest one among you must be like the youngest, and the leader must be like the servant. 27 Who is greater, the one who sits down to eat or the one who serves? The one who sits down, of course. But I am among you as one who serves.*

*28 "You have stayed with me all through my trials; 29 and just as my Father has given me the right to rule, so I will give you the same right. 30 You will eat and drink at my table in my Kingdom, and you will sit on thrones to rule over the twelve tribes of Israel.*

*31 "Simon, Simon! Listen! Satan has received permission to test all of you, to separate the good from the bad, as a farmer separates the wheat from the chaff. 32 But I have prayed for you, Simon, that your faith will not fail. And when you turn back to me, you must strengthen your brothers."*

*33 Peter answered, "Lord, I am ready to go to prison with you and to die with you!"*

*34 "I tell you, Peter," Jesus said, "the rooster will not crow tonight until you have said three times that you do not know me."*

**What a troubling, but encouraging promise**: "Your life is going to be thrown up in the air and everything is going to fly apart, but I have prayed for you." It's encouraging when you realize that the main reason you are still here is that Jesus prayed for you specifically. Knowing all of your weaknesses and struggles, all of your trauma and trials, all of your fears and insecurities, He passionately prayed for you.

Troubling in that fact that Jesus also said, "I prayed for you that your faith doesn't fail." When I first started out in this journey of faith called following Jesus, I thought it wasn't possible to lose your faith. Then down the road, life slapped me so hard that I started asking questions like…

- *"Where is God in this mess, anyway?"*
- *"I really don't know if there is a God or not at least that is what my feelings are telling me."*
- *"And I really don't know if He loves me or not, if he cares for me or not; I am confused!"*

Questions like that flooded my soul because my adversary was shouting poisonous one-liners at me like:

- *"Nobody is listening to you!"*
- *"Nobody really cares about you!"*
- *"You are in this mess all by yourself!"*

Moments like that are what I call "emotional exile moments" of the deepest kind. Exile simply means you are where you don't want to be in life. There is a truth about all the exile moments of life: **You only have to trust God in the moment you are in right now.** When your faith is in a fight, when you find yourself in exile, the enemy can cut to the core of your belief system. *And don't miss this.* Y*ou are no greater than what you truly believe.*

That is why you are never going to defeat the devil in an exile situation by trying harder, by your will power. **You absolutely need the power of God.** That is why it is so important to learn the discipline of staying in the enemy's face as you make statements like…

- *"I believe God when I don't feel a thing!"*
- *"I believe God when I can't see a thing!"*
- *"I believe God when things are getting worse instead of better!"*
- *"I BELIEVE GOD!"*

**Where in your life do you need to make such statements in the face of spiritual opposition?** List them below. At your next Pure Desire meeting give each man the opportunity to express out loud where he needs to get in hell's face!

**1.** I believe God when _____

**2.** I believe God when _____

**3.** I believe God when _____

**4.** I believe God when _____

**5.** I believe God when _____

I love how the King James translation expresses Luke 22:32:

> *But I have prayed for thee, that thy faith fail not:*
> *and when thou art **converted**, strengthen thy brethren.*

Think about the automotive term "convertible." I remember the old hard top convertibles. When you pushed the right button the car would go through this amazing metamorphosis. Right before your eyes it would change from a traditional "hard top" car into a convertible. There was no room in the trunk for any luggage because the hard top took up all the room, but it was still awesome! It is important that we understand that Jesus was not speaking to some belligerent sinner. Sure Peter messed up continually, but he was never openly defiant of Christ. He was a guy who had given up everything to follow Christ.

Jesus was saying to Peter just as he declares to us, "Pete, there is something inside of you that I want to deal with." We usually come to hear such words from Christ when we are in a place not of our choosing or when we feel uncomfortable.

---

**It is in exile that we come to clearly see our true condition.**

---

Here is the truth about all of us who are following Christ. Your spirit has been made whole, complete in Christ. In fact, Ephesians tells us we are seated in heavenly places with Christ. And your soul has been made whole, but you are frequently fighting past places in your head. Your body one day will be made whole. One day you will get a divine upgrade!

*Important point:* Every passage in the Bible referring to your salvation in the past tense is referring to your spirit. Statements such as you were redeemed or justified or sanctified. But at the same time there is a struggle going on within.

> *So get rid of all the filth and evil in your lives, and humbly accept the message God has planted in your hearts, for it is strong enough **to save your souls**.*
> James 1:21 (NLT)

You will never understand the Bible until you understand the finished work of grace in your spirit and the progressive work of grace in your soul. Our souls need to be converted just as Peter's did.

What am I talking about? Well for starters, let's define what we mean by the term "soul." Scripture describes it as our will, intellect, and emotions. And here is a key truth: The hardware or gateway of your soul is your brain.

Say you lived twenty plus years before you decided to follow Christ. That means you were making decisions for over twenty years out of your soul, from a soul that was uninformed by a born again Spirit. You were relating to God completely out of soul-ish wisdom. Now you might say, "But I came to Christ and that solved the problem, right?" I wish it were that simple. Your spirit was made whole, but your soul needs to be converted. And over time it becomes more and more obvious to you.

I remember reading statements like these in the Bible:

- *I can do all things in Christ.*
- *I am more than a conqueror in Christ.*
- *All things have passed away behold all things have become new.*

Those promises in scripture used to FRUSTRATE ME! They were frustrating because initially I didn't understand that my soul and my brain needed to be renewed if I was ever going to fully experience them.

This is not a simple process because our brains are such incredible gifts from God. One of the recent discoveries about the brain is the concept of neuroplasticity. Science has discovered that Paul was right in what he wrote two thousand years ago.

A human mind can be renewed. It can change and adapt to the environment. Previously science believed that your brain was hardwired and fixed in its structure. Now scientists realize that is totally untrue. For example, recent research has revealed that Braille reading individuals have a larger portion of their brain devoted to their index fingers. In fact, the seeing portion of their brain (the occipital lobe) was being used to process the sensations of touch. **The human brain will devote larger and larger areas to repeated behaviors.** This explains precisely why bad habits can be so hard to unlearn. Most of us think of our brains as a mental container. Learning just means putting something new into it, so when we are trying to break a bad habit we will do things like read more scripture or pray more. Those things obviously are good, but just those things alone will usually not break the deep sinful patterns that you have repeated for over twenty years.

Why is that true? Because each time we repeat the behavior or see it repeated, the use of that space is not available for good habits. As one neuroscientist put it, "It is best to get it right early before bad habits get the competitive advantage."[30]

Where our brain begins to react in the old survival patterns we have established, we, like Paul in Romans 7, will find ourselves doing the very thing we don't want to do. The exile times in our life help us to see those destructive patterns that have been carved into our brain—to see our true condition.

**Now listen carefully:** In exile times we don't get to see our true identity. We don't see our true self or our destiny, but the present condition that limits and restricts us from God's best in our life. Israel came to see who they were under their Egyptian taskmasters. It was in exile, in the frustration of their present condition that provoked them to call out for God's destiny for them.

In Luke 22, Jesus turned to Peter who I know anticipated hearing something like, "I will pray for you and you will have nothing but smooth sailing in your life." But the bewildered fisherman found profound hope in the middle of his chaos when he heard the words, "WHEN YOU ARE CONVERTED." Not "if" or "maybe" or "I sure hope so" but WHEN! You are coming out of this, my friend. God is saying that to you right now as you read this workbook.

> *There is a "when" to your mess, your trial, your tribulation.*
> *You are coming out of this battle with sexual bondage by His grace!*

How do you know when that time has arrived? "**When you are converted you will strengthen your brothers.**" You know you are coming out when you begin to instinctively look beyond yourself. The typical self-centeredness of an addict begins to lose its grip in your life. You begin to realize it is not about you; instead it is about what God wants to do in your life. It is about your destiny, your calling!

In John 21, the resurrected Christ openly challenged Peter to "Go feed my sheep." This was not the first time Jesus dared Peter to change the way he thought of himself. All the way back in Matthew 4 Jesus told Peter that he would make him a fisher-of-men. Peter's problem was that he just wouldn't let go of his boat. And in our struggles to walk in healthy sexuality we hold on to our boats as well.

Our boat in life represents the things we hold on to—**just in case what God told us doesn't work out**. Our boat is the thing we go back to for comfort, our sexual security blanket. It is how we spell relief. Every time Peter got in trouble you would find him heading back to his boat. Even after he was born again in John 20 still Peter went back to what was comforting to him. Despite the fact that it wasn't working he still keeps going back. Again and again he fishes all night and catches absolutely nothing. How many times I have sat in the counseling office and listened to men who have gone sexually fishing all night and it has left their souls only emptier.

 When we are dealing with sexual bondages we tend to keep our "boats" well hidden. The shame factor turns our boats into stealth vessels of bondage quietly moving deep within our soul.

In this lesson and the next I want to introduce you to one of the most powerful weapons I have discovered in this battle to help men truly get free, The **Arousal Template (AT)**[31] The AT is the stealth vessel of the soul that keeps leading men back into bondage. They are usually not even aware of the vessel within. At a subconscious level, they are not about to let go of the "boat." It is the thing that keeps carrying them back to comfort even though it is killing them.

So what is an Arousal Template? Well every one of us has one. It isn't inherently bad or good. It is simply part of how our brain has become "wired" so to speak.

## LET ME ILLUSTRATE SOMETHING.

❶ Close your eyes for a couple of minutes and think about the last time you were really angry or afraid. Picture the scene.

❷ Now what happened to your heart rate, breathing, blood pressure, field of vision?

❸ The next exercise will be a challenge. For just one minute, no longer, think about the most exciting sexual experience you have had in life.

Welcome back! I suspect that part of the exercise was a bit harder to turn off, but did you notice something? Your heart rate, breathing, blood pressure and field of vision did the exact same thing.

**Arousal is an automatic, neutral physiological experience of tension and energy related to what is happening in our limbic system.** Remember from the workbook introduction that this is the part of your brain that strongly responds to five things. The five are: 1) What you are afraid of, 2) what you will run from, 3) what is so terrifying that you will freeze in your tracks, 4) food, and 5) sex.

The male brain responds to sexual signals faster than anything else.[32] The AT (arousal template) is a mixture of physiology and learning. It is an unconscious decision tree of how we have become wired sexually. It is what guides us to what we respond to as being erotic or arousing. It determines decisions in **its own right and becomes a template for action.**

This is so critical for you to grasp: **You will have minimal success in stopping your compulsive behavior without understanding your Arousal Template.**

It organizes into a mental map all that we have learned about respect, trust, safety, dishonesty, domination, objectification, power and control. It has synthesized what we fundamentally believe about value, worth, excitement, desire and what to avoid. The limbic beliefs, ideas and responses become associated with triggers or cues for arousal. And almost anything can become an arousal trigger.

- **Locations:** hotels, cars, office, restrooms
- **Sensory input:** perfume, lingerie, alcohol, drugs, and certain smells
- **Physical characteristics:** height, hair color, body type, sound of the voice
- **Perceived personality:** vulnerable, professional, laborer, dominant
- **Feelings:** pain/loneliness, fear, anger/rage, guilt/shame or lust

You will begin the most challenging exercise in this book when you write responses in the Arousal Template chart that follows. You will finish the exercise in Lesson Three.

Why should you do it? Because if you have tried to stop your sexual behavior and can't, this could be the critical weapon to turn the tide in the battle. I have seen men who have struggled for decades, been to every type of Christian counselor, and tried everything they could think of or everything that was suggested to them, but couldn't get free. But once I walked them through this exercise the lights turned on for them. Their souls started getting renewed! They were able to let go of the one thing they had kept returning to for comfort that was also the thing that was destroying them. They let go of their boat—their distorted Arousal Template.

Obviously this information is not something you should share out loud in your Pure Desire group. It is too sexual and may be a turn on for someone else in the group who struggles with the same issues. And more importantly the shame factor can be enormous if you have never shared this with anyone else.

In the next lesson we will suggest certain portions of the completed AT chart that would be appropriate to share with your group. **But it is critical that you find someone who you can trust to share the *full results* of the chart.**

We are only as sick as our secrets and this is especially true with respect to our sexual secrets. Most men are not consciously trying to hide their Arousal Template; it has just operated on the subconscious level. They are unaware of the fact that it is constantly sabotaging their best efforts at walking in purity.

## MY AROUSAL TEMPLATE: PART ONE

| MY AROUSAL TRIGGERS OR SIGNALS | THE SPECIFICS FOR ME |
|---|---|
| **Locations**<br>(Hotels, malls, parks, beaches, etc.) | |
| **Sensations**<br>(Modem, perfume, drugs, etc.) | |
| **Body Types & Features**<br>(Tall, short, blonde, red head, etc.) | |
| **Personality Types**<br>(Unavailable, vulnerable, dominant, etc.) | |
| **Feelings**<br>(Danger, fear, pain, shame, etc.) | |
| **Culture**<br>(Older women, schoolgirls, Asian gay men, Hispanic, etc.) | |
| **False Beliefs**<br>(Sex= Love, Sex=Power, etc.) | |

## ✐ ASSIGNMENTS FOR NEXT TIME

❶ Be ready to share your "*I believe God when* ___" statements with the group.

❷ Complete the personal Arousal Template: Part One.

*Please note:* **There may be legal ramifications for any information about inappropriate sexual contact or behavior that involves minor children, the disabled or the elderly that is shared within your Pure Desire group. Please review the Memo of Understanding.**

❸ What is your reaction to completing the **Arousal Template: Part One** details in this lesson?

- Write a response below. Be prepared to share with the group.

_____

_____

_____

_____

_____

_____

_____

_____

_____

_____

❹ Read *Pure Desire* Chapter 13.

❺ Create a written list of what you are deeply grateful for in your life. (after you read Chapter 13.)

_____

_____

_____

_____

_____

_____

_____

_____

_____

_____

_____

# LESSON THREE

## TRAINING EXERCISES

Right about now you might be feeling a little weary and frustrated with all the exercises you have been asked to do in this workbook. I think a picture from the past might help at this point in your journey.

In the 1980's a movie came out about a skinny kid by the name of Daniel who runs into an old Japanese gardener by the name of Mr. Miyagi. That's right—I am referring to the movie *The Karate Kid*[33]. Not *Karate Kid XV*, but the very first one.

There is a scene in the movie that is an absolute classic. Daniel is being bullied by some local kids who are being taught karate by a sadistic leader at a local dojo. Mr. Miyagi shows up out of nowhere and rescues Daniel from a beating. Mr. Miyagi is a laconic character who quickly dispatches the arrogant bullies with some incredible martial arts moves. Daniel then asks Mr. Miyagi to teach him karate. And out of that request an incredible friendship develops between the two.

Daniel shows up on the first day of instruction raring to get involved in some sparring. Instead he finds himself polishing cars. You remember the routine...wax on...wax off! This is followed the next day with another menial job. Painting both sides of a six-foot fence with Mr. Miyagi pointing out spots that Daniel had missed. Next he finds himself sanding the floor..."Sand the floor!"

The young man is rapidly approaching the limits of his patience. He wants to learn karate. He wants to throw a few punches—anything except this mind-numbing routine. Nearly a week has transpired. Daniel shows up at Mr. Miyagi's house only to be greeted by a letter instructing him to paint the house. Daniel works all day fuming over the senselessness of the tasks he has been asked to do. He finishes painting the house only to be greeted by his mentor returning from a relaxing trip. Mr. Miyagi stoically once again points out a spot Daniel had missed.

That was more than the young man could take. He storms off slinging vindictive one-liners at Mr. Miyagi as he exits. Mr. Miyagi commands him to return. The totally frustrated youngster comes back and stands before his future mentor ready to explode. Suddenly Mr. Miyagi throws a karate punch his way and Daniel instinctively blocks the blow with the same hand motion he has been repeating all day long as he "paints the house." Then in rapid-fire succession Mr. Miyagi calls out "sand the floor," "paint the fence," and "wax on—wax off!" Each motion of Daniel's hands turns out to be the perfect counter punch to block the various karate blows Mr. Miyagi is throwing his way. It is a magnificent scene as Daniel's eyes light up with the realization that Mr. Miyagi has been teaching and training him the entire time. He thought he was in "exile" from his dream of learning karate.

What a profound portrayal of our difficulties with God at times, especially as we slug through the process of coming out of our sexual struggles. It feels at times as if all we are doing is just putting one foot in front of the other. You may have even said to yourself, "What is the purpose of all these exercises of looking at my feelings and wounds within? This doesn't make any sense to me. Is there a purpose to all of this? And why is God so picky about doing it this way instead of that way?" All great questions, but they are only answered as you realize...**You *are* in training!**

Doing an **Arousal Template** has brought more men, who struggle with sexual bondages, to what I call a "Mr. Miyagi Moment" than anything else I have them do. So frequently I have watched the lights turn on for a guy who has been mystified by his sexual behavior for years. Suddenly he understands how to block the enemy's punches against his soul.

I doubt that you will see the battle clearly until you pause **at the end of this exercise** and allow the Holy Spirit to open your eyes to what has been going on in your life for decades.

Therefore, it is critical that you answer the questions in each column with the utmost diligence. I am sure it will feel like a "sand the floor" experience as you answer some of the questions. And the floor will be your soul. These are not easy questions to answer. They can be difficult to deal with. But you have come this far by the grace of God. Now is the time to walk into a real breakthrough irrespective of the emotional effort required. You have been in training for such a time as this in your life.

This exercise will help you think through how the enemy keeps defeating you. Once you are sexually aroused you can't think that straight because you are limbically driven. Actor/comedian Robin Williams put it rather sardonically:

> *"God gave men both a penis and a brain,*
> *but unfortunately not enough blood supply to run both at the same time."* [34]

Neurologically that isn't true, but the point is that once we get sexually excited our higher reason ability usually drops to near zero. We have to do our critical thinking before we get sexually aroused and the **Arousal Template** on page 146 enables you to do exactly that. It enables you to deal with the bullies of hell that have so ruthlessly attacked your soul for years.

*Please note:* **There may be legal ramifications for any information about inappropriate sexual contact or behavior that involves minor children that is shared within your Pure Desire group. Please review the Memo of Understanding.**

## STEP ONE

❶ List ALL sexual behaviors that are arousing for you and have become problematic for you.

### EXAMPLES:
*Compulsive masturbation, pornography, strip clubs, one night stands, voyeurism, massage parlors, anonymous sex, masturbating w/or without 900#, seduction, adult bookstores, exhibitionism, flirtation, office romances, voyeuristic rape, S & M, conquest, affairs, high risk sexual behaviors, or _____.*

❷ Be very specific.

### EXAMPLES:
*What type of porn sites do you visit? What type of women or men do you like to view? (tall, short, young, old, red head, blond, muscular or heavy) What specific sexual acts do you find exciting? (couples having intercourse, more than two people, rape, violence, school girls, grannies, gay men, gay women, voyeuristic sites)*

*What do the individuals you view have in common? Do you pursue them or like to be pursued? Do you see yourself dominating the individual or being dominated? Do you like to exhibit images of yourself? Do you like to watch "hidden camera" views of sexual images? Do you view minors, elderly, or physically/mentally handicapped individuals?*

## STEP TWO

❯ **List all early painful sexual and relational experiences in your life. Pay particular attention to traumatic, abusive, and neglectful experiences.**

**EXAMPLES:**

*Rigid or disengaged family experiences, inappropriate exposure to sexually explicit information in your home, parent or parents having affairs, multiple marriages.*

*Boundary violations, spanked while naked, punished for normal childhood sexual exploration, failure to respect privacy when dressing or in the bathroom, ridiculing your body's development, exhibitionism by parent or parents.*

## STEP THREE

❯ **Identify childhood feelings and emotions or any themes related to abuse or neglect. Pay close attention to sexual or romantic themes.**

**EXAMPLES:**

*Being violated or having sexual boundaries intruded upon, getting something only when you were good (performance orientation), seeing sexual images prematurely (voyeurism), being flirted with (seduced), being subjected to abuse by a powerful parent (exploitive), experiencing abuse from a stranger (anonymous), being spanked while naked (pain), having no privacy (intrusive).*

*Remember trauma or pain, either a huge one-time experience or numerous small experiences, can become a hyper accelerator for sexual arousal. This is why individuals who have experienced abuse or neglect exhibit altered brain function.*

## STEP FOUR

❶ Identify emerging overall themes and core beliefs.

❷ List possible coping skills (disassociation, control, perfectionism, being passive, narcissism, silence, anger/rage).

❸ How have these coping skills become embedded themes or patterns in your life?

❹ How have these patterns expressed themselves sexually in your life?

❺ What triggers you to react sexually?

## STEP FIVE

❯ **Identify your arousal patterns, triggers and recovery strategies.**

Place your responses to each step in the chart on page 146. Some examples are given for Steps One, Two, Three, and Four.

## AROUSAL TEMPLATE: PART TWO

| STEP ONE The specific triggers and behaviors for me | STEP TWO Early painful sexual relational experiences | STEP THREE Childhood feelings | STEP FOUR Your overall themes and core beliefs | STEP FIVE Arousal patterns, triggers and recovery strategies |
|---|---|---|---|---|
| **Risk:** Constant masturbation and fantasies | *5/6 Older sister attempted to have sexual intercourse* | *Fearful and excited* | *I am worthless* | **INNER CIRCLE** |
| **Taboos:** Erotic writings on the Internet | *5/6 Began to masturbate* | *Shame and anger* | *Breaking taboos is exciting* | |
| **Quick and anonymous:** Frequent sexual encounters with anonymous males<br>• Tall, dark, & well-built<br>• Parks & public bathrooms<br>• Bath houses<br>• Porn shops<br>• Quick & dirty | *7/8 Sister and relative attempt intercourse with me; discovered by mother* | *Alone* | *Can't trust women* | **MIDDLE CIRCLE** |
| **Secrecy:** Sexually anorexic with wife | *Jr. High Mother discovered sister in bed with me* | *Hurt and anger* | *Don't get close to anyone; they will hurt you* | **OUTER CIRCLE** |
| **Non-relational:** Foul language is a turn-on at work & in public | *High School Forced to have oral sex with male student at knifepoint* | *Isolated and used* | | |

## MY AROUSAL TEMPLATE: PART TWO

| STEP ONE | STEP TWO | STEP THREE | STEP FOUR | STEP FIVE |
|---|---|---|---|---|
| All sexual behaviors that are arousing & problematic | Early painful sexual relational experiences | Childhood feelings and themes | Your overall themes and core beliefs | Arousal patterns, triggers and recovery strategies |

INNER CIRCLE

MIDDLE CIRCLE

OUTER CIRCLE

After you have completed your Arousal Template, find at least one other person, hopefully two, with whom you can share the result. By now you should have identified those individuals in your Pure Desire group with whom you feel safe.

Ask them to see if there are any themes or patterns you might have missed.

I don't think anyone can understand an addict quite like a fellow addict. Try not to get defensive if they question the conclusions you have come to; you desperately need an outside observer you can trust. You need such input to help you get clarity because you have been battling the problem at such close range for so long that, at times, you cannot see the forest for the trees.

## ✎ ASSIGNMENTS FOR NEXT TIME

❶ Complete Steps One through Five in the Arousal Template.

❷ Identify the individuals with whom you will share your Arousal Template.

❸ Meditate on Matthew 16:24-25.

# LESSON FOUR

## CONSTRUCTING A WINNING BATTLE PLAN!

> *Then Jesus said to the disciples, "If any of you wants to be my follower, you must put aside your selfish ambition, shoulder your cross, and follow me. If you try to keep your life for yourself, you will lose it. But if you give up your life for me, you will find true life."*
> Matthew 16:24-25 (NLT)

Meditating on this passage was part of the homework for Lesson Three. It was a very important exercise because it gives you a significant insight into how to mess with the enemy's head. Jesus is helping us to understand that the moment you deny yourself you have removed yourself from the realm of the enemy's control. Therefore, he can't mess with you anymore; instead you get to mess with him!

The principle: **Go Stealth...Embrace Your Cross**.

Please notice the fact that Jesus didn't say, "Take *my* cross but take up *your cross*." His cross was to die for the sins of the world; that is obviously not your cross. When Jesus faced the cross it meant death; when we face our cross it means life and abundance. Granted, it doesn't initially feel that way because your cross is found where your will runs counter to God's will in your life. But Jesus is saying to you right now, "That part of your life that is not working, that part of your life where we are at odds—I have a gift for you if you will surrender that part of your life to Me. I can touch that point of shame and pain and give you freedom."

You will never be able to hear those words until you understand that **every interaction with God is encased in grace**. That is why the Holy Spirit gets so excited about what God wants to give you; He is excited because He loves a good fight. And with the gift He would give you, the battle becomes a slam dunk, which is precisely why He gets so excited over what lies ahead for you.

Conversely, the enemy has nothing but contempt for you. Look at what he had to say about Job and all of mankind in the Old Testament.

> *Satan answered, "A human would do anything to save his life.*
> *But what do you think would happen if you reached down and took away his health?*
> *He'd curse you to your face, that's what."*
> Job 2:4-5 (MSG)

Satan is totally convinced that when push comes to shove, self-preservation will always rule in the hearts of men. He sees us as creatures completely run by fear, solely directed by our limbic system. Here is the bottom line: The enemy has no way to predict what you will do if you aren't being driven by your own self-interests. Satan can only forecast selfishness. He is helpless against a man who is living for a cause greater than himself.

- *When you decide that the Word of God settles it for you no matter what you are feeling—that messes with the enemy's head!*

- *Every time you obey God despite the difficulties you are going through—that messes with his head!*
- *Every time you do what is right despite the costs—that messes with his head!*
- *Every time you face your addiction and chose to accept God's grace and not be controlled by shame and fear—that messes with his head!*

**The way you really mess with the enemy's head is by constructing a winning Relapse Prevention Plan.** Your ability to accept God's grace and face your addiction is directly connected to you having a battle hardened *relapse prevention plan*. In the previous lesson we went through the difficult and challenging process of constructing your Arousal Template. Now we want to take the lessons and observations from Step Five of your Arousal Template and construct the Relapse Prevention Tool, which lies at the foundation of an effective battle plan.

The **Inner Circle** describes the place where you need to die to selfish impulses; otherwise the enemy will eventually kill you! These are the places, once you are there, you will **always act out**. It is what I call the "foxhole." It is where you find yourself with the enemy in close quarters combat. He has a bayonet and you are helpless. He will "gut" you when you go there!!

**❍ Inside this inner circle of the Relapse Prevention Tool, write down the compulsive, self-defeating behaviors from which you must abstain if you have any hope of being free.**

Abstinence is one day at a time. God is not asking you right now, instantaneously, forever to be sexual pure for the rest of your life. (When I share that with clients they usually breathe a sigh of relief.) Instead He is asking you to walk in purity TODAY by His grace. To keep your pants zipped TODAY. To keep your mind pure TODAY. I call it the Manna Principle.

When God led Israel out of the bondage of Egypt, He supplied them with what they needed—one day at a time. God will provide the grace you need one day at a time, but you have to know where to apply it, thus the priority of the inner circle. If you read the story of Israel's deliverance in Exodus, specifically chapters seven through ten, you will discover a fascinating phenomenon. Initially the plagues that God brought upon the land hit both the Egyptians and Israelites. But by the fourth plague things changed. God declared that He would make a distinction between His people and the Egyptians. All the rest of the plagues don't hit the camp of the Israelites. I find it interesting that initially the plagues hit the just and the unjust. As followers of Christ, we can't escape difficulties in this life and you definitely can't medicate them away. Our faith doesn't insulate us from problems, but on the other hand, there is what I call a "corporate anointing."

**A Holy Spirit anointing enables you to walk differently in this world. My point from Exodus is this: you usually find the grace you need to walk in purity when you are in relationship, in the community of faith. Your Pure Desire group is an absolute lifeline for you.** You will want to share the result of this exercise with them in detail. Make sure you listen carefully to their input and suggestions because you usually have a very incomplete understanding of yourself and the battle you are facing.

Your **INNER CIRCLE** might include comments like…

- *No sex outside of marriage.*
- *No viewing of porn and masturbation.*

- *No strip clubs or massage parlors.*
- *No medicating of my feelings of loneliness or worthlessness.*
- *No surfing of TV alone, secretly looking for sexual excitement.*
- *No gambling or overworking to the point of total exhaustion.*
- *No drinking or drugs.*

I also so call the **Inner Circle** the "crash." We are not planning on relapsing; but if we do, we must honestly look at the Inner Circle and ask the following questions:

- *How did I end up back here again?*
- *What were the steps that lead me to this crash?*
- *How do I need to revise my relapse prevention plan? What did I miss?*

The only relapse that can become fatal is the one I am not willing to learn from. Instead of turning against myself and spiraling into a deeper shame cycle, I must ruthlessly and graciously face my part in the process. **Relapses never just happen; they are always preceded by a clear sequence of choices that we make.** The problem is we are usually not even aware that we are making these choices. They are taking place beneath the radar of our conscious mind, at the unconscious level. Therefore, and this is HUGE, we must chart out a clear relapse prevention plan based on the insights we have gained from our Arousal Template or we will just continue the insanity. This is precisely why "trying harder" is a losing strategy.

Next is the **MIDDLE CIRCLE**. These are the "triggers" that lead you into the hellacious foxhole situations. The middle circle includes those behaviors that fall between the devastating addictions that totally demoralize you and the healthy sexuality you truly cry for in Christ. I call these the "trip wires" in my life. As a platoon commander, as well as a pilot, I became very familiar with the challenge of dealing with a crafty enemy. Whenever we set up a defensive position with our platoon, we set up trip wires on the outer perimeter of our encampment. The trip wires furthest out would be equipped with flares so that in the middle of the night as the enemy crept ever closer, suddenly a flare would rocket skyward. This was an objective indicator that our adversary was drawing near.

These **MIDDLE CIRCLE** behaviors will eventually lead us back into the INNER CIRCLE if we don't develop strong boundaries and stay in touch with the fact that we are powerless over our compulsions.

**❍ In this circle list people, places, situations, things, that you must avoid because they trigger you. (Refer back to your Arousal Template if needed.)**

List mental "slippery slopes" such as rationalizing, justifying, blaming, patterns of anger, isolating, etc. List activities that can set you up such as cruising for prostitutes, driving by the strip club, surfing the web, flirting at work, lying or choosing to omit certain facts, watching R-rated movies, etc.

The **MIDDLE CIRCLE** can also be seen from a positive perspective. It is where we construct the critical guardrails of our life. Guardrails are placed in areas in which it is safe to drive to keep us from driving into areas that are unsafe. Guardrails are designed to have us experience a little bit of pain to keep us from falling into devastatingly painful consequences. Guardrails are about a standard of personal behavior that reflects your unique personality and previous experiences in life. They define what you want to stay away from.

We live in a culture that constantly baits us sexually as men, then mocks us when we step over the line. Guardrails are not naturally and easily built in our life. The problem is we can feel like they keep us from something we want.

- *I don't want to save money I want to buy that car, power tool, or big boy toy, NOW!*
- *I know I am married, but I want to flirt with the gal at the office. I am not hurting anyone!*
- *I know I shouldn't eat that dessert, but I have been good all week. I will be better tomorrow!*
- *I know I shouldn't surf the Internet alone, but I am bored!*

The big problem with guardrails, as so many guys have told me, is they get in their way. It gets between them and what they crave. They restrict me! I am not experiencing as much fun as I possibly could. I am not as close to sin as I possibly could be without sinning. THEY ARE LIMITING MY LIFE! I am leaving stuff on the table. I am ignoring some fun things I haven't explored yet!

## BIG TRUTH NUMBER ONE

**Whether or not you have guardrails in your life, the pressure of temptation will not go away.**
Here is what I mean. The place you decide to put a guardrail in your life is where the temptation begins. If you decide to not place any guardrails in your life, the tension doesn't go away. It just moves closer to the cliff of horrendous consequences. However, the further back you construct the guardrails in your life, the easier it is to resist the magnetic pull of temptation and avoid plunging off the cliff. Compromise doesn't ease the tension; it only moves us closer to the cliff of losing sight of who we really are in Christ.

But we can so easily tell ourselves, "Oh, if I just give in to the temptation then I will not have this tension any more. The temptation will not be there anymore." The truth is if you lie to yourself once, it becomes much easier the next time. Eventually it will become such a lifestyle that you no longer know the truth or know who you really are in Christ.

> *But Daniel made up his mind that he would not defile himself with the king's choice food or with the wine which he drank; so he sought permission from the commander of the officials that he might not defile himself. Now God granted Daniel favor and compassion in the sight of the commander of the officials,*
> Daniel 1:8-9 (NASB)

Daniel made an insane choice. King Nebuchadnezzar has just offered him the gift of a lifetime! A free graduate education at one of the finest universities in the world at the time. If that is not enough he gets food right off the king's table. The vast majority of his countrymen, those who were still alive after Babylon destroyed Jerusalem, were wondering where their next meal was coming from. But Daniel made an incredibly wise choice; he knew where all this was headed. Nebuchadnezzar was a diabolically brilliant man. He ordered the best and brightest of the nations he conquered to be brought to and be trained in Babylon. Slowly, their culture and belief structures would be stripped away until they would become superb ambassadors for Nebuchadnezzar, his gods, and his way of life.

Daniel saw where all this "great stuff" was headed. He knew where this was going. He would eventually lose everything he held near and dear! "But Daniel made up his mind." He resolved that this is as far as it goes. He made up his mind even before he knew what the outcome would be. He had never read the book of Daniel, he was writing it. He was a teenager surrounded by the most powerful people in the world. They could have crushed him in an instant. He made the decision because he could predict the end of the story if he just went with the flow of events. He knew where this was leading, and yet he had no guarantees what would happen if he said "No!" to the king's offer.

## BIG TRUTH NUMBER TWO

I absolutely love the beginning of verse 9, "Now God." Here is the part we tend to forget in the stress of the moment. **God will not only use our guardrails to protect us. He will use them to direct us as well.** The Lord used this pivotal moment of decision to guide the rest of Daniel's life.

You have to make up your mind before you know the end of your story. Yet you can easily predict the end if you keep sliding towards the Inner Circle of destruction. **You will never know who you can be in God until you establish some solid guardrails in your life! You have to make up your mind! The only thing that goes away without guardrails in your life is your *God-given future!***

**◯ Inside the MIDDLE CIRCLE list the trip wires that can set you up and the guardrails you want to build in your life.**

Finally, the **OUTER CIRCLE** needs to be described. These are activities that support your healing and also describe what healthy sexuality looks like for you. The question of healthy sexuality can be a real puzzle for someone who has been struggling with sexual bondage for years. Usually when I ask a client to describe what healthy sexuality is for him, I get a blank stare. But it is vitally important you think that through because if your only goal is to stop your past behavior, you are defeated before you start. You must have a vivid picture of what your dreams and hopes are for your marriage or future marriage. Otherwise you will lack the passion and chutzpa (Jewish slang for courage) to win the war.

Your **OUTER CIRCLE** activities might include:

- *Faithfully doing my homework for my Pure Desire group.*
- *Play a sport for just the fun of it instead of having to win.*
- *Explore new healthy hobbies and interests.*
- *Develop a great ability to listen to and affirm my wife.*
- *Be totally honest in all of my dealings and admit when I am wrong.*
- *Develop some deep friendships.*
- *Develop a meaningful and deep devotional life.*
- *Learn **not** to focus on "all or nothing" in life, but to do something healthy every day.*
- *Develop healthy eating habits and a workout routine.*
- *Learn how to truly relax when I need to.*
- *Fall deeply in love with my wife once again.*
- *Be physically and emotionally present with and encourage my children.*

**◯ Inside the OUTER CIRCLE list what healthy sexuality looks like for you.**

Once you complete the **Relapse Prevention Tool** they will become a document in progress. At least once every three to six months you should revisit this exercise and adjust your responses to your current level of healing and understanding. You will find that this is an excellent indicator of the progress you have made and an invaluable tool in understanding your struggles.

It is important to understand that your Arousal Template is usually not a healthy sign of what "turns you on." If that was true, then you wouldn't be struggling with sexual bondage and have to go through this workbook! Your Arousal Template is instead a picture of the way you have learned to sexually medicate your inner wounds. That is a critical truth to understand. I had one guy finish his AT and say to me, "No wonder I am not attracted to my wife. She doesn't match my AT." That is when I smiled at him and said, "That is because your AT is telling you, you are one hurting guy!"

I have asked you to redo the **Relapse Prevention Tool exercise** every three to six months because as you get healed, your AT will begin to get healthier and healthier. As you redo your Relapse Prevention Tool, you probably will make a fascinating discovery. When you begin to walk in greater health and freedom you see two things take place:

❶ Your focus will move from the inner circle to the middle circle. You will begin to realize that the things that set you up to fall back into the Inner Circle are the things listed in the Middle Circle. Therefore, your Middle Circle begins to be combined with the Inner Circle. They become part of your Abstinence List! You don't want ever to go slamming into a Guardrail again in your life because you realize where that is headed…off the cliff!

❷ Real health begins to settle deep into your soul when your focus finally stops being what you don't want to do. Instead, your thoughts and focus is on what you really want to do in your life (the outer circle). Your focus has now dramatically shifted from the addiction to health!

## RELAPSE PREVENTION TOOL

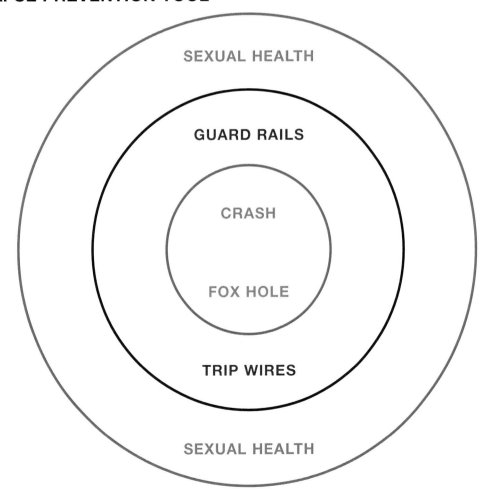

# ✐ ASSIGNMENTS FOR NEXT TIME

This is a very challenging lesson. Take your time and provide yourself opportunity for thoughtful responses. The battle plan you are constructing will in many ways determine whether or not you truly get free!

**❶** Be prepared to share and receive feedback on your work in the Relapse Prevention Tool.

**❷** Read through the exercise "**Who I am in Christ**" below.

**❸** Select a verse each day that deals with a limbic lie you have believed—a core belief that hell tries to control you with. When you feel insecure or intimidated by hell during the day, take the promise and **ram it down hell's throat**!

**❹** Review and sign the Commitment for Pillar Five.

**❺** Read *Pure Desire* Chapter 14.

## WHO I AM IN CHRIST[35]
### THE WORD OF GOD SAYS:

1. **I am God's child** for I am born again of the incorruptible seed of the Word of God that lives and abides forever. (1 Peter 1:23)

2. **I am forgiven** of all my sins and washed in the blood. (Ephesians 1:7; Hebrews 9:14; Colossians 1:14; 1 John 2:12; 1 John 1:9)

3. **I am a new creation.** (2 Corinthians 5:17)

4. **I am a temple where the Holy Spirit lives.** (1 Corinthians 6:19)

5. **I am delivered** from the power of darkness; Christ brings me into God's kingdom. (Colossians 1:13)

6. **I am redeemed** from the curse of the law. (1 Peter 1:18-19)

7. **I am holy and without blame** before God. (Ephesians 1:4)

8. **I am established** to the end. (1 Corinthians 1:8)

9. **I have been brought closer to God** through the blood of Christ. (Ephesians 2:13)

10. **I am victorious.** (Revelation 21:7)

11. **I am set free.** (John 8:31-32)

12. **I am strong** in the Lord. (Ephesians 6:10)

13. **I am dead to sin.** (Romans 6:2 & 11; 1 Peter 2:24)

14. **I am more than a conqueror.** (Romans 8:37)

15. **I am a co-heir** with Christ. (Romans 8: 16-17)

16. **I am sealed** with the Holy Spirit of promise. (Ephesians 1:13)

17. **I am in Christ Jesus by his doing.** (1 Corinthians 1:30)

18. **I am accepted** in Jesus Christ. (Ephesians 1:5-6)

19. **I am complete** in Him. (Colossians 2:10)

**20. In am crucified with Christ.** (Galatians 2:20)

**21. I am alive** with Christ. (Ephesians 2:4-5)

**22. I am free** from condemnation. (Romans 8:1)

**23. I am reconciled** to God. (2 Corinthians 5:18)

**24. I am qualified** to share in his inheritance. (Colossians 1:12)

**25. I am firmly rooted**, established in my faith and overflowing with gratefulness and thankfulness. (Colossians 2:7)

**26. I am called** of God. (2 Timothy 1:9)

**27. I am chosen.** (1 Thessalonians 1:4; Ephesians 1:4; 1 Peter 2:9)

**28. I am an ambassador** of Christ. (2 Corinthians 5:20)

**29. I am God's workmanship** created in Christ Jesus for good works. (Ephesians 2:10)

**30. I am the apple of my Father's eye.** (Deuteronomy 32:10; Psalm 17:8)

**31. I am healed** by the stripes of Jesus. (1 Peter 2:24; Isaiah 53:6)

**32. I am being changed** into his image. (2 Corinthians 3:18; Philippians 1:6)

**33. I am raised up** with Christ and am seated in heavenly places. (Ephesians 2:6)

**34. I am beloved** of God. (Colossians 3:12; Romans 1:7; 1 Thessalonians 1:4)

**35. I have the mind of Christ.** (Philippians 2:5; 1 Corinthians 2:16)

**36. I have obtained an inheritance.** (Ephesians 1:11)

**37. I have access** by one Spirit to the Father. (Ephesians 2:18)

**38. I have overcome** the world. (1 John 5:4)

**39. I have everlasting life** and will not be condemned. (John 5:24; John 6:47)

**40. I have the peace of God** that transcends all understanding. (Philippians 4:7)

**41. I have received power**—the power of the Holy Spirit; power to lay hands on the sick and see them recover; power to cast out demons; power over all the power of the enemy; nothing shall by any means hurt me. (Mark 16:17-18; Luke 10:17-19)

**42. I live by and in the law of the Spirit of Life** in Christ Jesus. (Romans 8:2)

**43. I walk in Christ Jesus.** (Colossians 2:6)

**44. I can do all things** (everything) in and through Christ Jesus. (Philippians 4:13)

**45. We shall do even greater things** than Jesus did. (John 14:12)

**46. I possess the Great One** in me because greater is He who is in me than he who is in the world. (1 John 4:4)

**47. I press toward the mark** for the prize of the high calling of God. (Philippians 3:14)

**48. I always triumph** in Christ. (2 Corinthians 2:14)

**49. My life shows forth his praise.** (1 Peter 2:9)

**50. My life is hidden with Christ** in God. (Colossians 3:3)

# ✔ PILLAR OF FREEDOM FIVE COMMITMENT

I have, to the best of my ability, completed all the exercises found in Pillar of Freedom Five. By God's grace I will do everything I can to live these truths out in my life on a daily basis.

My Name _____

Signature _____ Date _____

................................................................................................

## AFFIRMING WITNESSES:

❶ *I affirm the fact that* _____ *has grown in integrity and honesty in his life by the grace of God. Denial is no longer part of his life.*

My Name _____

Signature _____ Date _____

❷ *I affirm the fact that* _____ *has grown in integrity and honesty in his life by the grace of God. Denial is no longer part of his life.*

My Name _____

Signature _____ Date _____

................................................................................................

# TAKING ON THE "TOUGH ONE"

# 📄 LESSON ONE

## MIGS COMING OUT OF THE WEEDS

The title of this chapter is a term we used to describe a tactic the North Vietnamese Air Force used against us. We had extensive radar coverage of their airspace so we could anticipate when they would try to attack us. Instead of confronting us head on, they would stay as low as possible after take off. So low it would be below our radar coverage, all the while their radar operators would be calling out our position and vectoring them to attack us from the rear. Once they had us in sight they would zoom up to our altitude and start blazing away. Frequently we never saw them coming, thus the term "MIGS coming out of the weeds."

In Pillar Six we are going to be looking at one thing I have seen trap more men in their addiction than just about anything else. It is a killer because they never see it. That is why this issue frequently shoots them down into a flaming ball of shame and relapse. We are going to be taking on the tough one: **Trauma**!

What do we mean by the term trauma? I have seen the reality and accuracy of this definition again and again in thirty plus years of pastoral and clinical counseling.

> *Trauma is an overwhelming experience that has a negative impact on an individual's mental and emotional processing ability in the moment and in the future because of what they have experienced in the past. Trauma frequently refers to an experience beyond the capability of an individual to adapt to effectively. This can easily happen in the childhood years, resulting in a downloading of maladaptive mental software that negatively affects the individual's interpersonal abilities at the subconscious level well into adulthood.*

Trauma is one of the stealthiest weapons the enemy brings against us. In nearly thirty years of counseling guys who are struggling with sexual purity, not once have I ever had a guy walk into my office and ask me to help him deal with the trauma in his life. Yet every man who I have helped walk to freedom had to face trauma in his life. His biggest problem was he didn't even realize the enemy was using the wounds of his past like a heat-seeking missile to blow his commitment to Christ to smithereens.

So what is trauma? Let me start by using a simple, but painful analogy from my life. I had been struggling with a muscle in my left hip for over a year. I just figured I had pushed it too hard during one of my workouts and eventually it would heal. Despite my best efforts of increasing the workout load to strengthen that muscle group and extensive massage therapy, nothing seemed to work. Finally I hobbled into the doctor's office. I described the frustrating symptoms and the doc knowingly nodded at my comments. He grasped a rubber hammer to test my reflexes. Tapping my right knee, my leg jerked upwards in response. Then he tapped my left knee….NOTHING, ABSOLUTELY NOTHING. He hit it again with more velocity…still nothing. He paused, then looking up at me stated, "Looks like you have a bulged disk in your lower back which is putting pressure on the nerves. This is causing the pain. It doesn't appear to be a muscle tear at all. We have to deal with something much deeper." I had an incorrect understanding of the source of the pain and would never have solved the problem.

Pain is not just pain; there are different sources of pain in our life. Trauma is not just pain because it can go so deep into our soul. Hearing the word "trauma" usually brings up mental images of hellacious events, making it is so hard for most guys to recognize the power trauma has over their lives. The destruction of the World Trade Center, severe car crashes, violent physical abuse, or similar events come to mind at the mention of the word "trauma." They almost always say to me, "Hey, I have had some tough times in life but no worse than the next guy; besides that I grew up in a Christian home. Mom and Dad loved me." When I ask them how affirming and present their dad was in the early years of their life, or how supportive mom was, they grow silent. Sometimes they will respond by vehemently defending mom or dad.

You see the problem is **we cannot help but love certain figures in our life whether they have earned it or not**. Now relax! We are not going to blame all your problems on mom and dad. They probably did the best they could with what they had. Once you become a parent you quickly realize just how impossible the job is.

> *We are not trying to blame anyone. We are going to reclaim what hell stole from us through the weapon of trauma in our life.*

## FOUR BASIC FACTS ABOUT TRAUMA

The award winning documentary movie *Armadillo* (2010) followed a regiment of Danish soldiers from their emotional farewells through their months in combat and, finally, back to their family reunions. The film is a study of the inner lives of young men as they experience the excitement and camaraderie, the tedium and mostly the terror and trauma of war in Afghanistan.[36] These same soldiers were the subjects of another study as well, a very different kind of study. They were being scientifically observed and tested for emerging symptoms of post-traumatic stress disorder (PTSD). The results of the study revealed some surprising findings. First of all, PTSD does not appear to be automatically triggered by a traumatic battle experience. The vast majority of the soldiers were resilient to trauma's effects.[37]

Compared to the resilient soldiers, the soldiers who developed PTSD were much more likely to have suffered emotional problems and traumatic events prior to deployment. Childhood traumatic experiences actually **predicted the onset of PTSD** in these soldiers. Those who showed symptoms of PTSD were more likely to have witnessed family trauma growing up. They were also more likely to have past experiences that they could not, or would not, talk about.

### TRUTH ONE: THE FOUNDATION FOR TRAUMA IS FREQUENTLY LAID DOWN EARLY IN OUR LIFE

Humans are born with lots of neurons, but with few connections between them. We build the operating system of our brain from experience instead of being born with it being pre-programmed. We also are vulnerable and needy for much longer than animals are. Thus, vulnerability is the first experience we have of life and it lays at the foundation of our mental operating system. A toddler's brain develops so easily in response to stimulation that it absorbs everything uncritically. After age two, the brain starts to rely on the circuits it has rather than changing to fit every new input. This explains the phenomena of the "Terrible Twos," where the child's favorite word is "NO!"

If a neural pathway is repeatedly triggered, it gets myelinated which makes the firing pattern almost automatic. This process explodes in our youth. "Myelination" simply means the neurons are insulated the way plastic insulates wires. This transforms some neural circuits into superhighways whose processing speed is like optical fiber compared to old-fashioned copper wire. Myelination reaches its peak at two years of age and surges again during puberty, so the experiences of those two peak periods are central to a person's expectations about their world. And during adolescence the male brain becomes uniquely sensitive to sexual signals.

All of this tells us that the foundational software of our brain is downloaded very early in our lives. Therefore, trauma in your early childhood will become a significant part of your perception of your world at the **unconscious level**. Children build their mental operating system in an attempt to avoid pain and experience pleasure. This explains why as an adult you can end up struggling to respond to pleasure and pain in your life in ways that are redemptive. You are battling a mental operating system built into your life years ago. You are dealing with some viruses in your mental software that hell injected into your thought process at the unconscious level back at the beginning. Early learning is the foundation of adult responses, whether we like it or not. After puberty, myelination drops off significantly; therefore, it takes a great deal of effort and repetition to create new neurological connections. This is why we are significantly affected by our adolescent experiences, especially sexual ones, despite efforts to the contrary.

## TRUTH TWO: TRAUMA CAN RENDER US EMOTIONALLY ILLITERATE ABOUT CERTAIN ISSUES IN OUR LIFE

As the study showed, those wrestling with trauma could not or would not talk about it. It remained a stealthy adversary in their souls. The Chinese have a proverb that profoundly describes the dilemma, "The deepest pain has no words."

The vicious Double Bind here is that unless we process our trauma, which at some point involves finding words to express the hurt, then ongoing life issues such as anxiety, sleep disturbance, anger, feelings of betrayal, and trouble trusting and connecting in relationships can persist for years. The unresolvable nature of the pain leads the individual to seek pleasure or self-medicate through sex, porn, masturbation, alcohol, food, spending, or other addictions.

## TRUTH THREE: TRAUMA CAN FEED THE ADDICTION AT A VERY DEEP LEVEL

As you discovered in the book *Pure Desire*, sexual addiction is like a noose from hell around your soul. Unless you deal with the underlying issues, the harder you pull against it the worse things get. When trauma is added to the mixture, you experience the reality the noose graphic painfully depicts.

There is a love-hate relationship with sexually acting out. You fight the urge, but it is a losing battle most of the time because you love how it makes you feel for the moment. Why can't you stop this craziness? I mean, you love the Lord with all your heart. Now you understand the neurochemistry of the addictive cycle. You have done the recovery homework faithfully and developed new skills to combat your past mental patterns. Why isn't it working!?! The answer: **You have to deal with the noose beneath the noose**.

A stealth noose is at work. The noose beneath the noose that can make us crazy despite our best efforts is unprocessed trauma from our past. The problem is that usually we can't even see it, or if we do, we don't know how to talk about it. I have lost count of the number of times I have asked a client how he feels about a painful experience in his past and all I get is a blank expression. He truly has become emotionally illiterate through years of medicating his pain. This can be so deep-rooted, it turns our life into a series of "bad reruns." When basic life needs are not met adequately early on in life, we can develop an emotional hunger that is never met. It is characterized by seeking to redo the past—to meet early unmet needs with the wrong people at the wrong time and place. This is called trauma repetition. I know it sounds crazy, but I see it all the time in the counseling office. For example, I have seen so many guys drive themselves mercilessly, trying to get approval from some male authority figure. Or they play the role of a rebel or the critic still reacting to the specter of their distant or distracted dad.

Research has shown that trauma victims attempt to control their feelings of hyper-arousal, isolation, emotional pain, and anger by medicating their inner struggle to restore a sense of control over their chaotic emotions within.[38] The choice to medicate the pain through sexually acting out becomes a reliable source of **temporary** mood management. The problem is their access to what is going on in their soul is blocked by these choices. This is when the visible noose is built. Soon the addictive cycle takes on a life of its own, which results in further isolation, shame, and unresolved pain. The two nooses reinforce each other!

If the trauma issues that lie beneath the desire to self-medicate are not resolved the individual will simply lay one addiction down only to pick up another. It is just another form of trying harder instead of process the underlying trauma.

**The fourth truth is simple, but so important to grasp.**
## TRUTH FOUR: TRAUMA IS NOT JUST "TRAUMA;" IT COMES IN MANY FORMS
I know it is a gross simplification, but the two extremes of trauma may be called "whacks" (events of extreme impact) and "lacks" (small wounds that occur over and over and over again). On the surface, the lacks may appear to be totally insignificant, but their cumulative effect can be as crippling as a massive whack. Both kinds of trauma can lead to such high inner pain levels that they trigger compulsive behaviors to medicate.

## WHACKS AND LACKS GRAPH
**Whacks**

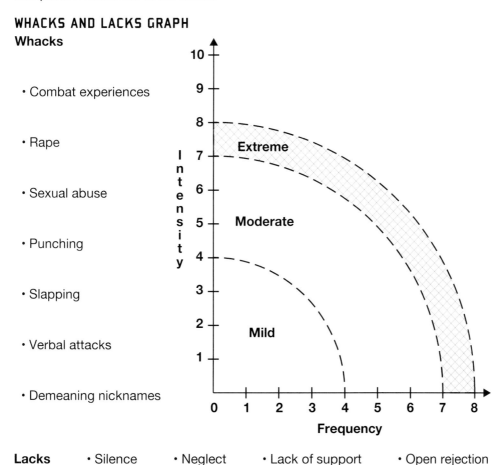

• Combat experiences

• Rape

• Sexual abuse

• Punching

• Slapping

• Verbal attacks

• Demeaning nicknames

**Lacks**   • Silence   • Neglect   • Lack of support   • Open rejection

For example, if dad repeatedly communicated to you that you weren't enough—either through his absence, neglect, or anger—it becomes an insufferable weight to bear within. Frequently the "lacks" were not purposed, they just were. One individual's mom was constantly sick and bedridden in his early years; he never had that sense of nurturing he needed growing up, and he battles with it to this day. For some this may be a tough concept to grasp when you are just reading a bunch of words on a page. So let me graphically display what I am trying to communicate.

*Note:* Sometimes a single "whack" can move someone into the extreme range of trauma. "Lacks" can also move a person into the extreme range through high frequency. For example, extreme trauma can result if someone is continuously treated with silence or neglect throughout their early years of life.

This is not psychobabble excusing for out-of-control addictive behavior. As you will learn in Lesson Two, a child's basic software for dealing with their world is downloaded from his Family of Origin. Yes, as we grow up we learn to think as an adult; but if that initial software is riddled with the viruses of trauma, the urge to medicate instead of process the pain within will be irresistible. Especially when we are under pressure. We will have to do what Paul so eloquently challenges us to do in I Corinthians 13:11: "When I was a child, I talked like a child, I thought like a child, I reasoned like a child. When I became a man, I put the ways of childhood behind me."

So let's look at your life. Note the examples in each category of "whacks" or "lacks" then add examples from your life. Since each person may categorize intensity within the context of their own experiences, don't limit yourself to the examples given. Write outside the boxes if needed.

## THE WHACKS OF MY LIFE

**High Intensity**

*Examples:*

- Parents divorce
- Family member dies
- Sexual abuse
- Failure in school
- Emotional abuse

*My life:*

**Medium Intensity**

*Examples:*

- Loss of a friend
- Being bullied
- Not making the team

*My life:*

**Low Intensity**

*Examples:*

- Name-calling
- Feeling unheard

*My life:*

*Note:* What may be a high intensity whack for you might be a medium or low intensity whack for someone else. The whacks can even come from ourselves if we are looking at the world through shame-colored glasses. Shame can affect us in all three levels of intensity from failing to make the team or failing at school, to being rejected by a girl, to self name-calling.

## THE LACKS OF MY LIFE

**High Intensity**

*Examples:*

- Abandoned by one or both parents
- Family unemployment

*My life:*

**Medium Intensity**

*Examples:*

- Moved frequently
- Felt rejected by older siblings
- Never had close friendships

*My life:*

**Low Intensity**

*Examples:*

- Little validation from parents or peers

*My life:*

Now back up a bit and look at all your responses.

**❯ What messages were communicated to you because of the whacks and lacks of life? What are the statements that hell has tried to use to bring you down? What are the traces of trauma in your life?**

Now relax! We will get to what God says about you. But to truly hear and receive words of grace and encouragement, you need to identify the lies that have been the background music of your soul for years.

Examples:

- *I am not enough.*
- *I have to prove myself or I will always have to do it myself.*
- *Those closest to me will abandon me.*
- *I have to protect myself—no one else will.*

1. _____

2. _____

3. _____

4. _____

**❯ What incident, event, or comments do you struggle with the most from your past?**

## ✎ ASSIGNMENTS FOR NEXT TIME

**❶** Complete the Trauma Checklist in Lesson Two and be ready to share your results at the next group meeting.

# LESSON TWO

## CHECK YOUR SIX!

A question always comes up when I share my experience of having enemy aircraft suddenly pop up behind you, "How do you avoid getting shot down?" The answer is simple, but difficult. You keep your head on a swivel and you especially check the airspace behind you. That is where the term "check your six" comes from. The airspace around your aircraft was referred to in a clock code fashion. Directly ahead of you was 12 o'clock, thus 6 o'clock was behind you. We flew in a type of formation that enabled us to constantly scan the skies for the enemy. But that is not easy to do when you are trying to set up the aircraft to attack a ground target and, at the same time, avoid anti aircraft fire and dodge surface to air missiles that were being unleashed your way. If you saw the enemy, then you could defeat him. **It was the stuff you never saw that would take you out.**

Trauma operates the same way in your life. If you never see it, it can control you at times without you even being aware of it. For example, a first of its kind study was done with Chinese adolescent Internet users.[39] The study discovered a strong correlation between increased Internet addiction and stressors from interpersonal problems, school problems, and anxiety. Once again, trauma doesn't have to be a big event or a huge whack to affect us. The stealthy noose of trauma can lie concealed in the frenetic pressures of our daily lives.

How do we see the trauma that may be ingrained in us and deal with it? Great question! The rest of Pillar Six will address that issue which is so critical in your recovery.

Let's "check your six" in life. Let's look in the rearview mirror of your life. Take a few minutes and walk through this Trauma Checklist and answer "yes" if the question is or has ever been true in your life. This is simply a list of questions I use with a client as we begin the counseling process to understand the depth of what we are dealing with.

## TRAUMA CHECKLIST

**1.** Yes___ No___ I had medical problems or was hospitalized early in life.

**2.** Yes___ No___ I get easily lost in my work.

**3.** Yes___ No___ I have periods of sleeplessness.

**4.** Yes___ No___ I feel bad at times about myself because of shameful experiences in my past.

**5.** Yes___ No___ There are actions I have trouble stopping even though they don't help me/are destructive.

**6.** Yes___ No___ My relationships are the same story over and over again.

**7.** Yes___ No___ I was adopted.

**8.** Yes___ No___ I am unable to recall details of painful experiences.

**9.** Yes___ No___ I avoid mistakes at all costs.

**10.** Yes___ No___ Unsettling thoughts or memories about something in the past have come to mind out of the blue.

**11.** Yes___ No___ Sometimes I have outbursts of anger or irritability.

**12.** Yes___ No___ Sometimes I spoil opportunities for success.

**13.** Yes___ No___ There is something destructive I do over and over that started early in my life.

**14.** Yes___ No___ I have difficulty concentrating.

**15.** Yes___ No___ Growing up I was separated from either one or both parents or my siblings for a lengthy period of time.

**16.** Yes___ No___ My parents fought a lot verbally and/or physically.

**17.** Yes___ No___ We moved a lot when I was growing up.

**18.** Yes___ No___ I am a risk taker.

**19.** Yes___ No___ I stay in conflict with someone when I could have walked away.

**20.** Yes___ No___ I often feel sexual when I am lonely.

**21.** Yes___ No___ I feel loyal to people even though they have hurt me.

**22.** Yes___ No___ I feel I must avoid depending on people.

**23.** Yes___ No___ I use TV, reading, eating, and hobbies as a way of numbing out.

**24.** Yes___ No___ I have a problem with putting off certain tasks.

**25.** Yes___ No___ I need lots of stimulation so that I don't get bored.

**❷ How many items did you mark "yes"?** _____

This is not a clinical test or a test that has been scientifically evaluated, but I have noticed that individuals who answer, "Yes." to four or more items have trauma in their life that is affecting them. In most cases, these individuals have no idea that their life has been impacted by the event or circumstance. If you scored eight or more, it is likely that you have been significantly affected by trauma. In that case, we recommend that you seek additional help from a trained clinical counselor.

**It is much like that pain I had in my left hip; the doctor told me there were three options:**

1. If it was just a muscle pull, it would heal on its own with some rest.
2. If I had a bulging disk in my back, then I would need some anti-inflammatory medication and physical therapy to mend.
3. Or the disk would require surgery.

The information in this Pillar can significantly help you if you scored below an 8 on the Trauma Checklist. Even then you may still need to seek clinical help. You can go to the Pure Desire website (www.puredesire.org > Counseling > Affiliate Treatment Providers) and look for an IITAP counselor affiliated with Pure Desire. One may be located near you, or you can contact one in your region of the country who can speak with you via a video connection.

I eventually had to go to a physical therapist for my hip pain. I couldn't just ignore it—and you can't do that either if there is unprocessed trauma in your life. We have found out that 20 to 30% of men who are part of a Pure Desire group need clinical counseling as well. It is important that you seek out a certified sexual addiction therapist who can deal with trauma.

You may have noticed that many of the questions in the checklist deal with the early years of your life. Why would trauma have such a foothold so early in life? The answer to that question is found in how the brain develops. The brain lays its foundational perceptions of the world very early in life. In the first year of life, the weight of a child's brain goes from four hundred grams to one thousand grams, more than doubling its size in twelve months. This rapid growth phase where the brain is particularly sensitive to outside stimuli continues until about twenty-four months. During the first six years of life, the limbic system, and the emotional brain (Scripture describes this as "our heart") develops its basic software.

Research has discovered that early childhood trauma affects overall health much more than trauma that has occurred in the last three to four years of our life.[40] The reason for this is the brain remembers best anything that has a high emotional charge to it, be it positive or negative. The intense emotional content literally burns the memory into the neurochemistry of the brain and acts as a **template** upon which **we print the future pages of our life**. There is nothing more intense in life for a child than the rupturing of the relationship between them and their caregiver. Their very survival is at stake. If someone has had such an experience it will be harder for them to bond to others. And it will be very hard for them to process subsequent ruptures in any relationship because it will return them to pain of the original wound.

It has also been discovered that each tiny interaction between child and primary caregiver becomes part of the hardwiring of the child's brain.[41] Self-regulation is one of the earliest tasks of childhood. Addicts, however, are characterized by poor impulse control, or a lack of ability to self-regulate. They bear the marks of trauma, resulting in a lack of their ability to self-soothe and deal with the harsh realities of a fallen world.

Dr. Bessel Van der Kolk points out the unique impact trauma has upon us, "A traumatized person does not have access to the left hemisphere of the brain which translates experience into language, therefore, they can't make sense out of what is happening. Traumatized people also have been known to have trouble tolerating intense emotions without feeling overwhelmed. Such individuals go from stimulus to response without being able to figure out what upsets them. They **overreact**, **withdraw**, or **freeze**."[42]

One of most confusing things about trauma in our life are the strong defensive structures we can build in response to the pain. The things that hurt us so deeply are the ones that we can be the most out of touch with at an emotional level. This is because a common defense we use when we are traumatized is to go numb. We mentally check out; therefore, we have little or no feeling in those areas of our disowned pain. We essentially apply emotional Novocain. Thus, we lose access to the feelings that would serve as indicators of the location of the wounds. Somewhere inside of us we hurt, but we don't know just where. This dilemma can drive the addiction ever deeper into our soul when we bump into that wound accidentally.

A particular action or statement from another person presses on the old wound, triggering a response in us that is clearly an overreaction. But we continue the overreaction by blaming others because this is where we are numb or out of touch. Instead of dealing with our overreaction and finding out why we acted that way, we project our unfelt pain onto the situation. This creates so many more problems on top of the original ones that we get lost and distracted by them. We are caught in a double noose keeping us tied up and blind to the original trauma that drives the whole cycle. Thankfully, although we cannot identify the pain, the Holy Spirit is crying out for us as Paul declared:

*In the same way, the Spirit helps us in our weakness. We do not know what we ought to pray for, but the Spirit himself intercedes for us through **wordless groans**. And he who searches our hearts knows the mind of the Spirit, because the Spirit intercedes for God's people in accordance with the will of God.*
Romans 8:26-27

There is a gracious aggression in the Holy Spirit's intercession for us. It is this aggressive nature of God at work deep within our soul that will enable us to overcome the passivity and paralysis we inherited from Adam. In Genesis 3, Adam doesn't engage or intervene to help Eve; he just stands passively by as Eve buys hell's sales pitch. Yet God created Adam to act. He was endowed with the image of a mighty and loving God who acts and intervenes dramatically. The trauma of the Fall, however, passed down a spiritual passivity or overreaction that affects us all today.

Unprocessed trauma within will push us to react in one of three ways; at times we will cycle through all three.

## TRAUMA-TRIGGERED REACTIONS
### 1. OVERREACTION USUALLY EXPRESSED IN ANGER
Your limbic system or emotional brain responds so frequently to major threats or trauma with anger. Why? For the simple fact that initially, it can feel effective. It drives others back and makes you feel more powerful and less vulnerable. Not all anger is bad, there is righteous anger that gives you the courage to fight for **others**. The problem is, our anger is almost never about helping others. Instead, it is about the survival brain overpowering higher reasoning and screaming at us, "You have to fight to survive!" The main role of reactive anger is to numb out our fears. Therefore, if we refuse to face and feel our fears they will always control us. The unchallenged trauma programing of our past will end up being the software that directs our actions in the present.

### TRAUMA PROGRAMMING
**A.** Who, what, when, or where can your anger buttons get pushed?

*Example: Lately I've gotten angry or gone limbic when I feel like I'm going to be left out of something. It's terrifying and reminds me a lot of high school. It's not so much anger as it is fear.*

Example from my life:

.................................................................................................................

**B.** Why is this person, place, or action so triggering for you?

*Example: I have a fear of not being good enough to be invited into things. It seems like people are avoiding me on purpose or something.*

Example from my life:

.................................................................................................................

**C.** What lies beneath that anger? What are the fears that reside beneath that anger?

*Example: I'm afraid I'm not good enough. If people really knew me they would definitely leave me.*

Example from my life:

..................................................................................................................................

**D.** Can you remember a time in your past where you first felt this deep response of fear and/or anger?

*Example: The first time I really remember a response of fear and/or anger was in high school when my girlfriend dumped me; I kind of made a vow with myself that I would never trust another woman.*

Example from my life:

..................................................................................................................................

## 2. SHUTTING DOWN, RUNNING AWAY OR WITHDRAWING

Adam started the downward spiral of male passivity. He was standing there, but he was "out of there" when it came to supporting and covering Eve. The fear of conflict is an excuse that so many men have given me when I challenge them to talk honestly with their wife. It is a challenge we all face as husbands. I have never met a man who doesn't want to be his wife's hero. The problem is he doesn't have a clue on how to have a healthy disagreement with his wife and he has all the traumatic pictures in his head of the conflicts he saw between mom and dad. Violence did not have to be part of the picture, just the icy silence between parents as they never faced their fears and disagreements. They were emotionally illiterate and passed on that pattern to their son.

### CONFLICT PATTERNS

**A.** When you were growing up, how did your parents deal with conflicts between them?

*Example: Honestly, it seems like things were pretty good. I've never really seen them fight, though they have disagreed for sure. But there wasn't like this eerie feeling in the air like they weren't fighting, but something was definitely wrong. I think they just handled things pretty well.*

Example from my life:

..................................................................................................................................

**B.** What issues or situations do you most fear and withdraw from?

*Example: Not being good enough and everyone finding out.*

Example from my life:

..................................................................................................................................

**C.** What causes you to worry the most in life?

*Example: Failing at this business and having to go do a job that I don't want and just being trapped in that. Also, people knowing that I failed and feeling really ashamed because I talk a big game, but then I can't actually make it happen. I'm afraid of being a fraud.*

Example from my life:

..................................................................................................................................

**D.** Do remember when you first started worrying about this issue? Is there a particular incident that comes to mind?

*Example: Well, mine is pretty specific to business stuff going on recently. I don't exactly know when this fear started, but this is definitely the biggest time in my life when I was stepping into something that I just literally didn't know if I could do. Almost everything else in life I felt like I could dominate.*

Example from my life:

..................................................................................................................................

## 3. THE FINAL OPTION: FREEZE OR APPEASE

*Why Zebras Don't Get Ulcers* is a great book. If you think about it for a moment, you can understand why the author chose that title. A zebra's life is fairly uncomplicated. The primary time of stress and trauma in their life occurs about once a week when the lions show up to eat somebody. However, if you can outrun the slowest zebra, no problem—you can go back to munching grass. Even if the lion catches you, you still have a backup plan…play dead. This triggers a profoundly altered state of numbing. In this state, the numbed-out animal is less encumbered by debilitating pain and is able to escape if the opportunity arises.[43] And if you saw the zebra narrowly escape the teeth of the lions, you would notice that afterwards the animal would literally shake; he is actually processing the trauma of the situation. We as human beings, however, face a huge problem in dealing with intense traumas in our lives. We can have the lion in our head 24 hours a day. Peter expressed it well; "**Be alert and of sober mind. Your enemy the devil prowls around like a roaring lion looking for someone to devour.**" 1 Peter 5:8.

The term prowling carries a sense of continual activity. Thus, through traumatic incidents in our life that are unprocessed, the feelings of that moment can be frozen within, so that we experience them as facts. For those who, like me, grew up in an alcoholic home, those feelings can become so ingrained that they seem like undeniable facts. We can let them run us; we can let them define who we are and how we relate to others in life.

I remember the first time I realized how differently I was acting around a strong male authority figure. I wasn't myself; I was withdrawn and anxious. As I instinctively placed my hand on my chin, I felt the scar and it all came back to me. One of my stepfathers threw me against a brick fireplace and cracked open my chin. I now have a large scar at the bottom of my chin.

When something doesn't make sense, usually your emotional brain or limbic system is overpowering your prefrontal cortex, the higher reasoning part of your brain. In other words, past trauma is turning your feelings into false facts.

169

Many of us try to "deal" with our emotions. We mistakenly work at trying to manage them, control them, tolerate or suppress them. We would be much better off simply noticing them and using the information they bring; acting on them is optional. These emotions are like the instruments on the aircraft's instrument panel. They give you information and can be misleading if you focus on just one instrument.

After I realized why I was acting so strange around the male authority figure, I asked the Holy Spirit how He was interceding for me at that moment. I still remember His response, "Ted, I am praying you would understand who you are. Your name means gift of God. You need to face your feelings of fear. They are not fact, so don't withdraw or puff up; instead, be who I have called you to be—and stand your sacred ground!" That realization began a significant process of healing in my life that continues to this day. That experience also underlines some very important truths about the healing of trauma.

## TRUTHS ABOUT THE HEALING OF TRAUMA

❶ Most people think of trauma as a "mental" problem. However, trauma is something that happens in the body. The mental states associated with trauma are important, but the body states or limbic states are equally important. The instinctive touching of the scar on my chin was part of the healing process. Therefore, it is important that you learn to listen to what your body is telling you as well as focusing on what is biblically true.

❷ Stay focused on what God says about you while tracking your bodily reactions and feelings, so you can begin to effectively process and release the trauma from your soul. Peter described our enemy as being "like a lion." As we allow ourselves to come out of freezing or appeasing we will discover that there is only one true lion—the Lion of the tribe of Judah and He wars on our behalf. He is for us not against us! This is not an easy process because you must develop the capacity to face uncomfortable physical sensations and feelings without becoming overwhelmed by them. In this process, you may need someone trained to deal with trauma to walk with you. And remember: it is a challenge worth taking on, because trauma is the noose beneath the noose. If you want to walk in freedom and purity you will have to process the trauma in your life.

**A.** What are you most afraid of and why?

*Example: Right now I'm afraid of failing and people don't like me because I'm a failure.*

Example from my life:

......................................................................................................................................................

**B.** When you bring to mind what you are most afraid of in life, what body sensations are triggered? Where do you feel it?

*Example: I thought about this a few minutes ago and felt the physical reaction to it. I felt like crying; I really am afraid of failing right now. I have been working so hard to show everyone that I'm not an idiot and I can figure things out.*

Example from my life:

......................................................................................................................................................

**C.** How do you think the Holy Spirit is praying for you when you have those feelings?

*Example: I think the Holy Spirit wants me to know that it's going to be OK. That it's OK if I fail because Jesus has my back. That people still love me regardless of how I perform and the Lord definitely still loves me.*

Example from my life:

..............................................................................................................................

**D.** What causes you to freeze or appease in life?

*Example: I freeze when I know I have some self-examining in life to do. If I know I should think through some aspect of my life, I'll just not think about anything and try to numb out.*

Example from my life:

..............................................................................................................................

**E.** Why do think that is such strong reaction for you? When do you remember freezing or appeasing for the first time in your life?

*Example: I think I definitely just shut down a lot growing up. I just appeased and did the easy thing when I was with my family and then came alive outside of that. I really was kind of dead with my family.*

Example from my life:

..............................................................................................................................

## ✐ ASSIGNMENTS FOR NEXT TIME

➲ **Be prepared to share with your group your preferred method of coping: fight, flight, or numbing out. And, more importantly, why do you respond that way?**

❺ Read *Pure Desire* Chapter 15.

# LESSON THREE

## LEARNING TO TURN INTO THE FIGHT

Hopefully, you have come to realize you have some trauma in your life. That is one of the reasons you ended up using sexual activity to medicate your pain. You may have never realized how trauma has affected your relationships, your responses on the job when you are under pressure, or in some other area of your life. Now that you have noticed an MIG from hell closing in on you, what do you do next? This is where the analogy really gets interesting. You can't outrun the MIG because it has a closing angle on you. You can't outrun trauma, either. If you try to ignore the threat, it is only a matter of time before things are going to get even more painful. So it is with trauma, just trying to ignore it or blaming others for your problems will only make matters worse.

**YOU MUST TURN INTO AND FACE THE ENEMY!** This is your only option to deal effectively with this threat. And it is critical that you execute your response with wisdom. Turning into an enemy aircraft too forcefully will cause you to bleed off your airspeed and energy. You will end up a sitting duck! Turning into your adversary too casually will only make his job easier. The same is true in dealing with trauma in your life. Reacting to your past pain too violently will only make you more reactive. Being passive about the pain of your past with statements like, "It is no big deal. Forget the past and let's move on in life!" are simply denial by another name.

So what do we do? Is there one solution we need to apply to the problem? After listening to men for three decades, I have come to see that you can't predict the effect of a traumatic event on a person in the way you can predict the effect of a gunshot on human tissue. Yet, the stress of trauma profoundly affects the health of the human body as well as the emotional, relational, and spiritual wellbeing. We cannot patch up the impact of trauma with a pill or with surgery. Yet, if left untreated, it grows and morphs into a destructive beast that erodes the very fabric of the soul. Trauma has the ability to make you so anxious, angry, dissociated, or spaced out that nothing you read or do will help. That is because your processing centers or prefrontal cortex is "shorted out" and shut down.

## THE "GIVENS"

I have discovered several "givens" in dealing with trauma. First, there is **no one-size-fits-all approach** to how people traverse the terrain of their trauma to health. There is no "one solution." There is no single prayer, spiritual exercise, or clinical protocol that will always make it all go away. Because trauma involves the wounding of multiple dimensions of our being, there is no "one solution"—be it spiritual, emotional, behavioral, or intellectual.

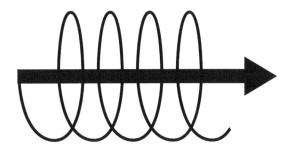

Second, **the healing process is not linear**. It is like a spiral moving forward rather than forward movement in a straight line. When we feel like we are going backwards, God is having us circle around and pick up some of the hidden aspects of issues at a deeper level. This is why you may feel out of control: you are moving in emotional spirals. But remember, the spiral circles around, eventually moving you forward again.

Finally, **you must go through stages or steps** despite the fact that each trauma story and experience is totally unique. Now, there is no agreement as to the clinical stages or steps for trauma recovery, but after walking through the trauma stories of hundreds and hundreds of individuals, I have seen at least four stages come up in every situation.

## 1. REBOOTING

Trauma literally stuns the mind. When the mind can't accept what it sees, or when it has no way to process the event it has encountered (such as a child experiencing mom and dad yelling angrily at each other), the mind goes into psychological shock. If you have ever come upon the scene of a horrific accident or been in combat, you have seen what I am talking about. The victims are openly staring into space, unsure of what just happened and are temporarily mute. The shock is like a system freeze or a computer crashing. Many people who are stuck in the past need to take the first step by recognizing the shock that has taken place in their life. That is precisely why the Trauma Checklist is such an important part of the healing process; it finally gives us a way to verbalize and express the fact that we have experienced trauma.

The rebooting challenge is dependent on the intensity of the trauma endured (the whack) or the number of previous traumas we have lived through (the number of "lacks"). Rebooting is initially about realizing what triggers a trauma reaction within us. I have seen men trapped in a repeating loop of trauma shock and rebooting for years because they are not aware of what triggers them to re-experience the wound again. They end up stuck on an emotional merry-go-round, endlessly circling their pain.

## 2. ACCEPTANCE

This is where the battle is usually won or lost. You can tell when someone is losing the fight because they live in the opposite of acceptance…denial. It can range from minimization to fantasy. Sexual addicts tend to have a well-developed fantasy sex life, usually because of the trauma of their family of origin. They learned at an early age to escape the pain through fantasy. Denial protects us from unbearable loss and pain, but it also puts us in a mental prison and throws away the keys. Acceptance always results in a shift from the current reality to a more difficult and painful reality.

### SUCH AS:

- *Your father abused you by his passivity and neglect.*
- *Your mother was involved in emotional incest in the way she related to you.*
- *Your father cared more about his job or the ministry than you.*
- *Your uncle was a pedophile, not just a caring relative.*
- *Your mother's illness when you were young left you feeling terrified and alone.*

Such realities may be very difficult to accept, but if they are true in your life, you will stay stuck in the past until you do accept them.

## 3. INTEGRATION

Once the feelings of trauma lose their grip, the next task is integrating a new sense of self and revising your life story based on your revised reality. Restoration begins when you begin to dream the dreams of God at the very points of the past trauma in your life. We can't change our past history, but we sure can **reframe it!** For example, I cannot change the fact that I had seven abusive stepfathers in my life, but I can reframe that fact by realizing that God has called me to be a "father to the fatherless." The trauma of my past then becomes a weapon against hell because I uniquely understand the pain of being fatherless and the deep wound that leaves in a man's life. Sometimes the deepest wound comes when you had a dad, but he was never there for you. Yet that can become a unique gift once you unwrap the struggle paper of trauma from around that fact in your life! Paul put it best in 2 Corinthians 1:3-5 (TLB).

*What a wonderful God we have—he is the Father of our Lord Jesus Christ, the source of every mercy, and the one who so wonderfully comforts and strengthens us in our hardships and trials. And why does he do this? So that when others are troubled, needing our sympathy and encouragement, we can pass on to them this same help and comfort God has given us. You can be sure that the more we undergo sufferings for Christ, the more he will shower us with his comfort and encouragement.*

## 4. RESTORATION

Forgiveness is not just an act of your will; without safety, forgiveness is impossible and undesirable. Premature forgiveness can be counter-productive because it can leave one open to re-victimization. When a Christian family of origin is the source of the trauma, it may be necessary to write a letter to your parents describing the abuse (whacks and lacks) you experienced from your perspective. The Cross of Christ and His shed blood boldly proclaim that we don't have to live in fear or unforgiveness. Christ has promised again and again for us not to live in fear. He will be with us. Yet it can be tough to believe those promises when it is mom or dad who wounded you, or members of your extended family.

The letter you may decide to write to your family of origin is not about venting your anger. Instead, it is the first step in reconciliation. Time and time again, I have seen a mom and dad who had no idea how deeply they had hurt their kids turn around and make amends after receiving a letter. **But reconciliation is not required for true forgiveness to occur. Forgiveness is something you do as part of dealing with the trauma of your past.**

## TOOLS FOR YOUR HEALING TOOLBOX

Hopefully by now you have picked up on the fact there is no one approach that cures all trauma. Therefore, what I will do is share with you five tools that I have found indispensable in dealing with trauma. I will share them within the context of the four stages of healing, but you may need to apply them to your life in different stages of the trauma healing process. God will give us the wisdom to receive what we need and when we need it.

### STAGE: REBOOTING
### TOOL 1: TRIGGER IDENTIFICATION

A trigger can be anything that pushes your buttons and is mentally paired with a past trauma **whether you remember it or not**. The body does not lie. Only the mind is capable of denial, which is why lie detectors work. The truth of what you experienced is stored in your body, which is exactly why mapping your triggers is so helpful. Triggers inform you about what trauma you have lived through, **even if you do not remember the original traumatic event**. Triggers do not excuse your abusive behaviors, such as yelling at your wife when you feel insecure. Yet understanding your triggers will certainly help you get a handle on working on your overreactions and help you to keep your limbic system from overpowering you. Since triggers often lead to the body's re-experiencing the feeling of the original trauma, it is little wonder that we avoid them both consciously and unconsciously. The problem is, if people have undiscovered traumas, no prayer or therapy in the world is going to make much difference until those traumas are brought into their present consciousness and dealt with. Now, some might say, "But God can heal anything!" Yet Scripture doesn't tell us that. In fact, Paul openly challenges us in Romans 12:2:

*Do not conform to the pattern of this world, but be transformed by the renewing of your mind. Then you will be able to test and approve what God's will is—his good, pleasing and perfect will.*

Please notice God is not into controlling you. He is very clear about our responsibilities. "You be transformed by renewing your mind" and "you test and you approve."

After speaking at a church service, it is not uncommon for a man to come up to me and ask, "Dr. Roberts, could you pray that this spirit of lust would be removed from my mind?" My answer is always the same, "NO! God is not going to pull your brain out and put in a new one! He is not going to abuse you. You have to get into a Pure Desire group and renew your mind through healthy relationships!"

The reason I have those kinds of discussions is that denial and dissociation are two of the most commonly employed defenses to deal with traumatic memories. I have never had a man walk into my office and overestimate their traumas. NEVER! In fact, I have never had a sexual addict walk into my office who didn't come for a "good Christian home." Denial is alive and well in the church when you realize that 69% of sexual addicts come from rigid and disengaged homes.[44]

**Mapping Your Triggers in Life**

❶ Four things that really upset me or make me angry:

**A.** _____

**B.** _____

**C.** _____

**D.** _____

❷ Four things I really avoid in life:

**A.** _____

**B.** _____

**C.** _____

**D.** _____

**Triggers fall into six categories: the five senses of taste, touch, smell, sight, and hearing, plus states of feeling.**

❸ Can you think of a significant memory (good or bad) that was so strong that a taste, touch, smell, sight, or sound brings it vividly back to mind?

**The Memory** _____

**Taste** _____

**Touch** _____

**Smell** _____

**Sight** _____

**Sound** _____

When I recently went to the movies with my wife, we watched the latest episode of *The Hunger Games*. Suddenly, I found myself wanting to get up and leave. The heroine was in the jungle where the adversary was watching her every move. And it seemed like every ten seconds something or someone was trying to kill her. All I felt was a compelling urge to get out of that theater! The sights and sounds were overpowering me! Then it hit me, I was experiencing the exact same feelings I experienced as a platoon commander in Vietnam. "That was forty years ago!" I told myself. "Come on, get a grip. Shake it off, Princess!" Once I stopped shaming myself, recognized the source of what I was feeling; the feelings subsided and I came back into my right mind. I became present.

❹ When have you recently overreacted? What event, situation, or circumstance from your past caused you to overreact, to not be present?

❺ Now back up and look at the results of your answers to questions one through four. What traumas from your past do you struggle with in the present?

**◗ Put your results on a timeline of your life and identify each major trauma. Also identify the lies that hell told you about yourself in the midst of each trauma.**

## MY PERSONAL TRAUMA TIMELINE

Divide your life into fourths and fill in the trauma and lies associated with that trauma. On this page is space for you to complete the first quarter of your life; on the next pages is space for you to complete the rest of your life. For example, if you are 40 years old, the first page would include ages 0 to 10; the second page would include ages 11-20 and 21-30, and the last page would include ages 31-40.

### AGES (FIRST ¼TH OF MY LIFE):
**Example: Age 0 to 10 (if you are 40 years old right now)**
...............................................................................................................................................................................

**Traumas: whacks & lacks** (during the first ¼th of my life)
*Example: my parents weren't planning to have another child when I came along*

...............................................................................................................................................................................

**Lies I believed** (during the first ¼th of my life)
*Example: I was unwanted from birth—a mistake.*

...............................................................................................................................................................................

## AGES (SECOND ¼TH OF MY LIFE):
**Example: Age 11 to 20 (if you are 40 years old right now)**

**Traumas: whacks & lacks** (during the second ¼th of my life)

**Lies I believed** (during the second ¼th of my life)

## AGES (THIRD ¼TH OF MY LIFE):
**Example: Age 21 to 30 (if you are 40 years old right now)**

**Traumas: whacks & lacks** (during the third ¼th of my life)

**Lies I believed** (during the third ¼th of my life)

## AGES (FOURTH ¼TH OF MY LIFE):
**Example: Age 31 to 40 (if you are 40 years old right now)**

.......................................................................................................................................

**Traumas: whacks & lacks** (during the fourth ¼th of my life)

.......................................................................................................................................

**Lies I believed** (during the fourth ¼th of my life)

.......................................................................................................................................

## STAGE: ACCEPTANCE
### TOOL 2: THE PHILIPPIANS PERSPECTIVE

In Philippians, Paul took pen in hand and expressed his heart in one of the most joy-filled epistles in the New Testament. What was the context of such joy? Was he staying in a beautiful condo on the beach in Maui? Hardly! Paul wrote the letter to the Philippians while he was in prison in Rome. In fact, he had to leave Philippi after a storm of persecution and an illegal imprisonment. The context of the letter is one of personal pain and injustice. He was eventually pulled out of the prison in Rome and beheaded. Paul experienced trauma at a deep and personal level. So what gave Paul an ability to process so much trauma in his life?

I think Philippians gives us an incredible clue into the way he thought about the struggles of life. Please realize that Paul didn't simply ignore his problems or try to pray them away religiously. He had a mental resilience that enabled him to withstand incredibly pressure-packed situations in life. And his response to traumatic situations is vividly revealed in Philippians 4:8.

*Finally, brothers and sisters, whatever is **true**, whatever is **noble**, whatever is right, whatever is **pure**, whatever is **lovely**, whatever is admirable—if anything is excellent or praiseworthy—think about such things.*

Now let's take this passage and apply it in depth to our lives. Approach it from a right brain perspective, from the context of our emotional lives by honestly answer the following questions. Don't write down what you think you should say. Write down what you really feel and think!

❶ Who triggers anger within you? What is it about them that you don't like?

..............................................................................................................................................

❷ How do you want them to change?

..............................................................................................................................................

❸ What should or shouldn't they do? What should they do so you can be happy?

..............................................................................................................................................

❹ How do you feel about them? Make a list.

Name _____ is _____

Name _____ is _____

Name _____ is _____

Name _____ is _____

❺ What don't you want to have to deal with them about again? What don't you want to feel again?

..............................................................................................................................................

❻ Now sit with your feelings for a moment after answering those questions. Don't shove them away. Be present, because those feelings are present whether you recognize them or not.

...................................................................................................................................

Next, take Paul's challenge and lets look at your thoughts.

### *"Whatever is true"*

After identifying the thoughts that are troubling you, ask yourself this: "It is true? Does that thought truly match reality?" Go inside yourself and ask if you **know** 100% the thought is true.

What you will discover is that most of the time, your thoughts don't match reality. Many of our hurtful thoughts are focused on figuring out the behavior of people we care about. Many of our painful thoughts come when we try to "mind read" others. Simply writing down the painful thoughts we have within, as you just did, can be a powerful first step in processing some of the trauma of our lives.

❷ **Write down your observations about what is true, based on the person you identified who triggers your anger.**

...................................................................................................................................

### *"Whatever is noble, pure and lovely"*

Noble is from the Greek term *semnos* that is difficult to translate; but when describing a person, it means one who moves through the world as if it were the temple of God.[45] In other words, they are conscious of God's presence in their life and thinking. Pure is from the word *hagnos* meaning holy or undefiled. Lovely is derived from *prosphiles* referring to that which calls forth love.[46]

How do we apply all of this to our thinking process when we are hurt or traumatized? When I ask someone if what they wrote down in questions one through five is true, 100% true, they say, "YES!" Then I ask, "How does it feel to be gripped by those thoughts and feelings? How does it affect you emotionally and physically when you think those thoughts? How does it cause you to treat yourself and others?"

**◐ Why don't you answer those questions for yourself in the space below.**

•  How I feel emotionally and physically when I have that thought:

..........................................................................................................................................

•  How do I treat others?

..........................................................................................................................................

•  How do I treat myself?

..........................................................................................................................................

Paul continues his cogent comments in verse 9, "*Whatever you have learned or received or heard from me, or seen in me—put it into practice. And the God of peace will be with you.*"

If there is one thing that trauma removes from us, it is our sense of peace. Paul was full of false beliefs prior to his Damascus Road encounter with the One who was the Truth. Blinded by the brilliance of the resurrected Christ, he got up off the ground and he began to think new thoughts.

**What would your life be like and who would you become without the thoughts you delineated in questions one through five?** When people take a fearful and rigid thought as absolute truth, it often brings about what they are trying to prevent. New God-given thoughts open up space for a different reality to be seen. They allow you to see how things can work out in a peaceful way, beyond what you had considered when you were defending a position.

**❷ Who would you become and how would your life be without the thoughts you wrote down in questions one through five?**

For example, say you have come to believe your wife or girlfriend or boss doesn't care about you. Think of how you live when you are in the grip of such a thought. How does that thought affect you? Do you feel hurt and angry? Do you snap at your coworkers or your kids? Does it affect your sleep?

**❍ Describe yourself and your life *without* those thoughts in the space below. Imagine for a moment what your life would be without that thought.**

....................................................................................................................................................

When Jesus was asked repeatedly who He was and what He was about, He frequently referred to Isaiah 61. He literally saw it as His divine job description. Verses one and two describe the outward acts that Jesus did: proclaim good news to the poor, bind up the brokenhearted, proclaim freedom for the captive. But verse 3 describes the divine transfers that made verses one and two possible.

> *To bestow on them a crown of beauty instead of ashes, the oil of joy instead of mourning, and a garment of praise instead of a spirit of despair.*
> Isaiah 61:3

Christ brought divine turnarounds everywhere He went. He was the proclaimer of "divine insteads." Healing deep trauma within isn't ultimately about going back and reliving the painful event again and again until you stop being reactive. You may have been so young when it occurred it is not even part of your explicit memories. Your reactivity is based on implicit memories. It became the window through which you looked out on the world. How about changing the window through which you see your world? You see, your mind at times is like a mirror. It has a way of getting things right, but backwards. So let's take some of those thoughts in questions one through five and experience a divine turn around. This means reversing them in as many ways as possible. Then ask yourself if these revised answers seem more true that the original thoughts.

For example, you are convinced that your boss doesn't care about you. Yesterday he walked right past you and he didn't even greet you; he publicly ignored you! Now let's have a divine turnaround starting with self!

**I insulted him**

*I jumped to my conclusions when he didn't greet me. I judged him harshly.*

**I insulted me**

*I turned a possibly innocent situation into an insult. I was the one who created the insult. It was a creation in my head. My angry and hostile thoughts made me feel insignificant and worthless.*

**He didn't ignore me**

*Maybe he was so busy in thought he didn't even see me. I can't really know what he was thinking. I am not a mind reader.*

Let the Holy Spirit lead you to divine turnarounds by considering if the opposite conclusion could possibly be true. It is such an important skill to develop when you are mentally stuck. It is similar to rocking a car back and forth when it is stuck in the mud.

If you can find even a possibility that the opposite is true, it will greatly diminish your fear response. Being stuck is when your mind totally refuses to look at the opposite conclusion. Take your responses in questions one through five and turn them around until you find the truth that probes deeper into the problem.

There are an infinite number of "insteads" you can ask yourself out of those five questions as you probe deeper in your life. Here a few suggestions.

❶ INSTEAD...what don't I like about myself?

❷ INSTEAD...how do I need to change so that an environment of change could be created?

❸ INSTEAD...are they really responsible for making me happy? How is God revealing himself to me in a unique way in the midst of this disappointment?

❹ INSTEAD...how do I REALLY feel about myself?

❺ INSTEAD...what in my past reminds me of how I feel when I am upset with this person?

⊙ **Now write some observations you have made about yourself:**

## ✍ ASSIGNMENTS FOR NEXT TIME

⊙ **Be ready to share with your group which tool worked best for you and why.**

# LESSON FOUR

## POWER TOOLS

The final three tools are what I call the "power tools" in dealing with the vestiges of trauma in our lives. As they apply these tools with disciplined consistency, I have witnessed many men walk forth into amazing freedom.

### STAGE: INTEGRATION
### TOOL 3: WITH THE END IN MIND: THE VIKTOR FRANKL FOCUS

The enemy is relentless in his attack on our soul through the weapon of trauma. The enemy I faced in combat in the skies of Vietnam was constantly adjusting to our efforts against them. The enemy of your soul operates in the same manner. Therefore, the challenge isn't just to process the trauma we may have in our past, many times the more difficult adversary can be the processing of our present trauma. We live in a fallen world and sometimes it falls on us. Stuff happens!

Developing the ability to deal with the present tense traumatic situations we may be facing also can keep us from being embedded in our past hurts and wounds. We can learn to live our lives from a present-future perspective and prevent the past from blocking our experiencing the love of God in the present difficulty we may be facing.

Viktor Frankl, an Austrian neurologist and psychiatrist as well as a Holocaust survivor, is a classic example of the type of response to tragic circumstances I am referring to. In his classic book *Man's Search for Meaning* he shares how he was able to keep his mind and hope alive by rehearsing talks he imagined he would give after he was released from imprisonment. In the environment of a Nazi death camp, he discovered in a reality saturated in trauma that purpose and meaning were central to his mental strength and health. Or as he expressed it, "Those who have a 'why' to live, can bear with almost any 'how'."[47] In others words, once you have a clear understanding of where you are headed in life, you can effectively deal with deeply traumatizing situations.

In his book, Frankl tells of one freezing winter day. While being forced to march outside the concentration camp, Frankl developed a violent cough. He fell to the ground, coughing uncontrollably. A prison guard, irritated by Frankl delaying the group's progress, began beating him. He collapsed on all fours in the snow, convinced he could not get up or move another step. The guard threatened to kill him on the spot. Without conscious effort, he did something he had done endless times in his mind. Frankl found that he was no longer in the field on his hands and knees, but transported in his mind to the future. He explicitly pictured himself giving a lecture in Vienna on "The Psychology of Death Camps and the Psychology of Meaning." As the imagery swept over his mind and body, he no longer felt pain and weakness. He got to his feet as he saw himself telling of his experiences to his audience. He pictured this talk all the way to the work detail and all the way back to the concentration camp. He ended the imaginary talk to an standing ovation!

It is critical to realize that when Frankl was traumatized, instead of staying frozen (literally) in the traumatic experience, he reoriented to a future without the trauma. He literally saw a preferred future. Now he wasn't escaping to a better place, that would have been nothing more than a pleasant fantasy to ease the pain as he died. HIS PERCEIVED FUTURE INFLUENCED HIS BRUTAL PRESENT.

The Apostle Paul always saw things from a present-future perspective, not a present-past perspective. His stirring words at the end of Romans 8 are a classic example of his way of dealing with difficult times in life.

*For I am convinced that neither death nor life, neither angels nor demons, neither the present nor the future, nor any powers, neither height nor depth, nor anything else in all creation, will be able to separate us from the love of God that is in Christ Jesus our Lord.*
Romans 8:38-39

Paul's perspective is totally present-future in the midst of his overwhelming difficulties. It is fascinating to note that Paul doesn't say the past can't separate you from the love of God, because emotionally it can—especially if trauma has ensnared you in your past. Obviously, from a purely theological perspective, the past cannot separate us from God's love. The Cross of Christ forever broke the power of our past, no matter how violent it may have been. For example, in the military I used to kill people for a living; that troubled me for years. Intellectually, I knew of the power of the Cross. The left side of my brain totally accepted that fact, but the emotional side of my brain struggled for years to **feel forgiven**. It was so hard for me to perceive my reality from a present-future perspective. Then I finally asked myself the question, "Had Jesus suffered enough on the Cross? Or did I still need to pay for my sins? Had Christ even taken on himself the sins of those who abused or neglected me growing up?" Once I emotionally, right brain realized that Christ had profoundly paid it all, then I could forgive myself and those who had betrayed me early in life! I could present tense, right now, begin living the future the Lord had for me! The outrageous love of God began to take up residence deeply in my soul!

As followers of Christ, the future He has planned for us enters into us to transform us, long before it happens. Everything can be taken from us but one thing: the last of human freedoms—to choose one's attitude in any given set of circumstances. We always have the freedom to trust God and choose His future for us no matter what may have happened to us or is presently happening. Viktor Frankl walked through absolute hell by looking forward to a speech he was going to give some day. We can also become overwhelming conquers in this life as we come to understand what God has prepared for us and how He sees us.

❓ **Once you have finished the Seven Pillars and are walking in the purity you have sought for so long, what will be happening in your life?**

**❷ What could you do, think, or focus on during the next six months that would help you move a little bit closer to that preferred future?**

.........................................................................................................................................

**❷ Have your "future self" write a letter to your current self and describe:**

1. What you had to go through to get where you are.
2. The critical turning points that got you to where you are.
3. Sage and compassionate advice that the "future self" might share with the current self.

---------------------------------------------------------------

---------------------------------------------------------------

---------------------------------------------------------------

---------------------------------------------------------------

---------------------------------------------------------------

---------------------------------------------------------------

---------------------------------------------------------------

---------------------------------------------------------------

---------------------------------------------------------------

---------------------------------------------------------------

---------------------------------------------------------------

---------------------------------------------------------------

---------------------------------------------------------------

---------------------------------------------------------------

---------------------------------------------------------------

## STAGE: INTEGRATION
### TOOL 4: GOD ESTEEM VERSUS SELF ESTEEM

As I sat watching a History Channel special, I was stunned to learn about a powerful tool the Navy Seals had developed to help trainees face their fear of drowning. The pool competency test is a grueling underwater experience that only 25% of the trainees pass. For twenty minutes straight, the instructors push the students right to the edge of running out of air underwater. As a result, their survival brain frequently kicks in and overpowers their higher reasoning powers and the student panics and fails the test. So, the Navy developed a mental toughness program to enable more of the trainees to pass the test. In other words, they enable the students to renew their highly stressed minds and not forget who and where they were.

I am thinking, "This is awesome! It will help so many of my clients to not be panicked by that trash-talking voice within. It will give them incredible tools to renew their minds even when they are under tremendous stress!" Through the years I have found it to be a profound tool for renewing the mind.

The mental toughness program the Navy developed includes four elements: goal setting, mental rehearsal, self talk, and arousal control.

## GOAL SETTING

All of these steps have powerful biblical foundations, especially the first. I will ask an individual struggling to renew their mind to initially do one thing. They may be struggling with an addiction, a deep hurt, habit, or hang up. It doesn't matter. The first step is always the same. I will ask them before our next appointment to remember four times when God encountered them in life. Not just when they read a good Christian book or heard a great sermon, but times where they **experienced God**! Their right brain has to be involved. Then I ask them to write down who God said they were in that moment of encounter. Not what He asked them to do, but who He said they are! They are a human "being," not just a human "doing." Next they are to write those moments down and find a passage of Scripture that reminds them of that experience (left brain) and attach it to that moment.

Why don't you do that before we proceed?

❯ **Write down four times God has encountered you in life and who He said you are. Then find a Scripture to attach to that moment. Don't go on in the book until you finish this assignment. It may take you a while, but I guarantee you it will be worth the effort!**

| ENCOUNTER WITH GOD/WHO YOU ARE! | DEFINING PASSAGE |
|---|---|
| *Ted's example: I'm adopted by Father God who loves me unconditionally.* | *Romans 8:15 You have received a spirit of adoption as sons…* |
| 1. | 1. |
| 2. | 2. |
| 3. | 3. |
| 4. | 4. |

## MENTAL REHEARSAL

You don't simply have some mental goals, but four powerful and personal Prophetic Promises. I want you to do something each morning. I "double-dog-dare-you" to do it! It will transform your morning and day! The first thing each morning, when your feet hit the floor, these promises should be coming out of your mouth. This should occur even before you pray each morning so that you will **learn to pray in light of your promises instead of your problems**.

Then, when you feet hit the shower each morning give God thanks for the good things He did in your life yesterday. As Scripture declares, "We enter his gates with thanksgiving." It may be hard to think of anything positive that occurred in the previous day because you were hit with such troubling times. Yet, if you pause for a moment in the shower, you will realize that God was at work in your life despite the difficulties. Once again, as you lift praise you realize God will never leave you or forsake you—no matter what hell may throw at you!

## SELF TALK

We mentally talk to ourselves at the rate of 300 to 1000 words per minute. Yet we talk out loud at 200 to 250 words per minute. That means you can't out-talk that trash-talking voice in your head! You can't out-talk hell! You can't out-talk hell, but you sure can "out-truth" hell! When Jesus was tempted by hell in the wilderness, he didn't debate with Satan; He simply declared, "It is written." He took God's word and counter-punched hell. That is exactly what we must do from a full brain perspective; by that I mean with our right brain and our left. Usually when hell triggers us, it is from an emotional perspective; we go limbic out of our fears and shame and we can't think straight. Therefore, now this is HUGE, we have to be aware of what is happening within us emotionally. Once we identify the fact that we are being triggered emotionally, we need to ask ourselves why are we reacting. What fears, hurts or hang-ups lie beneath that reaction? We need to respond to this challenge by confronting the limbic lie that hell is attempting to use to control us. We do this by taking our Prophetic Promises and ram them down hell's throat. I know that image may seem a bit violent for some, but it simply underlines the depth of the warfare.

We will have to develop two skills. The first is being fully present in the moment and being aware of what our body is telling us. Since our limbic responses occur at the subconscious level, we usually are not aware of what is happening. We are reacting in the moment, but our body is sending us signals all the time about what is going on in our soul. We need to be aware of what our body is telling us and ask questions like: Why is my heart speeding up right now? Why is my breathing becoming more rapid and shallow? Why do I feel this tightness in my stomach or shoulders? Why is my voice rising in pitch? Why are my hands clenched? Why do I want to run and get out of here right now? What fear or pain am I tempted to medicate right now?

What limbic lies has hell thrown at you recently? What are some of the comments that the trash-talking voice in your head fires at you? To help you understand how to respond to these questions, look at your Personal Trauma Timeline (created in the previous lesson).

**◗ List the lies on the next page; more importantly, identify the Prophetic Promise God has given you that will counter those lies.**

| THE LIMBIC LIE FROM HELL | THE PROPHETIC PROMISE |
|---|---|
| *Example: You are not enough…you are worthless* | *Example: I am a warrior for God (Joshua 1:7-9)* |
| | |
| | |
| | |

Now we come to the other skill found in the fourth element of the Navy's mental toughness program—meditation.

## STAGE: RESTORATION
### TOOL 5: BIBLICAL MEDITATION

Abram is totally frustrated; decades have passed since God promised him a son, yet nothing has changed. Ever been there in your life? Once you believed God's promise to you concerning your son, or daughter, or your job, or your marriage. Once you were filled with faith and hope, but everything now appears dead. Abram knew exactly how you feel! Sari, his wife, is now experiencing menopause she is well into meno-stop! There is no way the promise from God could ever come to pass in their lives. The dream of God seems to be a cruel joke, almost taunting him as the years passed. You pick up Abram's despair in the intensity of his complaint to God.

*But Abram said, "Sovereign Lᴏʀᴅ, what can you give me since I remain childless and the one who will inherit my estate is Eliezer of Damascus?" And Abram said, "You have given me no children; so a servant in my household will be my heir."*

*Then the word of the Lᴏʀᴅ came to him: "This man will not be your heir, but a son who is your own flesh and blood will be your heir." He took him outside and said, "Look up at the sky and count the stars—if indeed you can count them." Then he said to him, "So shall your offspring be."*

*Abram believed the Lᴏʀᴅ, and he credited it to him as righteousness.*
Genesis 15:2-6

Here is an interesting question. What did God encourage Abram to do in the midst of his frustrations? What moved him to faith? That is a critical question because living in a fallen world is an extended experience in fighting our way through personal disappointments to faith. The answer: God was teaching Abram to meditate.

189

I had a seminary professor, Dr. Tom, who was a great mentor of my soul. But the process wasn't always easy or enjoyable for me, which is true of most experiences of significant spiritual growth. One of the most frustrating things for me was to learn how to "Practice the Presence" as Dr. Tom called it. He had been good friends with Frank Laubach, a man who began an amazing spiritual quest. On January 20,1930, as a missionary to the Philippines, he made a decision.

> *I have started out trying to live all my waking moments in conscious listening to the inner voice, asking without ceasing, "What, Father, do you desire said? What, Father, do you desire done this minute?" It is clear that this is exactly what Jesus was doing all day every day. But it is not what His followers have been doing in very large numbers.*[48]

Frank Laubach made a commitment to bring Christ to mind at least one second of each and every minute of his day. My initial reaction to his quest was, "That is fine if you have nothing to do in life!" Yet I discovered Laubach wasn't someone who just sat around in life. He was a missionary to the fierce Moros, an Islamic tribe on Mindanao. There, in the village of Lanao, he set about his inspiring quest to experience God, and simultaneously developed a technique for bringing the Moro language to writing. This not only made it possible to teach them to read, but also permitted them immediately to teach others. The famous "Each One Teach One" program was born, which laid the foundation for his worldwide efforts to promote literacy, beginning with India in 1935. During the last thirty years of his life, Laubach was an international presence in literacy, religious, and governmental circles.

After discovering those facts about his life I was challenged to join him in the quest of practicing the presence of God, but I failed miserably. As we have discovered, our minds don't easily stay focused. My "monkey mind" was jumping from tree to tree mentally and I quickly lost sight of my commitment. Paul's challenge to renew our minds isn't some spiritual quick fix response to our struggles in life. I realized I needed to develop more "mind muscles" –some strengthened neurological connections to walk this path of practicing the presence of Christ.

My first clue came after reading Genesis 15 and a statement Laubach made after watching the sunset sitting atop Signal Hill, a knoll just outside the town he ministered to in the Philippines.

> *"This concentration upon God is strenuous, but everything else has ceased to be so. I think more clearly, I forget less frequently…. Even the mirror reveals a new light in my eyes and face. I no longer feel in a hurry about anything. Everything goes right. Each minute I meet calmly as though it were not important. Nothing can go wrong except one thing. That is that God may slip from my mind."*[49]

> *"Having had this experience, which comes to me several times a week, the thrill of filth repels me, for I know its power to drag me from God. And after an hour of close friendship with God my soul feels as clean as new-fallen snow."*[50]

I hungered for that! So how does that happen? Then I realized Frank was sitting on Signal Hill meditating just as Abram meditated on the heavens. They were experiencing the fact that God is the Great I AM. Our default state of mind is so frequently about agonizing over our past mistakes or worrying about future problems. I need to learn how to be PRESENT, spiritually, emotionally, and mentally. In other words, I need to learn how to meditate.

Meditation was not invented by Buddha. Abraham was meditating hundreds of years before Eastern religions ever came up with the idea. Unfortunately, Christians today believe meditation experiences are all about New Age beliefs. Nothing could be further from the truth! The Psalms are loaded with David crying out for the words of his mouth and the *meditations* of his heart to be acceptable to God. We, like David, can come to a biblical understanding of what meditation is and how it is such a powerful part of the process of renewing our minds. But first we will need to address several "false brain beliefs" that can cloud our understanding.

## FALSE BELIEF ONE
*The brain can only be shaped by experiences from the outside. The brain itself cannot be changed by the mind or by thoughts.*

Psychiatrist and researcher Jeffrey Schwartz, who works with patients with severe obsessive-compulsive disorder, has proved that intentional and willful thoughts can literally alter the brain's physical wiring and connections.[51] Alvaro Pascual-Leone of Harvard University had half a group of volunteers learn a simple five-finger keyboard piece. They practiced it over and over again for a week with their right hand. Then using neuroimaging, they determined how the brain had expanded in the areas relevant to that motor skill. This was not at all surprising, but what astonished them were the results from a second group. This group was told to mentally practice the same musical piece without touching the keyboard. The region of the brain that controls the fingers of the right hand had expanded in the virtual pianists just as it had in the group that had physically practiced the piece! Thinking and thinking alone can change the physical structure of the brain.[52] It has taken nearly two thousand years for science to realize that what Paul said is true. You can renew your mind.

## FALSE BELIEF TWO
*You don't have to pay attention to something for it to physically affect your brain. For example, if your arm is constantly stimulated, that part of your brain will automatically be activated and increased. It doesn't matter if you are paying attention to it or not.*

Attention is what stimulates neuronal activity. Attention is like a neurological scalpel that restructures the brain. If someone is listening to music and having their arm stimulated at the same time, change in the brain only occurs in those areas where they have focused their attention. Recent research has uncovered the fact that when we focus our attention, an area adjacent to the brain stem secretes a chemical that enables any neurons that are activated at the same time to strengthen their connections to one another.[53] This simply means that you literally shape who you are each and every moment by what you choose to pay attention to. The question is not how do we change, but what direction are we consciously directing the changes that are occurring in our brain.

## FALSE BELIEF THREE
*The brain essentially has an emotional set point that it always returns to. There are various ups and downs emotionally but the brain always returns to its "normal."*

The power of meditation to change the brain in response to stress has recently been documented by Professor Richard Davidson. He discovered that we can literally change specific areas of our brain connected with our emotions. We can down-regulate our fears and reactive parts of our brain.[54] In other words, we can directly change our limbic system or heart. We can come to a place of peace deep within and a freedom to meditate on life instead of just reacting. The process of meditating is exactly what David did so frequently in the Psalms. It involves using the mind to look at itself; observing and naming your feelings, for example, can inhibit the reactive part of the brain.[55]

One study found that just three hours of meditating led to improved attention and **self-control**. After eleven hours, the researchers could detect actual changes in the brain itself. They found increased neural connections between regions of the brain important for staying focused, ignoring distractions, and controlling impulses. They were amazed that our brains can reshape themselves so quickly. But it makes sense because meditation increases blood flow to the prefrontal cortex. It is a lot like lifting weights, which increases blood flow to your muscles and, in the process, brings strength and change.

Probably by now some of my readers are getting a bit anxious for two reasons:

- You are expecting me to say, "just empty your mind and open up to God!" *That is not what biblical meditation is about. David didn't turn off his brain in the Psalms; he was passionately focused.*

- You have tried meditating and you are terrible at it, as I once was. *Being bad at meditation is actually good! It helps you do what you need to do in daily life. Catch yourself moving away from a goal and then redirect yourself back towards it. It is the process of learning to be present.*

**Biblical meditation is learning to fill our minds and mouths with God's truth.**

*"This book of the law shall not depart from your mouth, but you shall meditate on it day and night, so that you may be careful to do according to all that is written in it; for then you will make your way prosperous, and then you will have success."*
Joshua 1:8 (NASB)

Meditating on the promises of God is something we are called to do as believers. I don't know about you, but I have thoughts in my head that I am sure God doesn't have in His. I need to replace my thoughts with His. It is impossible for me to consistently be fulfilling God's purpose and calling in my life unless I am training my mind to think about myself the way that God does. I need to learn how to see myself the way heaven sees me! This is critical because I can never consistently operate in life above the way I see myself. If I see myself as a loser or worthless at some point in my life, when I succeed I will engage in self-sabotage. It usually takes place at the subconscious level. So I will end up wondering why things never work out for me.

**So how do you get started? How do you meditate biblically so your mind can be renewed?**
Meditating pivots around three learnable skills: Intention, attention, and observation.

### Intention
Meditation is a skill that must be developed. Therefore, you must make time for it in your busy schedule. Frank Laubach found time in his highly pressured life of being a Christian missionary in a Muslim community. The results affected the world. After I finally realized that meditation wasn't about trying really hard to focus on God, but learning to enjoy Him, it started changing my life as well.

### Attention: Being Present
One of the most effective tools I have found in our stressful world to help folks seeking meaningful change in their life is to teach them how to breathe. In other words, I help them with **arousal control** or enable them to be present. I love the title of the book, *Why Zebras Don't Get Ulcers*, which I mentioned in a previous lesson. It's true, zebras only have to outrun the slowest zebra about once a week when the lions show up. The rest of the time they just walk around munching on grass. But so frequently, we live with the lions in our heads roaring twenty-four hours a day. As a senior pastor

of a mega church I was constantly battling the lions in my head for years. You can graphically see the struggle most folks have when you ask someone to close their eyes and place one hand on their chest and the other on their stomach. Then have them breathe deeply for the next three minutes.

**Brain Exercise!**

Try it! Get comfortable in your chair and place your feet flat on the floor. Place one hand on your chest and the other on your stomach. Then spend the next three minutes breathing deeply.

How did you do? Feel a bit calmer? Which hand moved? The hand on your chest, the hand on your stomach, or both? If you are like most people, the hand on your chest moved the most or both did. What you want to occur is have only your stomach move. Here is why. Deep breathing pushes on the diaphragmatic wall, which presses on the vagus nerve that runs along the inside of your spine. This triggers a physiological relaxation response causing the gut to release serotonin in your bloodstream. Shallow breathing (the hand on your chest) reinforces the body's fight or flight response. You end up trying to run faster from the lions in your head. This affects both your judgment and ability to rapidly respond to stressful situations.[56]

*Your adversary the devil walks about **like** a roaring lion,*
*seeking whom he may devour.*
1 Peter 5:8b (NKJV)

I underlined the word "like" because as a follower of Christ, you have been given authority over the enemy. The problem is until you renew your mind, he frequently convinces you it is not true when you are under stress.

Learning to program your mind for deep diaphragmatic breathing is one of the most basic skills to renew of your mind in our stress filled world. I have lost count of the number of times my clients have been amazed at the deep breathing's effectiveness for helping them walk in faith. And if you can do what Abraham did—walk outdoors and meditate as you breathe deeply—that is especially powerful.[57]

**Observation**

*"Surely I have calmed and quieted my soul; like a weaned child with his mother, like*
*a weaned child is my soul within me [ceased from fretting]."*
Psalm 131:2 (AMP)

Notice that David is meditating with a "weaned soul." He has confronted his fretting within.

**❍ Now I want you to spend five full minutes in a deep breathing meditation exercise. And walk through the following progression:**

**❶** Start with simply noticing your breathing pattern. Don't fret if it is initially hard to breathe from your diaphragm. Be gracious towards yourself! You are learning a new skill.

❷ Next take a short scriptural phrase. Use it as a centering prayer/focus. Here are some favorites:

- *The joy of the Lord is my strength*
- *The peace of God*
- *Have mercy Lord Jesus*
- *By His stripes I am healed*
- *I can do all things through Christ*
- *I am precious in God's eyes*
- *Fear not for I am with you*

Speak the phrase mentally to yourself in time with your breathing. It becomes especially powerful when you find a scriptural phrase that uniquely applies to your life and begin to deeply meditate on it. Occasionally the enemy will try to throw me back in my PTSD from the past. I will find myself tossing and turning in bed until I remember the devil is LIKE a roaring lion. Christ has pulled all his teeth and claws out at the Cross! Once I begin to breathe and use a centering prayer, I have ALWAYS fallen back to sleep.

If you have been faithful to practice deep diaphragmatic breathing as suggested, there will be a neurological reprogramming that has been built in your brain. When you sense your limbic system is firing up and trying to take over your prefrontal cortex or higher reasoning, you now have the ability to engage deep diaphragmatic breathing. It is a choice you can make and it is amazing in its ability to calm you down so you can think straight. And your Prophetic Promises define what clear thinking is with respect to yourself. If you diligently apply these biblical responses in stressful situations you will truly be able to get a grip on who you really are in Christ.

Stressful situations are actually where God does His best work in our lives. That is why Christ always wraps His greatest promises in *struggle paper*. God doesn't just want us to get to a particular place of blessing, but to get His richest blessing down into our soul. That always takes place in the midst of stress, struggle, and pressure.

**◑ For a more detailed understanding of how trauma is affecting your life, refer to Appendix Two: PTSI.**

## ☑ ASSIGNMENTS FOR NEXT TIME

**◑ Write down your Prophetic Promises (the memory and the defining Scripture) and read them daily. Be prepared to share them with your group.**

# ✔ PILLAR OF FREEDOM SIX COMMITMENT

I have, to the best of my ability, completed all the exercises found in Pillar of Freedom Six. By God's grace I will do everything I can to live these truths out in my life on a daily basis.

My Name _____

Signature _____     Date _____

..............................................................................................................................

## AFFIRMING WITNESSES

**❶** *I affirm the fact that* _____ *has grown in integrity and honesty in his life by the grace of God. Denial is no longer part of his life.*

My Name _____

Signature _____     Date _____

**❷** *I affirm the fact that* _____ *has grown in integrity and honesty in his life by the grace of God. Denial is no longer part of his life.*

My Name _____

Signature _____     Date _____

..............................................................................................................................

# LESSON ONE

## DISCLOSURE

One of the major lies that hell tells us is that our kids, our wife or other loved ones will not be hurt by our addictive behavior. Nothing could be further from the truth; in fact, scripture is vividly clear about the consequences of our actions.

> *You must never worship or bow down to them* (the surrounding pornographic gods),
> *for I, the LORD your God, am a jealous God who will not share your affection with any*
> *other god! I do not leave unpunished the sins of those who hate me, but I punish the*
> *children for the sins of their parents to the third and fourth generations. But I lavish my*
> *love on those who love me and obey my commands, even for a thousand generations.*
> Deuteronomy 5:9-10 (NLT, *Comment in parentheses is added for clarification*)

This is where the phrase, "The sins of the fathers shall be passed down to the third or fourth generation" comes from. I doubt you will find that passage in a list of Bible "promises," but it does contain a phenomenal promise that we want to get a grip on in this final pillar. The promised legacy for us: Through our lives, God will lavish His love and blessings on those closest to us.

I can usually tell when a man has turned the corner in the healing process. He suddenly begins to grasp just how deeply his sexual addiction has hurt his wife. It is a difficult place for him. His tears are now not just about the fact that he got caught. They are not generated by his embarrassment and shame. Instead they come from deep within, out of a perspective on life that is no longer just built around a narcissistic focus on self. He is developing the heart of a servant leader.

The expansion of that growth process becomes profound as he moves into a disclosure process with his wife and children. This is usually where he will cry out "Lord, I believe you, but help me with my unbelief." Normally he will resist the challenge of telling his entire family, but as a Christ follower, it is not an option. **If he wants to leave a blessing for his children instead of a curse, transparency is mandatory.**

In every disclosure process I have participated in, the children either *knew or suspected* something. Once the dad discloses his struggle, it allows the kids to make sense of their family life. Otherwise, the children can perceive it as being their fault: their father's detachment, isolation, or irritability. **The emotional distancing between mom and dad that sexual addiction always brings about can lay a subtle foundation of insecurity in the hearts of children.**

The question for you is: **Do you want a thimble of God's blessing or a lavish bucket full of blessing on your life and on your family?**

Bring God a thimble—ask God for a little bit of healing, a little change in your life. "Just help me stop this addiction, Lord." And He will probably fill your thimble prayers. But bring God a bucket—ask him to make your life an adventure of honesty and faith, ask him to use you way beyond yourself. Ask that He make your heart a radical agent of sacrificial love. Bring God a bucket and He will fill it. What are you bringing to God in your battle with your addiction?

This week you met a good friend of mine as you meditated on **Mark 9**. This dad had great dreams for his son as all fathers do. He wanted to raise him to honor God and love the Torah (The Bible). He planned on teaching him the family trade, and someday giving him the family business. But that wasn't going to happen; for some reason his son was stricken with a disease that was destroying him. An evil spirit tormented the boy, throwing him into convulsions and life threatening situations.

Add to that the fact that the young man was mocked and ridiculed by his peers. The situation rapidly became unbearable. The condition also affected his ability to speak. It totally robbed him of the ability to even talk to his dad.

Then one day my friend heard about Jesus. The disciples had gone ahead, healing the sick and casting out demons. So he came to the disciples and they were quite confident the problem could be easily solved. But soon it became apparent that despite their best efforts, the situation was only getting worse. When Jesus arrived on the scene he asked the father a critical question, "How long has he been like this?" I find it fascinating that Jesus doesn't ask the disciples the question—you know, kind of like a group consultation of physicians' questions. Jesus is up to something; he knows the boy's healing is tied to the father.

That's when the father reveals his heart. He prefaces his plea for healing with a great big fat "IF YOU CAN." The disciples all the while have been arguing in the background as to why they couldn't heal the boy, essentially debating who was the greatest among them. But when the father spews forth that "IF," I picture them stopping in their tracks and turning to see what the Master's response will be. And it is a classic!

*Jesus said, "If? There are no 'ifs' among believers. Anything can happen."*

*No sooner were the words out of his mouth than the father cried, "Then I believe.*
*Help me with my doubts!"*
Mark 9:23-24 (MSG)

I introduced this father as being a friend of mine. The reason I say that is I have so frequently responded to Christ in the same way. After Jesus' statement, the dad declares…

*…I do believe; help me with my unbelief!*

*…I believe, but I have deep doubts at the same time!*

*…I want to risk and hope again, but I am afraid!*

*…My faith is a mess!*

Oh how many times I have stood in that dad's sandals!

Here is my point. When I start telling a man that he has to have a disclosure with his entire family, you can see the blood drain right out of his face and terror fill his eyes. He can't believe that secrecy isn't the best policy. He keeps missing the truth that we are only as sick as our secrets; that is especially true when it comes to our families.

I love how the scene ends. Jesus simply walks over to the son and rebukes the spirit. Then he takes him by the hand and lifts a totally healed young man to his feet. For the first time, he can turn to his dad and say, "Dad, I love you. Dad, thanks for caring for me; I am so grateful that you are my Dad."

The initial part of your disclosure may be filled with anger and attacks against you because of your wife or children's deep hurt. But if the disclosure is sincere, totally honest and *there has been a clear and apparent change in your behavior*, the results will eventually be deeply healing for the family. You will have the joy of one day having your children thank you for being their dad. I have seen it happen in some of the most severe cases imaginable.

The foundational element of honesty and demonstrable change in your life is the key to the whole process. That is why I have waited to deal with the issue of disclosure until Pillar Seven. Disclosure with your wife (or girlfriend if you are single) may have to come much earlier because there has been an arrest, a discovery, an affair. But full disclosure is never an option in light of Deuteronomy 5. The only question is one of timing. And it is always preferable to have a clear track record of change in your life, not just a promise to change as you approach the process of disclosure. Most wives have heard hundreds of promises from their addicted husbands. That is why I always tell the wife, "*Don't believe his words, believe his actions.*" This is not to condemn the husband, but to give the wife a realistic basis for hope.

**How much faith is it going to take to do this?** Good question. The same amount of faith it took the father in Mark 9. "If you can," the dad said. Demonstrated by this scripture, it takes just enough faith to come to Jesus and ask him for help. It is not our job to conjure up enough faith. It is our job to come to Jesus and it is his job to increase our faith as we do.

How much faith does it take? It takes just enough to be authentic. A very critical point in the story is when Jesus declared, "Everything is possible for the one who believes." At that point I would have been tempted to fake it—to say to Jesus, "Alright, I want my son healed so I believe. I don't have a bit of doubt. You are the Man!"

The dad doesn't do that; instead he responds with staggering transparency. "Rabbi, that is my problem. I am not sure you will come through for me." How many times I have heard the same response from a man facing the challenge of the disclosure process!

But guess what? This story tells us that it is okay because **Jesus always prefers honesty to certainty**. You don't have to be sure, you just need to be real and honest. If faith is nothing more than being certain about something, then his disciples had it. But they forgot one thing. They forgot to pray. They were operating out of their own strength. In fact there is only one person in the story who prayed. And his prayer was a jello-filled, dilapidated appeal. The dad, however, got it right; he just kept bringing his bucket to God. So the question for you is this: Are you coming to God with a bucket or a thimble? Are you going to get honest and disclose your struggle or not?

## HOW DO YOU GO ABOUT THIS DISCLOSURE PROCESS?
### FIRST. REALIZE THE BENEFITS OF DISCLOSURE.

❶ It finally destroys the secret life you have been living.

❷ It makes your commitment to accountability real.

❸ It enables you to start letting go of the shame and guilt.[58]

❹ It enables your spouse to have the ability to make healthy choices and feel empowered.

❺ It initiates the process of your spouse facing her own trauma that your addiction has triggered.

## SECOND. BEGIN TO UNDERSTAND HOW PAINFUL THIS IS FOR YOUR WIFE.

The recent research of Dr. Omar Minwalla, Licensed Psychologist and Clinical Sexologist, has revealed that most wives are severely wounded by their partner's sexual addiction.[59]

❶ The symptoms are strikingly similar to those of post-traumatic stress or of a rape victim.

❷ The problem is further complicated because the disclosure is usually staggered in nature. Initially the man denies everything, then discloses what he thinks he can get away with, then a bit more and finally, after he is confronted as more details come out, he discloses everything.

❸ This is the typical sequence that 58.7% of addicts follow[60] and it is absolutely horrific for the spouse. It's as if she is being repeatedly traumatized again, and again, and again. **Therefore, it is absolutely critical that you hide nothing in the disclosure. The last thing you want to do is end up repeating the process because you were still in denial during the first disclosure.**

❹ I understand that the disclosure process is challenging. You are like the man in Mark 9 struggling to believe God. In a study of 80 addicts and their spouses[61], 60% of the addicts and 81% of the spouses felt that disclosure was the right thing to do. After the disclosure, 96% of the spouses and 96% of the addicts felt it was the correct choice. Hint: You will never fall into the 4% that thought it was the wrong thing to do because you are a Christ-follower.

❺ The only time disclosure is the wrong thing to do is when you are disclosing out of anger to hurt your partner or you are dumping on your spouse to deal with your guilt. I have placed this disclosure information in Pillar Seven because disclosure works best when you deal with your stuff before you approach the process with your wife.

## THIRD. PREPARE YOURSELF FOR THE DISCLOSURE.

❶ You need to be in a place of accountability and honesty. A Pure Desire group is a great choice. Stop the denial!

❷ Write out your disclosure and discuss it with your Pure Desire group leader thoroughly before you disclose to your spouse or family.

❸ Disclose significant details that your spouse needs to know such as:

    **A.** The time frame when referring to each incident where you acted out.

    **B.** Include sex acts that don't involve a physical act, such as fantasy, flirting, planning to act out.

    **C.** Include financial information.

    **D.** If there are health issues she needs to know include them.

    **E.** If there is someone else who the spouse may know or run into, the spouse has a right to know.

    **F.** Refer to your spouse in the second person (I betrayed YOU when…)

    **G.** Stick with information sharing; do not justify any of your addictive behavior.

❹ If at all possible have someone you both trust help you through the process, such as a pastor or a counselor who is familiar with sexual disclosures. This is important for several reasons.

  A. When things get emotional, that third party can serve as a tempering factor who helps you stay honest and help you deal with toxic shame that can so easily push you back into denial.

  B. If the third party is skilled, they will also be able to help the spouse not go "pain shopping," wanting all the painful details. ("What did she look like? What was she wearing? What type of women were you looking at on the porn site?") Your wife needs to not feel like a victim in the process. She has a right to decide what she needs to know, and what pain level she can tolerate.

❺ Your wife *will need strong peer support following the disclosure*. It is critical for her to be part of a Women's Pure Desire group.

  • The goal in all of this is to *repair* not to *re-traumatize* your spouse.

## FOURTH. THE DISCLOSURE MUST INVOLVE THE ENTIRE FAMILY IF YOU ARE GOING TO WALK IN THE BLESSING PORTION OF DEUTERONOMY 5.

This part of the disclosure is especially difficult; frequently it is forced because your activity became public. Forced disclosure can come from an angry spouse who is so traumatized that she strikes out in anger and tells the kids about what you have done. Or the children can discover your acting out behavior. How often I have had a man sitting in my office say something like, "The worst day of my life was when my son/daughter walked in on me watching Internet porn and masturbating."

### SUGGESTIONS FOR THE DISCLOSURE PROCESS:

❶ The information needs to come from you, not someone else. Face your pain. Be there for your kids.

❷ Share in an age-appropriate manner with each child.[62] Kids don't need to know the specific details of your acting out or about the hurt and anger that exists between you and their mom.

**For Preschool Children:**

  • They need to know you are not going to leave them.

  • They are not in trouble and they did not cause the problem.

  • They need to know you love them.

**For Elementary Children:**

  • It is not their fault.

  • Will something bad happen? (Fear of divorce?)

  • Are you getting help?

**For Middle School Children:**

  • What will happen to me if you and mom divorce?

  • What is so bad about sex? (They need to understand healthy sexuality.)

  • How are you going to get better?

**For Teens and Young Adults:**

  • How could you do this to our family?

  • How does this relate to me? (You ruined my life.)

❸ The best situation is a delayed disclosure where you and your wife have experienced enough healing that you can both meet with the children. The two of you speaking with them will help them deal with the fear of divorce. Then it is helpful to…

- Be guided by the child's desire to know. Let them determine the level of disclosure; it will limit the gory details.
- Assure the child about the recovery process, which will save the child from instinctively trying to be a caretaker.
- Provide emotional support for the child after the disclosure through the church or a therapist.
- Teach about healthy sexuality out of what you have learned in the healing process.
- If your child is struggling in life, wait for disclosure until you as a couple are in agreement that the time is right.

The father in Mark 9 had an evil spirit harassing his child. You are facing the same challenge because sexual bondage at its core is always demonically energized. Do not let that scare you away from healing for yourself and your kids. Simply, honestly come to Jesus with your doubts and lack of faith. Come to him and begin to take the next steps that he calls you to take, such as the disclosure process. If you do what Jesus asks with all your heart despite your fears and hurts, someday your wife and kids may turn to you and say, "Thanks for trusting Christ!"

## ✍ ASSIGNMENTS FOR NEXT TIME

❶ If you haven't had a disclosure time with your spouse, discuss that with your group. With their help, begin writing out a disclosure letter that you will read to your wife.

❷ Read *Pure Desire* Chapter 16.

# LESSON TWO

## HELPING YOUR WIFE MOVE THROUGH HER HEALING

### TO HEALTHY SEXUALITY (PART ONE)

By Diane Roberts

You have come a long way in your healing journey and now is the time to ask the question, "How can we move into healthy sexuality as husband and wife?" Because your wife has been so wounded, this is one of the most difficult places for her to grow. In this lesson and the next, I want to share the things you can do to help her move toward healthy sexuality.

The first step is to help you understand your wife's reality. It is very different than your own.

In the diagram below, notice that most men try to approach life from the physical (the left-hand side). That means when it comes to problem solving, men tend to look for physical solutions to problems.

As I have counseled over the years, women often ask the question, "Why does my husband want to have sex when we have an argument?" Again as you can see from the diagram, when the husband feels the gap in their relationship, the most normal way for him to want to fix it is to do something physical, which usually translates into having sex. Most women approach problem solving from the right side of the triangle. Their approach is spiritual and emotional.

## BEHAVIORAL RANGES

*Female Reality*

*Male Reality*

Male starts here & expands outward

Logical/ Objective

Area of Balance

No cause
No effect
Intuitive/Subjective

Female starts here & contracts inward

**Physical**
Logical
Organization
Executive
Verbal
Analytical
Linear
Rational
Objective

**Emotional**
Poetic
Musical
Artistic
Humorous
Irrational
Subjective

**Spiritual**
Vision
Non-Verbal
Inclusive
Intuitive

Behavioral Ranges is adapted from Joe Tanenbaum. *Male and Female Realites: Understanding the Opposite Sex.* Grand Rapids: Eerdmans. 1990.

204

Add to the equation sexual addiction and the wife's tendency is to avoid the physical and focus on the emotional and spiritual. You could have made some huge changes in your life and be strongly on the healing path away from your addiction, but most likely she is stuck in a totally different place.

---

*Her healing must come by working through her emotions and leaning on God.*

---

Disclosure often creates such trauma in the wife that she literally freezes in her pain. She will tend to ruminate on the issues and be preoccupied with your addiction. The state of shock and trauma can be accentuated if there has been what I call "dribbling" or, as Ted calls it, staggered disclosure. Only when she knows the bottom line can she begin to heal.

One woman dealing with betrayal issues scored high on the PTSI (Post Traumatic Stress Index) that measures trauma. Her husband asked if he had caused her high scores. Because she had early childhood trauma, I told him that he wasn't the complete source. But, I added, chances are her scores would have been dramatically less had there been no sexual addiction.

You could be walking on water—doing everything right—and her pain would not allow her to see how much you have changed. Even when there is change, she is not sure it will last and therefore is usually very guarded. She is often stuck rehearsing the past and questioning everything about you and your years of marriage. What was real and what was a lie?

1 Corinthians points out the fact that sexual sins have far reaching effects:

> *There's more to sex than mere skin on skin. Sex is as much spiritual mystery as physical fact. As written in Scripture, 'The two become one.' Since we want to become spiritually one with the Master, we must not pursue the kind of sex that avoids commitment and intimacy, leaving us more lonely than ever-the kind of sex that can never 'become one'. There is a sense in which sexual sins are different from all others. In sexual sin we violate the sacredness of our own bodies, these bodies that were made for God-given and God-modeled love, for a sacred place, the place of the Holy Spirit. Don't you see you can't live however you please, squandering what God paid such a high price for?*
> 1 Corinthians 6:16-18 (MSG)

Paul is underlining the fact that sexual intercourse is more than a biological experience. In fact, when a person sins sexually, it is sin against his or her own body (and the spouse's body) which makes this sin like no other. God created sexual commitment in marriage to bond two people together as one. Therefore, when sexual sin occurs it can also become the most wounding in the relationship as husband and wife. A wife not only feels violated physically, but also emotionally and spiritually. Statistics show that the backlash of this kind of violation can have a huge impact in the marriage.

Women whose husbands have been involved in sexual addiction have exhibited the following:[63]

## DEPRESSION:
- 39% of women struggled with depression prior to their relationship with a sexual addict.
- 82% of women struggled with depression during their relationship with a sex addict.

## EATING DISORDERS:

- 40% of women struggled with eating disorders prior to the relationship with a sex addict.
- 62% of women struggled with eating disorders during their relationship with a sex addict.

## SEXUAL HEALTH:

- 50% of women participated in sexual behavior of which they were later ashamed while in the relationship with the sex addict.
- While in the relationship with the sex addict, 23% of women contracted 1 STD and .05% of the women contracted 2 STDs.

## TYPICAL BEHAVIORS WOMEN ADMITTED TO WHILE IN RELATIONSHIP TO THE SEX ADDICT:

- 85% were checking up on the addict
- 78% were controlling
- 76% were looking for more proof
- 68% felt threatened and insecure around other women when with the addict
- 65% spent time trying to read the sex addict's mind
- 61% used sarcasm
- 58% were not having sex or were being hypersexual
- 54% would rage
- 52% shamed the sex addict
- 46% fantasized about his acting out

When disclosure takes place or when the wife discovers for herself the extent of the addiction, often contempt settles in her spirit. She feels contempt for herself, for the addict, and even for the marriage.

Contempt for herself might look like this: "If I were prettier, weighed less, were taller, were more shapely, etc., this wouldn't have happened; there must be something wrong with me." She feels disdain and worthlessness towards herself. Sex is often the farthest thing from her mind.

She usually feels contempt and disdain towards her spouse because of the lies, the betrayal and sometimes for the pressuring to do things that were against her values. From the previous listed statistics, one can see that 50% of women were ashamed of what they did sexually with the addict.

Emotions can vary and are mixed among the women. Some feel entitled and can respond as one woman did: "The betrayal made me feel entitled to be cruel with my words toward him and to spend as much money as he spent on his addiction." Besides the entitlement your wife may feel, you will also have to learn to tolerate her anger and hurt. She will tend not to believe you, even when you are being honest; listening is always a better strategy than trying to be heard. If you try to defend yourself or make demands, it will only push her father away from you.

At this point you may be saying to yourself, "If disclosure creates this much pain, maybe I will skip that part of my recovery!" Let me remind you that **part of your recovery is facing the pain and taking responsibility for your behavior regardless of the consequences**.

I will never forget a picture the Lord gave me that might help you at this point. I was praying with some-one who had sinned, and confessed their sin and was ready to make things right. The Lord showed me this person standing in water waist deep, with ripples of waves going out from them because of the sin. But as they repented and turned 180 degrees in the water (repentance means turning from your sin and going in the opposite direction), the ripples were buffered. There were still ripples, but the impact had been curtailed because of this person's willingness to turn from sin and go in a different direction.

Your repentance and disclosure will give you a clean slate, will reinforce your desire for accountability and honesty, and will facilitate the letting go of shame. It will also make healthy sexuality a possibility in the future.

Your disclosure to your wife will empower her with truth and the ability to make informed choices based on truth. It will also allow her to see her need to embrace recovery and, hopefully, pursue healthy sexuality.

Finally, because of the wife's roller coaster emotions during this healing process, most husbands have a hard time knowing what to say. The usual response is to go limbic when she goes limbic and dismiss or react to her emotions. The worst things you can say are, "You should be farther along by now," or "When are you ever going to forgive me?" I recommend a little book to all our male clients titled *How to Help Your Spouse Heal From Your Affair* by Linda MacDonald. Even if you haven't had an affair, this book helps you understand what your wife needs to hear you say when she is on the emotional roller coaster. Remember, she will tend to approach relationships emotionally, and this book will help you meet that need.

Meditating this week on Psalm 55 will help you to get in touch with the pain of betrayal your wife is now experiencing. Understanding her emotional pain is your first step in helping her to heal and allowing for the possibility of healthy sexuality in the future.

## ✒ ASSIGNMENTS FOR NEXT TIME

❶ Read *Pure Desire*, chapter 16: *His Realities and Her Realities*

❷ Obtain a copy of Linda MacDonald's book *How to Help Your Spouse Heal From Your Affair* (available on Amazon.com as book or ebook). Begin reading this book!

❸ Meditate on **Psalm 55** (on the following pages) and *answer the questions below each segment.*

## PSALM 55 (NLT)

*1 Listen to my prayer, O God.*
*Do not ignore my cry for help!*
*2 Please listen and answer me,*
*for I am overwhelmed by my troubles.*
*3 My enemies shout at me,*
*making loud and wicked threats.*
*They bring trouble on me*
*and angrily hunt me down.*

❷ **What emotions does David express?**

..................................................................................................................................

❷ **How are his enemies treating him?**

..................................................................................................................................

❷ **How might your wife see you as the enemy?**

..................................................................................................................................

❷ **What emotions might your wife be feeling as she deals with her present troubles?**

..................................................................................................................................

*4 My heart pounds in my chest.*
*The terror of death assaults me.*
*5 Fear and trembling overwhelm me,*
*and I can't stop shaking.*
*6 Oh, that I had wings like a dove;*
*then I would fly away and rest!*
*7 I would fly far away*
*to the quiet of the wilderness.*

❷ **Do you see evidence of depression or trauma and stress (fight, flight or freeze)?**

..................................................................................................................................

❓ **Have you seen symptoms of depression, trauma or stress in your wife's life? Describe those symptoms.**

..................................................................................................................

> *12 It is not an enemy who taunts me—*
> *I could bear that.*
> *It is not my foes who so arrogantly insult me—*
> *I could have hidden from them.*
> *13 Instead, it is you—my equal,*
> *my companion and close friend.*
> *14 What good fellowship we once enjoyed*
> *as we walked together to the house of God.*
>
> *20 As for my companion, he betrayed his friends;*
> *he broke his promises.*
> *21 His words are as smooth as butter,*
> *but in his heart is war.*
> *His words are as soothing as lotion,*
> *but underneath are daggers!*

❓ **How have you experienced what David has with a close friend that has betrayed you?**

..................................................................................................................

❓ **How could your wife relate to this scripture in terms of your relationship?**

..................................................................................................................

*15 Let death stalk my enemies;*
*let the grave swallow them alive,*
*for evil makes its home within them.*

*16 But I will call on God,*
*and the L*ORD *will rescue me.*
*17 Morning, noon, and night*
*I cry out in my distress,*
*and the L*ORD *hears my voice.*
*18 He ransoms me and keeps me safe*
*from the battle waged against me,*
*though many still oppose me.*
*19 God, who has ruled forever,*
*will hear me and humble them.*

*22 Give your burdens to the L*ORD*,*
*and he will take care of you.*
*He will not permit the godly to slip and fall.*

**❷ What does David wish upon his enemy? (15)**

.............................................................................................................................................

**❷ Has your wife seen you as the enemy and wished negative things upon you because of her pain? Explain your answer.**

.............................................................................................................................................

**❷ What does David decide to do instead? (16)**

.............................................................................................................................................

**❷ Write out a prayer for your wife, asking God to draw her close and care for her as she is processing her betrayal and hurt.**

.............................................................................................................................................

## HELPING YOUR WIFE MOVE THROUGH HER HEALING

### TO HEALTHY SEXUALITY (PART TWO)

By Diane Roberts

Often an addict is dealing with more than one addiction. Initially when Ted and I got married, I didn't see the sexual addiction with which he was struggling, but I did see his lust for aluminum. I felt I was always competing against the "other woman," jet airplanes! In fact, when we first got married he warned me that if he had to choose between airplanes and me, I'd lose. I naively thought I could change him, but instead ended up crying and frustrated for the first two years of our married life.

When Ted came to Christ and was filled with the Holy Spirit, I was no longer competing with his addictions. I became second to Christ rather than his addictions.

As you read Proverbs 4, see Wisdom as a gift of the Holy Spirit that can be that transforming agent in your life, like He was in Ted's life.

### PROVERBS 4:1-27 (MSGB)

*1 Listen, friends, to some fatherly advice;*
*sit up and take notice so you'll know how to live.*

*2 I'm giving you good counsel;*
*don't let it go in one ear and out the other.*

*3 When I was a boy at my father's knee,*
*the pride and joy of my mother,*

*4 He would sit me down and drill me:*
*"Take this to heart. Do what I tell you—live!*

*5 Sell everything and buy Wisdom! Forage for Understanding!*
*Don't forget one word! Don't deviate an inch!*

*6 Never walk away from Wisdom—she guards your life;*
*love her—she keeps her eye on you.*

*7 Above all and before all, do this: Get Wisdom!*
*Write this at the top of your list: Get Understanding!*

*8 Throw your arms around her—believe me, you won't regret it;*
*never let her go—she'll make your life glorious.*

*9 She'll garland your life with grace,*
*she'll festoon your days with beauty."*

*10 Dear friend, take my advice;*
*it will add years to your life.*

*11 I'm writing out clear directions to Wisdom Way,*
*I'm drawing a map to Righteous Road.*

*12 I don't want you ending up in blind alleys,*
*or wasting time making wrong turns.*

*13 Hold tight to good advice; don't relax your grip.*
*Guard it well—your life is at stake!*

*14 Don't take Wicked Bypass;*
*don't so much as set foot on that road.*

*15 Stay clear of it; give it a wide berth.*
*Make a detour and be on your way.*

*16 Evil people are restless*
*unless they're making trouble;*
*They can't get a good night's sleep*
*unless they've made life miserable for somebody.*

*17 Perversity is their food and drink,*
*violence their drug of choice.*

*18 The ways of right-living people glow with light;*
*the longer they live, the brighter they shine.*

*19 But the road of wrongdoing gets darker and darker—*
*travelers can't see a thing; they fall flat on their faces.*

*20 Dear friend, listen well to my words;*
*tune your ears to my voice.*

*21 Keep my message in plain view at all times.*
*Concentrate! Learn it by heart!*

*22 Those who discover these words live, really live;*
*body and soul, they're bursting with health.*

*23 Keep vigilant watch over your heart;*
*that's where life starts.*

*24 Don't talk out of both sides of your mouth;*
*avoid careless banter, white lies, and gossip.*

*25 Keep your eyes straight ahead;*
*ignore all sideshow distractions.*

*26 Watch your step,*
*and the road will stretch out smooth before you.*

*27 Look neither right nor left;*
*leave evil in the dust.*

Notice that addictions to evil can become as natural as sleeping, eating and drinking (verse 17). And verse 19 underlines the darkness of that road and the consequences of following that path. But sandwiched in between in verse 18 is God's promise of a shining destiny for those who follow His ways.

In this lesson we want to explore the **power of trust** and how it can help couples move into healthy sexuality. Studies of a woman's brain as she is having an orgasm revealed that "Fear and anxiety need to be avoided at all costs if a woman wishes to have an orgasm; we knew that, but now we can see it happening in the depths of the brain."[64]

This research clearly underlines the fact that if a woman is not experiencing peace in her relationship with her spouse, she is not likely to enjoy sex or feel fulfilled sexually.

**A woman's number one priority is safety**, especially if there has been betrayal and trauma in her life. As pointed out in chapter 16 of the *Pure Desire* book, "Some women feel so violated they don't know if they even love their husbands any more, let alone trust them. This is a normal response. There is a numbness that develops for her own self-protection. She doesn't want to be hurt again."[65]

In the previous lesson we talked about understanding how your wife is feeling and why she most likely is reacting and even over-reacting to situations out of her woundedness and trauma. In chapter 16 of *Pure Desire* it was also stated that "For trust and reconciliation (and healthy sexuality) to take place, the husband has to be willing to meet the emotional needs of his wife, which in many cases have been ignored over the years because of his need to feed his own addiction. Ephesians 5:25-26 says "Husbands, love your wives, just as Christ also loved the church and gave Himself up for her, that He might sanctify her, having cleansed her by the washing of water with the word" (NASB).[66]

## THREE ACTION STEPS

For a woman's heart toward her husband to change, she needs to see three actions steps. Then and only then will she begin to trust him and feel safe.

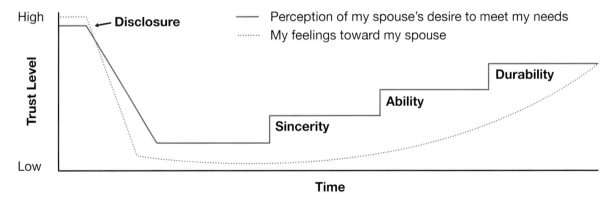

### THE FIRST ACTION STEP IS SINCERITY.

A sincere heart is not only repentant, but is also willing to walk in behaviors that show sincerity. Notice in Proverbs 4:23-27 (MSG), there are action steps with outward evidence of guarding your heart, mouth, eyes and feet.

*Keep vigilant watch over your heart;*
*that's where life starts.*
*Don't talk out of both sides of your mouth;*
*avoid careless banter, white lies, and gossip.*
*Keep your eyes straight ahead;*
*ignore all sideshow distractions.*
*Watch your step,*
*and the road will stretch out smooth before you.*
*Look neither right nor left;*
*leave evil in the dust.*

Your wife needs to see these actions being practiced daily. Again, she is the one that defines what it will take to regain trust. Some of your action steps might be participation in a Pure Desire group, checking in with your sponsor daily, getting professional counseling if needed, being proactive with recovery practices. Evidences that you are changing and are truly in recovery may include:

- Fewer outbursts of anger
- Less demanding or controlling behavior
- Consistency in what is said and done
- Dependability and accountability (with time, finances, etc.)

As she sees these outward behaviors, which are hopefully motivated from the inside out, trust begins to be restored.

## THE SECOND ACTION STEP IS ABILITY.

The question that arises in her mind is, "He seems sincere and is trying, but does he have the ability to follow through and continue to grow?" Her greatest fear is that although the commitments seem sincere, in one year will he still be growing and moving toward health? Will he allow the Holy Spirit to help him move into new healing areas and is he willing to face whatever the issues are that drive his addiction?

One specific way you can allow the Holy Spirit to move you in a new way of healing is to break the soul ties of the past. About 8 months into the wife's Betrayal & Beyond class, we talk about breaking soul ties. If you have had sex outside the marriage or even had premarital sex with your wife, the following information can help you take the lead in breaking soul-ties.

### SOUL-TIES[67]

If infidelity has occurred, soul-ties must be broken. When we have intercourse, soul-ties are formed. Genesis 2:24 (KJV) says that we "become one flesh" and Matthew 19:3-10 also says we are "not longer two, but one." This is a profound mystery (Ephesians 5:32), that goes beyond neurochemical bonding in the brain, physical familiarity, and emotional intimacy, to a complex bonding that occurs in the spiritual realm.

In the Pure Desire Sexy Christians seminars,[68] I share a powerful illustration of soul-ties and how they impact us. I take a pink and a blue piece of paper and glue the two together. Then I pull the papers apart; in that tearing process, some of the blue is left on the pink and some of the pink is left on the blue paper. God intended that our sexual relationships literally glue us together as husband and wife. If infidelity has taken place, there are still "appendages" attached between the lovers due to the neural imprints of their sexual, emotional, and physical unions, as well as the thought patterns associated with their relationship. The enemy can use these attachments as hooks that continue to jerk the spouse around, even if he has removed himself from the relationship.

*Do you not know that your bodies are members of Christ himself? Shall I then take the members of Christ and unite them with a prostitute? Never! Do you not know that he who unites himself with a prostitute is one with her in body? For it is said, "The two will become one flesh." But he who unites himself with the LORD is one with Him in spirit. Flee from sexual immorality. All other sins a man commits are outside the body, but he who sins sexually, sins against his own body. Do you not know that you are the temple of the Holy Spirit who is in you, whom you have received from God? You are not your own: you were bought at a price. Therefore honor God with your body.*
1 Corinthians 6:15-19

As you can see from this scripture, when a man engages in sex outside of his marriage, the sin is not only against God and the wife, but also against the husband's own body. For sexual freedom to resume between husband and wife, it is important that the husband walk through these steps of praying for the soul-ties to be broken:

1. Ask forgiveness for sinning against God. (Psalm 51:4)

2. Ask forgiveness for sinning against his own body. (1 Corinthians 6:18)

3. Ask forgiveness for sinning against the other person's body. (1 Corinthians 6:18)

4. Ask forgiveness for sinning against his wife's body. (Matthew 5: 23-24).

This is a sample prayer a husband can pray that declares freedom from the union that took place outside of marriage and created soul-ties with another person:

**Husband's Prayer for Breaking His Soul-Ties:**
*Father, You have heard my confession and my asking for forgiveness in these four areas. Thank you that You forgave me of my sin and cleansed me from all unrighteousness. Because of the blood of Jesus and my repentance, I ask right now that You break any sexual, emotional, and physical soul-ties between me and the other woman. I declare the enemy will no longer have any hooks in me because You have broken any power he has had over me because of my past sins. In the name of Jesus, I release my heart tie to this person and sever and renounce any bonds that were formed. Thank you, Jesus, for new freedom and a sense of cleansing within my spirit. As I reconnect with my wife, let our spirits become one as you intended and let nothing separate us in Jesus' name.*

A soul-tie is not limited to a sexual union but can be rooted in an emotional attachment to another person, place or even an object.

You may also want to lead your wife through the four steps if you had premarital sex as a couple. Asking each other and God for forgiveness will allow you to wipe the slate clean and start over in your sexual relationship.

*Husbands, love your wives, just as Christ also loved the church and gave Himself for her, that He sanctify and cleanse her with the washing of water by the word.*
Ephesians 5:25-26

## THE THIRD ACTION STEP IS DURABILITY.

She needs to know you are not doing these things to placate her now, and then later down the road go back to old habit patterns. Dr. Patrick Carnes has studied sexual addicts for years and has determined it takes two to five years for substantial healing and change to take place.[69]

In watching Ted go through these action steps, my trust and respect for him has grown through the years. He realized many years ago that his father wound was the main issue driving his addictions. He has allowed the Holy Spirit to walk with him, guide him, give him revelation and then make changes that are manifested in his outward behavior.

How are you doing in these three areas? Remember that we are not talking so much about performance as we are a heart attitude—what is in the heart is being worked out and shows in the behavior.

## ASSIGNMENTS FOR NEXT TIME

❶ Acknowledge honestly where you are in the three action steps.

**Sincerity:** What is the outward evidence of this in your life? What kind of commitments have you made that show outward evidence?

**Ability:** On a scale of 1 to 5, how consistent have you been in following through with commitments you have made? Circle where you are today:

Low in consistency                                                    High in consistency

❶                    ❷                    ❸                    ❹                    ❺

• If you are struggling with consistency and circled a 1 or 2, what action steps could you take to help you move into a higher place of consistency?

• If you circled 4 or 5, what are you doing now that helps you maintain that consistency?

**Durability:** In your journey, what have you identified as the wound that is driving your addiction?

• What are some steps you are taking to heal that wound?

................................................................

❷ Re-read the section of Proverbs 4 (MSG) printed below. Under each segment, list your proactive behaviors or choices that will help you walk on God's path and in His light.

*Keep vigilant watch over your heart;*
*that's where life starts.*

*Example: Allow God's Word to read my heart daily*

................................................................

*Don't talk out of both sides of your mouth;*
*avoid careless banter, white lies, and gossip.*

*Keep your eyes straight ahead;*
*ignore all sideshow distractions.*

................................................................

*Watch your step, and the road will stretch out smooth before you.*
*Look neither right nor left; leave evil in the dust.*

................................................................

❸ **Continue reading** Linda MacDonald's book, *How to Help Your Spouse Heal From Your Affair* that was recommended in Lesson Three. In the space below, write down a couple of things you are learning from that book. Remember, the more you can empathize with your wife and her pain, the healthier you are becoming.

................................................................

# LESSON FOUR

## SELF-CONTROL & VISION

David of the Old Testament is not an ancient historical figure to me, but a close personal friend. He was a rascal who deeply loved God. His life gives me hope because I can see how I will be able to finish well this race called life. Acts 13 tells us an amazing fact about David's life.

> *But God removed Saul and replaced him with David, a man about whom God said,*
> *'I have found David son of Jesse, a man after my own heart.*
> *He will do everything I want him to do.'*
> Acts 13:22 (NLT)

David was a man who broke every law God ever made, yet at the end of his life, he ended up with a heart for God and did everything God wanted him to do. Not many men in the Bible finish well, but I don't want to follow that pattern—which is why David's life has become a deep resource for my soul. So what was the key for David living a life that pleased God despite his continual failures? There are several factors, but the central one might surprise you.

**❯ Read 2 Samuel 5:1-10**

Finally David is ready to step into the promise God had given him over a decade before that he would be the next King of Israel. This is an event he has looked forward to for years. There is one problem: new levels, new devils. It never fails as you step into your God-given promises; there will always be some kind of devil to fight. David doesn't have much to assist him in the battle. He is surrounded by a bunch of broke, busted, and disgusted guys. They haven't become David's mighty men yet. David makes a critical decision in the midst of that daunting situation. **He decides to fight with what he has!** Let me tell you something, if you are going to finish well in life then you have to learn to win with what you have.

*You may only have five loaves and two fish, but you have more than enough to defeat the enemy and meet the need! You may only have a rag and a rock, but you can take out a Goliath!*

God knows what you need; in fact, He has given you more than enough to get the job done. You can win with what you've got!

**❯ In what area in your life is it hard for you to believe that God has given you more than enough to win the battle? List it below.**

To the casual observer it didn't remotely look like God had given David what he needed. David's army was down in the Kidron Valley and his enemy was on a ridgeline overlooking them in an impregnable fortress. The area the Jebusites controlled prevented David from ruling as God intended. No matter how much territory he controlled in the valley from their fortified position, the Jebusites limited him. They blocked his freedom to become who God called him to be.

But David realized the Jebusites were on land that God had promised him. That was when David declared, "Now we are going to fight!"

## YOU HAVEN'T REALLY LIVED UNTIL YOU FIND OUT WHAT GOD HAS CALLED YOU TO FIGHT FOR!!!

❷ What has God called you to fight for in life? List your responses below.

1. _____

2. _____

3. _____

4. _____

David faced a difficult stronghold. When the enemy has anything he consistently uses against you… It is a stronghold. Every time you get ready to take a couple steps forward and he pulls you back… that is a stronghold.

Every time you move forward to get victory over this hurt, this habit, the hang-up, and he pulls you back…that is a stronghold.

Strongholds rob you of the upgrades God has for you. You know you should be further along by now, but the enemy keeps pulling you back. Let me be crystal clear about what I am referring to. I am not talking about deep addictions and bondages. We have looked at the monster of sexual addiction at close range throughout this workbook. Instead, I am pointing to the little things that drive such addictions. The little things that keep pulling you back. As we near the end of the Seven Pillars, it is critical that we deal with the little things that lie underneath the addiction. If you don't deal with these little things, they will control you and set you up to slowly slide back into addictive behavior.

❷ What are the strongholds in your life—the little things that limit the freedom Christ wants to bring into your life?

Here is the bottom line in the battle: You will never conquer what you are not willing to confront. The question is how is David ever going to be able to confront the Jebusites? To take out their fortified position his men will have to climb a 15% grade slope with nothing to cover them from the withering fire raining down from above them!

David's words give us an insight into his plan of attack, "We are going to use the *water shaft* to take those guys out." The term "water shaft" is only used twice in the Old Testament. Once in Psalm 42 to refer to a waterfall and in 2 Samuel 5. More than likely, David was referring to a sinkhole inside the mountain on which the Jebusite city is perched. It is known today as Warren Shaft, a thirty-foot vertical sinkhole caused by water percolating through the dolomite rock inside the mountain. In essence, it is drainage for the city, a gutter.

The Jebusites told themselves, "David doesn't want it bad enough to go through the gutter to get here." But they seriously underestimated him. David declared, " I want that city so bad I will crawl through the gutter if I have to! I WILL HUMBLE MYSELF!"

How bad do you want that stronghold to come down in your life? I know you have prayed about it. You have brought it before God a number of times. BUT HOW BAD DO YOU WANT IT?!

Now listen carefully. I am not going to communicate to you the typical evangelical message of TRY HARDER, meaning you need to pray more, read your Bible more, be a better Christian. Obviously those things are not bad in themselves, but they will never be powerful enough to deal with a stronghold from hell. I WILL POWER is never enough. A classic illustration of this fact is a humorous study done in 2007. It compared the self-control of two groups; chimpanzees and Harvard graduate students. They gave the two groups two options: have two treats immediately or wait and delay gratification for six treats. An impressive 72% of the chimps waited for the treats. Only 19% of the Harvard students chose to delay gratification. I love the conclusions of the researchers. "When we are on our best behavior, humans' ability to control our impulses are amazing…because of our large prefrontal cortex. But it is good for more than self control; it can also rationalize bad decisions and promise I will be better tomorrow."[70]

We have all eaten the chocolate cake and promised, *I will be better tomorrow*. I WILL POWER is not enough. The upper left side of your brain specializes in "I WILL POWER." It helps you to start and stick to boring tasks, such as getting up early in the morning to pray instead of sleeping in. Come on, let's be honest; sometimes praying early in the morning can become boring. The I WILL POWER, however, is useless without self-awareness. The problem is without self-awareness, the brain automatically reverts to whatever is the easiest. And taking out a stronghold in your life is never an easy task. I think that is why God said to Abraham what he did in Genesis 15. Abraham gave up believing God's promise would ever come true in his life. He was sick and tired of waiting on God's promise of a son, and delaying gratification. God's response to him is fascinating. He challenged Abraham to go outside of his tent in the middle of the night and count the stars.

What is God doing? He is calling Abraham to meditate on the greatness of creation. Meditation wasn't invented by Buddha. God-seekers were doing it hundreds of years before Buddha came up with the concept. Meditation has been shown to increase the neural connections improving the brain's ability to stay focused, ignore distractions, and control impulses.[71] The huge problem is I WILL POWER isn't powerful enough. Remember, Abraham eventually went for the chocolate cake. Sarah came up with the bright idea of her husband having sex with her young maid to produce a son.

Of course, Abraham smiled from ear to ear and went along with the idea. Thanks, Abe, we now have perpetual war in the Middle East between Isaac and Ishmael because you couldn't delay gratification.

The upper right side of your brain handles the I WON'T POWER of your life. It holds you back from following every impulse and craving. But how many times have you said something stupid to your wife when you were under stress? How many times have you eaten junk food when you were stressed? The answer is embarrassing isn't it? My point? We live in one nation under_____. Not under God; our nation turned from God years ago. We live in one nation under STRESS! And nothing drains brainpower more than continual stress. Again, I comment on the great book titled *Why Zebras Don't Get Ulcers* and why the title makes sense once you stop and think about a zebra's life. All he has to do is outrun his slowest zebra friend about once a week when the lions show up to eat somebody. Then he can go back to munching the grass. Our problem is we can have the lion in our heads 24/7!

*Your enemy the devil prowls around like a roaring lion looking for someone to devour.*
1 Peter 5:8b

I WILL POWER is not strong enough. I WON'T POWER isn't strong enough. So what is the answer?

The University of Albany tested a number of willpower-drained students. They took them through an exhausting number of stressful and distracting tests. They found that only two things would motivate these stressed out students. 1) Not surprisingly, money helped these poor undergraduates find a new strength to proceed with another stressful test. 2) Secondly, the more powerful incentive was being told that doing their test could help the researchers discover a possible cure for Alzheimer's disease. The researchers commented, "While being the less obvious motivator, it proved to be the determining factor in whether people stuck with difficult challenges in real life."[72]

The I WANT FOR OTHERS turned out to be the most powerful factor in self-control. Not just I want it for me, but for others. That mental function takes place in the Orbitofrontal Cortex, which is located directly behind your eyes.[73]

Why did David want Jerusalem so badly? At the time, there was no way Israel could deal with all the vicious enemies that surrounded them unless they were united. Yet they were split into ten tribes to the north and two tribes in the south. If David had made his capital in the north, the tribes to the south would have never joined him, and the opposite would have been equally true. Jerusalem was located precisely in the "no man's land" between the north and south tribes. David desperately wanted Jerusalem, not for his own glory, but also for the survival of Israel. That is precisely why David finished so well in life despite all of his hellacious failures; he ultimately wanted to leave a legacy for others that would last. And today the Star of David still flies over the city of Jerusalem in the flag of Israel.

What will be your legacy? What gifts has Christ called you to leave behind in this hurting world?

Let's start with the present. At times we need to see what Christ is currently doing in our life before we can grasp the future He has for us.

## THE LEGACY I AM PRESENTLY LEAVING BEHIND

**ACHIEVEMENTS TO DATE   GREAT EXPERIENCES   GREAT RELATIONSHIPS**

**1.**

**2.**

**3.**

**4.**

**5.**

## THE LEGACY GOD WANTS ME TO ULTIMATELY LEAVE BEHIND!

| THE LIFE GOALS AND CHARACTER DEVELOPMENT I WANT TO EXPERIENCE IN THE YEARS AHEAD | THE LEGACY I WANT TO LEAVE FOR FUTURE GENERATIONS AND MY FAMILY |
|---|---|
| 1. | |
| 2. | |
| 3. | |
| 4. | |
| 5. | |

## ✎ THE FINAL ASSIGNMENTS FOR NEXT TIME

❶ Take your time on your legacy assignment; it will profoundly affect how much freedom you will be able to walk in.

• Revisit this exercise on a regular basis.

❷ Talk through this assignment in your group at your next meeting; make sure everyone has time to share ALL their responses. It may take more than one session.

❸ Review and sign the "Pillar Seven Commitment" prior to the next group meeting.

❹ As a group, discuss what your next step will be:

**A.** Begin to walk through the *Genesis Process for Change Groups*[74] (www.genesisprocess.org)

**B.** Move into a couple's group and go through the *Sexy Christians Workbook*[75] (www.puredesire.org)

❺ Read *Pure Desire* Chapter 17.

# ✔ PILLAR OF FREEDOM SEVEN COMMITMENT

I have, to the best of my abilities, completed all the exercises found in Pillar of Freedom Seven; by God's grace I will walk into the new life and dreams God has for me. I will walk with integrity, honesty and transparency in relationship to my wife and family in all things. I will dream the dreams of God for my life!

My Name _____

Signature _____ Date _____

..........................................................................................................................

## AFFIRMING WITNESSES

**As the wife of _____, I affirm that he is making progress toward integrity and health. I make a commitment to pray for him and our marriage in the days ahead as we both seek to walk in freedom and purity in Christ.**

Wife's Name _____

Signature _____ Date _____

..........................................................................................................................

***Witness Two:*** *I congratulate _____ for having completed this work-book and preparing his heart to walk in freedom. I make a commitment to pray for him and stand beside him in the days ahead cheering him on to even greater heights in Christ!*

Name _____

Signature _____ Date _____

***Witness Three:*** *I congratulate _____ for having completed this workbook and preparing his heart to walk in freedom. I make a commitment to pray for him and stand beside him in the days ahead cheering him on to even greater heights in Christ!*

Name _____

Signature _____ Date _____

..........................................................................................................................

## READING RESOURCES

### A SEXY BRAIN!

Years ago I remember a Hollywood starlet coming out with a memorable one liner. She smiled at the camera and jutted forth her sizable cleavage and cleverly commented, "Do you know that the sexiest part of the human body is the brain?" Initially I was so distracted by her actions that I missed the wisdom of her words. Since I have the typical male brain, it is hard to get my higher reasoning powers to engage in the presence of such overt female sexual signals. The fact that the male brain responds more rapidly to sexual signals than anything else is a subject we will investigate in the next lesson.

The ultimate battlefield in your life is always located between your ears, not your legs. The New Testament only uses the term "war" or "warfare" five times, but its focus is intriguing. Let's quickly look at each incident so you can have a clear understanding of the conflict in which you are involved.

*For though we live in the world, we do not wage war as the world does.*
*The weapons we fight with are not the weapons of the world.*
*On the contrary, they have divine power to demolish strongholds.*
*We demolish arguments and every pretension that sets itself up against the*
*knowledge of God, and we take captive every thought to make it obedient to Christ.*
2 Corinthians 10:3-5

This is Paul's classic statement about the nature of the battle every man faces. Please notice that the warfare is about pulling down mental bondages or strongholds of the mind. Notice that the focus is not on Satan taking charge, but rather on our minds and us taking our thoughts captive for the glory of God.

*Timothy, my son, I give you this instruction in keeping with the prophecies once*
*made about you, so that by following them you may fight the battle well...*
1 Timothy 1:18

Paul is challenging his apprentice to stay in the fight and to be faithful to his calling. Once again the focus is not on the devil, but on Timothy's mind.

*No one serving as a soldier gets involved in civilian affairs*
*but rather tries to please his commanding officer.*
2 Timothy 2:4

Paul is calling Timothy to clear out the clutter in his life to be single minded. He is exhorting him to stay committed to the call of God regardless of the cost and to focus his mind.

*What causes fights and quarrels among you?*
*Don't they come from your desires that battle within you?*
James 4:1

James is calling the reader to not be controlled by the self-orientated thinking that can so easily become part of our daily thought processes.

*Dear friends, I urge you, as foreigners and exiles, to abstain from sinful desires,*
*which wage war against your soul.*
1 Peter 2:11

The New Testament is vividly clear—**The Battlefield of Our Lives Is In Our Mind**! Therefore, if you are ever going to win the victory over your sexual struggles, the Hollywood starlet was right—the sexual battle is in your brain.

So let's begin by looking at the incredible gift of your mind. Take your right hand and curl it into a fist wrapping your fingers around your thumb. Then do the same thing with your left hand. Now bring your two fists together knuckles touching. Look down at your two fists. They are a good approximation of the size of our brain.

Your brain is only about three pounds in weight. It makes up about 2% of your body mass, yet it uses up 20% of the oxygen and calories you consume on a daily basis. It is a very delicate organ composed of about 80% water with the consistency of butter at room temperature. Yet it is the most complex of God's creation. For example, it contains somewhere over 100 BILLION neurons or nerve cells. This is approximately the number of stars in our Milky Way galaxy. And that is not even counting all the supporting glia cells. Now, here is the fascinating news. Each of those individual neurons has upward of 10,000 connections with other neurons. This means your brain has more neurological connections than there are **stars in our entire universe**!

## A TYPICAL NEURON

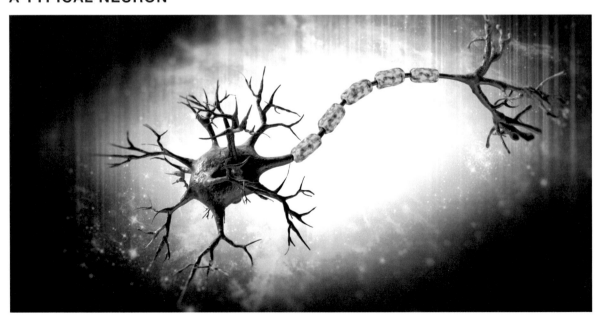

The way the individual neurons communicate with each other is intriguing. The signal initially travels down the length of the neuron electrically. Then the neuron sends a chemical signal across the gap between itself and the adjoining neuron. The neurons don't actually touch each other. The chemical nature of the signal sent across the gap or synapse gives you a hint as to why drugs like cocaine, meth, pot, and alcohol can so powerfully affect your brain.

We think our laptop computers are complex and sophisticated, but they are so primitive in comparison to the human brain. For example, your computer sends signals in binary form. In other words, the signal is either a "zero" or a "one," "on" or "off."

## A BRAIN SYNAPSE

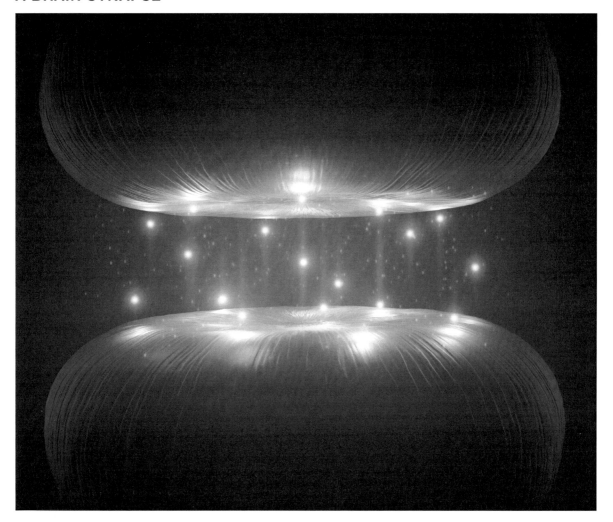

Scientists have been able to identify over 50 different types of neurotransmitter chemicals so far and have just begun to study the brain at this level. In other words, there are millions of unique signals that can be sent across the synapse of a single neuron with the various permutations and combinations of 50 different neurotransmitters. Your computer only has two options. Your brain is like an F-18 fighter and your computer is like a rock in comparison. And that is a severe over-simplification of the actual complexity of your brain.

Let's take a tour of the battlefield. Following is a rough diagram of your brain and its primary structures.

## THE HUMAN BRAIN

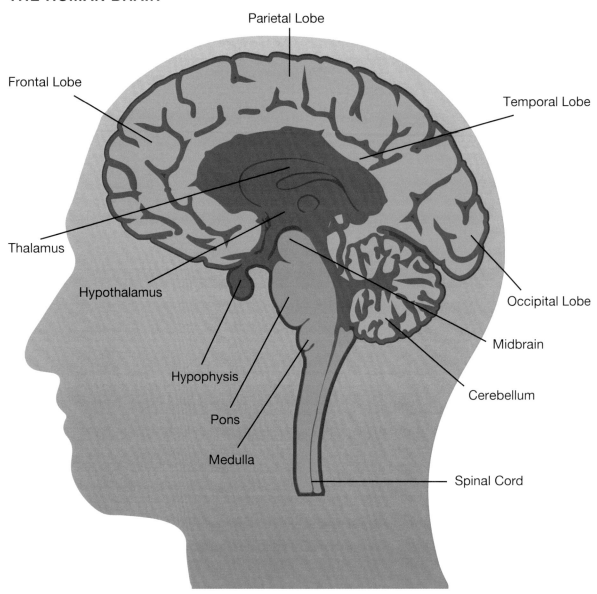

Parietal Lobe

Frontal Lobe

Temporal Lobe

Thalamus

Hypothalamus

Occipital Lobe

Hypophysis

Midbrain

Pons

Cerebellum

Medulla

Spinal Cord

Starting up front is the **frontal lobe**, specifically the **prefontal cortex**—the arena of your working memory and concentration.[76] This is where executive planning and social awareness and impulse control take place. This is the area of your brain that shuts down when you are acting out. I will tell you how and why later in the workbook.

Further back on the top of your head is the **parietal lobe**. This is where spatial awareness is created along with problem solving, and where attention and association take place.

The visual process occurs in the back of the brain in the region known technically as the **occipital lobe**. At the bottom and back of the brain is the **cerebellum** that controls voluntary muscle moments and processes information coming from muscles throughout the body. Our final stop in this general overview are the **temporal lobes** located on both sides of your head. These are an amazing part of your brain; they deal with word recognition, language, memory, music, face recognition and your moods. If you struggle with anger frequently, you probably have some "hot temporal lobes."[77]

The brain doesn't come fully programmed, which is one of its great strengths, because of its infinite adaptability. The brain usually isn't fully developed until our mid-twenties. Specifically, your Prefrontal Cortex isn't fully matured until then, which means impulse control and judgment can be lacking.

The first five years of growth in your brain are critical. Our brains are deeply social organisms. For example, from approximately six months to about a year and a half, the right side of your brain is rapidly developing. Some have termed this the "social side" of your brain. It is interesting to note that approximately 70% of the time a mom will carry her infant in her left arm.[78] Whether she knows it or not, this is so she can access the right side of the child's brain. In the constant interchange of comfort and care that occurs between an emotionally healthy mom and her child, a fascinating thing takes place. The mom's brain is serving as scaffolding for the formatting and construction of the child's social brain and affects regulation. *Stick with me on this; it will explain why some men struggle so deeply with sexual addiction.* "Affect regulation" is a fancy term for emotional stability. The child grows into a young man who can control and deal with the negative emotions of life. However, if there is abandonment, abuse or lack of care in the family of origin, the brain can be set up for some profound struggles. I think you could sum up the impact of early neglect by saying **that early childhood trauma in the form of emotional and physical abuse, sexual abuse and neglect shape the structure and functioning of the brain in ways that negatively affect ALL STAGES of social, emotional and intellectual development**.[79]

If you have ever seen three-year-olds roaring around the kitchen getting into everything, you are seeing neurons making new connections like crazy. Their little brains are experiencing everything for the first time and it is exciting! Compare that to the jaded 17-year-old standing in the kitchen responding to questions with one word cryptic answers, "NOPE" or "NOTHING" or the classic "WHATEVER!" One of the reasons for this extreme difference in behavior is that the teen has one-half the effective neurological connections of a three-year-old. They both have the same number of neuron connections, but the critical term is "effective."

The teen has neurological freeways in his brain. Instead of thinking all over the place like a three-year-old, the teen has fixed ways of thinking. The neuron connections have pruned down the options. In the brain, the old phrase is true, "Use it or lose it." The neurons that fire together actually wire together. Some of the neurological connections a person had at three have atrophied, withered away due to a lack of use.

Now for the critical question, "Where did those neurological highways come from? How were they constructed?" If you pause and think about it for a moment, the answer becomes glaringly obvious. Their family of origin taught them how to think either in a positive way or in reaction to the pain they experienced in their homes.

Here is an amazing fact: **You really don't leave home; you take it with you in your brain**. We carry our family of origin with us in our brains. This is where the biblical term "a generational curse" clinically comes from. I have never counseled a man struggling with sexual issues who wasn't carrying a negative family freeway around in his head.

Sexual addiction and bondage is frequently about medicating the family pain that the individual has carried around in his soul for years. The killer is, he usually can't even recognize it. It is like faulty software that was downloaded into his head as a kid. He has lived with it for so long he thinks it's normal to have these thoughts and feelings. It's similar to the background music stores play as you shop; you don't even recognize it's playing. But stores go to the financial expense of having it because when you emotionally connect with the music, you buy more! The music is controlling you and you don't even know it. In much the same way, painful neurological freeways of the past can control us. And some of the most powerful ones originate from the home we were raised in, which is precisely why the Bible speaks so much about generational curses.

Your brain can also become vulnerable in another way. You may have grown up in a great family, but your teen years were very painful. The vast majority of men I have listened to throughout the years struggled with sexual battles that began in their early teen years. Recent research has clearly demonstrated that teens have very unique brains that are quite different than the brains of adults and children.[80] Teen brains are uniquely susceptible to risk-taking and the impact of such behavior. Their Prefrontal Cortex is not fully developed, thus reducing their ability to control impulses. Add to that the fact they are experiencing elevated levels of the neurotransmitter dopamine that is connected with thrill-seeking behavior.

Here is the scene: A teen is driving a high-powered sports car with the accelerator to the floor, but the car only has the brakes of a go-cart. It is a recipe for disaster. Translate that illustration into sexual terms, and throw in the hyper-sexualized nature of our culture, and a sexual decision can be made as a teen that can affect someone for the rest of his life. The adolescent brain is distinctively sensitive to risky behavior. Studies have shown that teen brains form stronger connections to reward stimuli (drugs and sex) and these associations last longer than they do for adults.[81]

The bottom line is that **our history can be significantly affecting our present**. This is especially true when it comes to sexual issues because they are such a foundational part of our identity. This is not to say we aren't responsible for our behavior because of our past. Instead, I am saying **you will have little, if any, ability to move into a new beginning until you understand and redeem your past**. And let me passionately add that if you had a difficult childhood, you are not blaming your parents for your struggles. Instead, reclaim what is yours in Christ. Mom and Dad may have done the best they could, considering the family in which they were raised. But the curse stops with your generation. You will not pass on a sexually addictive mindset to your kids. Deal with your stuff, stop medicating the pain within, and learn how to walk in purity before your God and family!

## FAMILY TABLE EXERCISE

- Complete this exercise on your own.
- Bring your drawings to your Pure Desire group meeting.

❶ Get six clean sheets of paper and a box of crayons. You get to be a kid again!

⊃ **Complete 2 & 3 using your NON-DOMINANT HAND.**

❷ On the first sheet draw a picture of your family of origin at the dinner table, using your NON-DOMINANT HAND.

❸ On the next sheet of paper draw a picture of your present family at the dinner table several years ago, using your NON-DOMINANT HAND.

⊃ **Complete 4, 5, 6, & 7 using your DOMINANT HAND.**

❹ On the third sheet draw a picture of your family of origin as it is today if you all met for dinner.

❺ The fourth sheet is to be a picture of your present family at the dinner table today.

❻ The fifth sheet will be a picture of your family of origin as you wished it had been.

❼ Finally, draw a picture of your present family at dinner as one day you hope it will be.

❥ **Debrief yourself on the exercise!**

❶ Describe the experience of drawing using your non-dominant hand.

....................................................................................................................................

❷ Describe the experience of drawing using your dominant hand.

....................................................................................................................................

❸ If the drawings with your non-dominant hand represent your lifestyle of addiction and the drawings with your dominant hand represent your lifestyle in recovery, what can you learn from this exercise?

....................................................................................................................................

## "HELP! SOMEONE HIJACKED MY BRAIN!"

*I decide to do good, but I don't really do it;*
*I decide not to do bad, but then I do it anyway.*
Romans 7:19 (MSG)

I still remember the first time I read those jarring words of Paul. I thought, "That is me!" Those words so succinctly described the deepest frustrations of my life. I was totally committed to Christ trying to serve him with all my heart yet I kept being drawn to porn or _____ (You can put your area of sexual struggle in the blank).

"What is wrong with me?" I would cry. I thought that if I only tried harder the problem would go away. But that only made it worse because as I kept driving myself and shaming myself, the relapses only became more painful and crippling to my soul. The turning point came when I understood that hell had hijacked my brain. Like Paul, I was literally a double-minded man at war with myself.

The brain creates patterns and templates of action to help us deal more effectively with the demands of our day. Thus we don't have to decide which hand we will use to sign the check or which side of our face we will start shaving first in the morning. Have you noticed you always start with the same side of your face?

231

Your brain makes over three billion decisions per second, most of which are unconscious. In fact, it has been estimated that 90% of the decisions you make on a daily basis are unconscious in nature. You are on autopilot most of the time, which frees up your Prefrontal Cortex to develop and analyze new situations. This isn't a problem—until the autopilot is hijacked. We all have had the experience of rushing around the house finding ourselves in a room and we can't remember why we are there. Then we remember we needed to go to the garage to find a screwdriver, but we end up standing in the living room because of our fatigue. We just walked into that room out of habit. Like Paul we were headed one place and ended up in another.

We ended up in the wrong place and we were under stress. More than likely we walked into the living room because that is where we frequently go when we want to relax.

**Our autopilot was trying to help us, but instead, it ended up hijacking us from our desired destination.** This is a common experience of someone struggling with sexual bondages. Sexual addiction is driven by the fact that you are dealing with a hijacked brain. That doesn't mean you can't help yourself; instead it means you are going to have to work hard at recalibrating and reprogramming your brain. You will have to purposefully restructure the neurological connections of your brain that are setting you up to spend your life in the wrong places.

I was flying a long over-water flight and the refueling range of a fighter aircraft is notoriously short. Therefore, we had to engage in a number of rendezvous with tanker aircraft. This is normally not a challenging endeavor but that day I had an autopilot that wouldn't easily disengage and it was pulling the plane off the correct headings. The autopilot should have been my best friend. Long over-water flights can be very boring because you have to navigate by the instruments. There are no ground references to tell you where you are, so you are glued to the instrument panel. The autopilot can save you a lot of work, but in this case the autopilot was increasing my load. I flew for hours battling with the thing, anxious that I might miss the tanker. The Pacific Ocean can be a very lonely place when you are frantically looking for the refueling tanker as your fuel gauge rapidly drops to zero.

This illustration is a lucid picture of the mental battle the addict goes through because his faulty autopilot is trying to ignore the judgment or "common sense" of his input. When you are struggling with sexual bondages your Prefrontal Cortex commitment to Christ is usually being pulled off course by the autopilot of your Limbic System deep within your brain. When you continue to make choices that don't make any sense in your life, when you repeatedly make destructive sexual decisions, mark it down as a **limbic system problem**.

Your limbic system is comprised of the amygdala, hippocampus, medial thalamus, nucleus accumbens, and basal forebrain, all of which connect to the anterior cingulate gyrus, which is the major gateway to the prefrontal cortex.[82] Don't let all those technical terms freak you out. We are going to look at just three parts of the limbic system that drive your addictive behavior.

## 1. THE HIPPOCAMPUS

This part of your inner brain consolidates learning by converting working memory into long term memory and storing it in various regions of your brain. The hippocampus is constantly comparing working memory with long term memory, creating a sense of meaning in your thought process. For example, Alzheimer's progressively destroys neurons in the hippocampus resulting in memory loss.

## 2. THE AMYGDALA

This part of the brain works in association with the hippocampus. It is survival central. The amygdala is your early-warning system. It processes information even before the prefrontal cortex gets the message that something has happened. When you smile at the sight or sound of someone you love even before you consciously recognize her, the amygdala is at work. Some recent research indicates that of all stimuli, the brain (especially the male brain) codes erotic scenes 20% faster than anything else.[83] The amygdala defines what you see as being critical for your survival. It underlines in your memory what you should flee from or what you are willing to fight for so that you can survive. The amygdala identifies things so terrifying to you that you will just freeze, being unable to respond to the threat. It defines what food is critical for your survival and what is vital for you sexually.

An essential feature of brain anatomy is the fact that there are more connections running from the amygdala to the cortex than the other way around. That means that the amygdala will win the battle every time. That explains why Paul is in such despair in Romans 7. When these two parts of the brain are at war with one another it is a bit like Mike Tyson facing off with Woody Allen.

Fear, anger, sexual lusts, which all stem from the amygdala, are notoriously resistant to our ability to reason ourselves out of them. Once fearful reactions or traumatic memories (especially sexual ones) are burned into the amygdala, they tend to lock the mind and body into a recurring pattern of arousal. We have a great deal of difficulty restraining an excited amygdala. Noted neuroscientist Joseph LeDoux, author of *The Emotional Brain*[84], states that all strong emotional memories are neurobiologically indelible. I would agree with that statement apart from the power of the Holy Spirit. But if we allow the Holy Spirit's work to take place deep in our lives, our brains can be changed. I want to underline the fact that this process will not take place in a single prayer or Christian experience. It can only take place through the renewing of our minds. Much like a stroke victim, the addict has to re-grow various parts of his brain. You will have to renew your mind!

The first step is facing the pain. You will initially be experiencing a greater level of pain, not less, because for years you have been medicating the pain within. Once you start getting in touch with what has been going on deep within your thought processes, the pain will rise to the surface. In this workbook you will be engaged in a lot of written responses that are usually found at the end of each lesson. This **is not academic busy work**! Instead, this is a process of getting your prefrontal cortex involved. I want to increase your "common sense" factor. By that comment I am not implying you are not smart. Addicts tend to be very sharp. But when they are in a mental battle with their limbic system, the limbic system almost always wins the fight against reasoning powers.

The workbook questions are not random, but are created to help your brain focus. Please complete **ALL THE EXERCISES** because research has shown that the physical process of handwriting instead of typing on your computer engages the brain. Handwriting engages you in a refining way, much like adjusting the lens of a telescope so you can see the object clearly. The actual physical act of writing enhances mental change. *The commitment form to sign at the end of each pillar is designed to encourage you to follow through on your commitment to your own healing. You will not get better unless you do the work necessary to renew your mind!*

## 3. NUCLEUS ACCUMBENS

The third element of your limbic system we will look at is your Nucleus Accumbens. In 2005, *Discovery* Magazine listed the discovery of the *endogenous* (which means internal) *reward system* as one of the greatest discoveries in the last 25 years of scientific research. The reason it is so significant is the fact that all drugs and behaviors that are addictive appear to involve the nucleus accumbens.

The nucleus accumbens identifies a certain activity as one that needs to be repeated. The nucleus accumbens releases dopamine in the brain that floods across the synapse of the prefrontal cortex. This causes the "good feelings" from certain activities. But this reward system can be hijacked. For example, cocaine can flood the brain with a "super high" because it blocks the uptake pumps of the dopamine receptors in the brain. This results in a tidal wave of dopamine at the synapse, creating an abnormal firing pattern in the neurons. Over a period of time this literally rewires the brain. Brain scans of cocaine addicts clearly show a reduced overall brain function and specifically reduced prefrontal cortex activity. This is precisely why addicts can make dumb decisions.

Here is the connection with sexual addiction. Brain scans of sex addicts and gambling addicts show that the mere thought of sexual activity or gambling lights up their nucleus accumbens like a Christmas tree, much like what happens with a cocaine addict. Sexual addiction and gambling are "process addictions." The high is created by the action, not a drug, because the individual's own brain creates the drug.

This makes process addictions much more difficult to deal with for two reasons.[85] First, the rationalization structures are harder to break through. That is why Pillar One deals with breaking denial. If someone is taking a drug and has needle marks up and down his arms or his nose is being destroyed by snorting cocaine, it is harder for him to rationalize. A sex addict, however, can keep his activity hidden from view.

Second, process addictions have the capacity to create the immediate onset of a high, similar to cocaine, through things like sexual fantasy. Your battle with sexual fantasy will lie at the core of your ultimate victory and will be covered in Pillar Five.

Every time you act out, there is a surge of dopamine creating pleasure that triggers neurons and synapses in your brain. That sequence activates a set of beliefs and reinforces limbic dysfunctional experiences that may have begun in early childhood. Old destructive ways of coping with the pain in your life continue to be reinforced. Most of this takes place beyond the awareness of your conscious beliefs.

Paul wrote about this brain pattern in Romans 7:19. "I want to do what is right (conscious beliefs), but I keep doing what is wrong (unconscious dysfunctional beliefs and patterns)." We just keep repeating the old patterns of dancing with destruction. Just trying harder will not solve the problem because we are engaging conscious processes trying to solve unconscious destructive processes.

The ministry of the Holy Spirit is so important in our healing. God the Holy Spirit is not Casper the Friendly Ghost. He is the one who reveals Jesus to us (John 16) and he will uniquely reveal our unconscious processes that are entrapping us. (Romans 8:11-17, 26-27)

All addictions, and especially sexual addictions, are deadly traps. Once you experience the dopamine spike of destructive sexual activity the brain tries to balance itself. Being a sexual addict means your limbic system is "on" most of the time through your sexual fantasies. Therefore, the brain, in an attempt to balance things, reduces the production of dopamine that in turn weakens the reward system. Now the trap has been sprung because you are compelled to act out, not to feel high, **but just to feel normal**. This is why your sexual addiction has slowly been escalating over time. You have developed what is called "Tolerance." What sexually excited you previously doesn't turn you on now. This is why most sex addicts experience a decreased enjoyment of sexual relations with their wife. Or the addict will pressure his wife to engage in sexual behavior he has observed in the pornography he has been viewing.

Your pain and shame level have only increased as you acted out because of your commitment to Christ, but your ability to medicate the pain through porn, voyeurism, masturbation, and prostitutes has continued to diminish. Welcome to insanity!

As the process continues, the brain is significantly changed. Dr. Eric Nestler of the University of Texas has recently discovered that a hijacked dopamine cycle will produce a protein called Delta Fos B in the brain.[86] It will accumulate in the neurons. As it accumulates it eventually throws a genetic switch that causes changes that persist long after the reward cycle has stopped.

The addict is now far more prone to addiction because he experiences stronger cravings. His brain has become **sensitized** to the experience. Sensitization is different than tolerance. As tolerance develops, the addict needs more and more sexual acting out to get a pleasant affect. But as sensitization develops, the addict needs less and less of the experience for the cravings to increase. There are two separated systems in your brain, one for excitement and the other has to do with the satisfying the pleasure cycle. The man is caught in the vice of a vicious bondage. He is getting excited more and more easily, but experiencing less and less fulfillment. Welcome to totally insanity!

Because your brain has literally been hijacked in battle, you need some incredibly powerful weapons to set you free. This workbook is based on the latest research in neurochemistry. I have used the exercises time and again and have seen the deepest levels of bondage broken in men's lives.

However, you can have the finest clinical advice in the world and still be hopelessly in bondage. Two commitments are essential if you are ever going to get free. Both of these attitudes are foreign territory for sexual addicts.

## 1. A COMMITMENT TO HARD WORK AND HONESTY

You may be a hard worker and deeply honest in many areas of your life but with respect to your sexuality this hasn't been true for a long time. The hard work with respect to you getting free is going to be especially difficult because you can't be in control, which is where the honesty comes in. Your Pure Desire group will be a place where your honesty will be tested. In answering the questions in the workbook you can hide if you want to, but I pray that your group becomes a place where nothing is hidden in your life. I pray that your group becomes a place where you finally open up about your life. Chose to trust some other men totally and be open to their feedback even when it is painful and revealing.

## 2. A COMMITMENT TO TAKE UP THE SWORD OF THE SPIRIT IN YOUR LIFE!

In Paul's description of the warrior God has designed you to become, he makes a critical observation.

*Take the helmet of salvation and the sword of the Spirit, which is the word of God.*
Ephesians 6:17

The sword is the only offensive weaponry Paul mentions in the complete description of armor for a Roman soldier; everything else enables the soldier to stand against the enemy's assaults. Therefore, you must have this spiritual weapon in your battle. What is Paul talking about? Fortunately, he makes it very clear. It is the Word of God that you need, but not just in a general sense. Paul uses the phrase "The sword of the Spirit which is the rhema of God." This structure is called a "genitive of origin," meaning that the sword was given to you by the Holy Spirit.[87]

God the Holy Spirit will be speaking promises to you as you walk through this workbook. When He speaks, **write them down and review them every morning in your quiet time**. You must have a God-given dream to make it through the battle. You need something with which you can cut into the enemy when you feel like quitting or when your "Delta Fos B" is driving you crazy with cravings. You need that God-given dream when you are feeling worthless and like a failure, or when your mind is sliding towards the cliff of relapse, once again thanks to hell.

Take a stand with God's promise to you in your hand, His dream in your heart, and with your band of brothers in the Pure Desire group standing beside you. Then you will realize you have been condemned by God's grace to total victory!

## LIST BELOW THE PROMISES GOD HAS GIVEN YOU SO FAR IN THIS BATTLE.

1. _____

2. _____

3. _____

4. _____

**❯ What are your dreams of how your life will be when you win this battle? Write your description in the box below**

## THIS IS MY GOD-GIVEN DREAM...

being free.

**Note about suggested exercises and assignments:** Please complete all the exercises and assignments contained within the Pillars of Freedom Introduction sections. Bring your notes or other work to your Pure Desire group meeting so that you can discuss your ideas and responses with your group.

# FOR FURTHER READING

Arterburn, Stephen. *Every Man's Battle: Winning the War on Sexual Temptation One Victory at a Time* (Colorado Springs: Waterbrook Press, 2009).

Brown, Brene. *The Gifts of Imperfection: Let Go of Who You Think You Are Supposed to Be and Embrace Who You Are* (Center City: Hazelden, 2010).

Carnes, Patrick J., Ph.D. *The Betrayal Bond*, (Deerfield Beach, FL: Health Communications, Inc., 1997).

Doidge, Norman. *The Brain that Changes Itself*, (New York: Viking, 2007).

Dye, Michael, CADC, NCAC II, *The Genesis Process for Change Groups* (Auburn, CA: Michael Dye, 2006). www.genesisprocess.org.

Dye, Michael, CADC, NCAC, and Patricia Fancher, CAC III, MFCC, Ph.D. *The Genesis Process. A Relapse Prevention Workbook for Addictive/Compulsive Behaviors*, (Auburn, CA: Michael Dye, 1998; 3rd Edition 2007). www.genesisprocess.org.

Lynch, John. *TrueFaced* (book) and *TrueFaced Experience* DVD, 2nd Edition. (Phoenix, Az: Leadership Catalyst, Inc., 2007). www.leadershipcatalyst.org.

MacDonald, Linda J., M.S., LMFT. *How To Help Your Spouse Heal From Your Affair* (Gig Harbor, WA: Healing Counsel Press, 2010). Available on Amazon.com.

Roberts, Dr. Ted and Diane Roberts. *Sexy Christians* (Grand Rapids: Baker Publishing Group, 2010). www.puredesire.org.

Roberts, Dr. Ted and Diane Roberts. *Sexy Christians Workbook* (Grand Rapids: Baker Publishing Group, 2010). www.puredesire.org.

Sittser, Jerry L. *A Grace Disguised: How the Soul Grows Through Loss* (Grand Rapids: Zondervan, 2005).

Van Vonderen, Jeff. *Tired of Trying to Measure Up* (Minneapolis: Bethany House Publishers, 1989).

Wiles, Jeremy & Tiana. *Conquer Series: The Battle Plan for Purity*. Hosted by Dr. Ted Roberts. DVD Series & Workbook. (West Palm Beach, FL: KingdomWorks Studios, 2013) www.kingdomworks.com.

# APPENDIX TWO[88]

## PTSI (POST TRAUMATIC STRESS INDEX)

**THE FOLLOWING STATEMENTS TYPIFY REACTIONS TRAUMA VICTIMS OFTEN HAVE TO CHILD ABUSE.**

⊘ Please check those that you believe apply to you.

⊘ Although the statements are written in the present tense, if the statements have *ever* applied in your life then place a check next to that item.

⊘ Statements are considered false only if they have *never* been a part of your life. If in doubt, let your first reaction be your guide.

⊘ Given these guidelines, check the statements you feel apply to you.

### PTSI

_____ **1.** I have recurring memories of painful experiences.

_____ **2.** I am unable to stop a childhood pattern harmful to myself.

_____ **3.** I sometimes obsess about people who have hurt me and are now gone.

_____ **4.** I feel bad at times about myself because of shameful experiences I believe were my fault.

_____ **5.** I am a risk taker.

_____ **6.** At times I have difficulty staying awake.

_____ **7.** I sometimes feel separate from my body as a reaction to a flashback or memory.

_____ **8.** I deny myself basic needs at times like groceries, shoes, books, medical care, rent and heat.

_____ **9.** I have distressing dreams about experiences.

_____ **10.** I repeat painful experiences over and over.

_____ **11.** I try to be understood by those who are incapable or don't care for me.

_____ **12.** I have suicidal thoughts.

_____ **13.** I engage in high-risk behaviors.

_____ **14.** I eat excessively to avoid problems.

_____ **15.** I avoid thoughts or feelings associated with my trauma experiences.

_____ **16.** I skip vacations because of lack of time or money.

_____ **17.** I have periods of sleeplessness.

_____ **18.** I try to recreate an early trauma experience.

_____ **19.** I keep secrets from people who have hurt me.

_____ **20.** I have attempted suicide.

_____ **21.** I am sexual when frightened.

_____ **22.** I drink to excess when life is too hard.

_____ **23.** I avoid stories, parts of movies, or reminders of early painful experiences.

_____ **24.** I avoid sexual pleasure.

_____ **25.** I sometimes feel like an old painful experience is happening now.

_____ **26.** There is something destructive I do over and over from my early life.

_____ **27.** I stay in conflict with someone when I could have walked away.

_____ **28.** I have suicidal thoughts.

_____ **29.** I often feel sexual when I am lonely.

_____ **30.** I use depressant drugs as a way to cope.

_____ **31.** I am unable to recall important details of painful experiences.

_____ **32.** I avoid doing "normal" activities because of fears I have.

_____ **33.** I have sudden, vivid or distracting memories of painful experiences.

_____ **34.** I attempt to stop activities I know are not helpful.

_____ **35.** I go "overboard" to help people who have been destructive.

_____ **36.** I often feel lonely and estranged from others because of painful experiences I have had.

_____ **37.** I feel intensely sexual when violence occurs.

_____ **38.** My procrastinating interferes with my life activities.

_____ **39.** I sometimes withdraw or lack interest in important activities because of childhood experiences.

_____ **40.** I will hoard money and not spend money on legitimate needs.

_____ **41.** I am upset when there are reminders of abusive experiences (anniversaries, places, symbols).

_____ **42.** I compulsively do things to others that were done to me as a young person.

_____ **43.** I sometimes help those who continue to harm me.

_____ **44.** I feel unable to experience certain emotions (love, happiness, sadness, etc.)

_____ **45.** I feel sexual when degraded or used.

_____ **46.** Sleep is a way for me to avoid life's problems.

_____ **47.** I have difficulty concentrating.

_____ **48.** I have attempted diets repeatedly.

_____ **49.** I have difficulty sleeping.

_____ **50.** My relationships are the same story over and over.

_____ **51.** I feel loyal to people even though they have betrayed me.

_____ **52.** I have a dim outlook on my future.

_____ **53.** I feel sexual when someone is "nice" to me.

_____ **54.** At times I am preoccupied with food and eating.

_____ **55.** I experience confusion often.

_____ **56.** I refuse to buy things even when I need them and have the money.

_____ **57.** I have difficulty feeling sexual.

_____ **58.** I know that something destructive I do repeats a childhood event.

_____ **59.** I remain a "team" member when obviously things are becoming destructive.

_____ **60.** I feel as if I must avoid depending on people.

_____ **61.** I sometimes feel bad because I enjoyed experiences that were exploitive of me.

_____ **62.** I abuse alcohol often.

_____ **63.** I tend to be accident prone.

_____ **64.** I spend much time performing "underachieving" jobs.

_____ **65.** Sometimes I have outbursts of anger or irritability.

_____ **66.** I do things to others that were done to me in my family.

_____ **67.** I make repeated efforts to convince people who were destructive to me and not willing to listen.

_____ **68.** I engage in self-destructive behaviors.

_____ **69.** I get "high" on activities that were dangerous to me.

_____ **70.** I use TV, reading, and hobbies as a way to numb out.

_____ **71.** I go into a "fantasy" world when things are tough.

_____ **72.** I am "underemployed."

_____ **73.** I am extremely cautious of my surroundings.

_____ **74.** I have thoughts and behaviors repeatedly that do not feel good to me.

_____ **75.** I attempt to be liked by people who clearly were exploiting me.

_____ **76.** I engage in self-mutilating behaviors (cutting self, burning, bruising, etc.)

_____ **77.** I use drugs like cocaine or amphetamines to speed things up.

_____ **78.** I have a problem with "putting off" certain tasks.

_____ **79.** I use "romance" as a way to avoid problems.

_____ **80.** I feel very guilty about any sexual activity.

_____ **81.** I often feel that people are out to take advantage of me.

_____ **82.** I revert to doing things I did as a child.

_____ **83.** I am attracted to untrustworthy people.

_____ **84.** I endure physical or emotional pain most people would not accept.

_____ **85.** I like living on the "edge" of danger or excitement.

_____ **86.** When things are difficult, I will sometimes "binge."

_____ **87.** I have a tendency to be preoccupied with something else than what I need to be.

_____ **88.** I have a low interest in sexual activity.

_____ **89.** I am distrustful of others.

_____ **90.** Some of my recurring behavior comes from early life experiences.

_____ **91.** I trust people who are proven unreliable.

_____ **92.** I try to be perfect.

_____ **93.** I am orgasmic when hurt or beaten.

_____ **94.** I use drugs to escape.

_____ **95.** I use marijuana or psychedelics to hallucinate.

_____ **96.** I sometimes spoil success opportunities.

_____ **97.** I am startled more easily than others.

_____ **98.** I am preoccupied with children of a certain age.

_____ **99.** I seek people who I know will cause me pain.

_____ **100.** I avoid mistakes at any cost.

_____ **101.** I love to "gamble" on outcomes.

_____ **102.** I work too hard so I won't have to feel.

_____ **103.** I will often lose myself in fantasies rather than deal with real life.

_____ **104.** I go "without" necessities for periods of time.

_____ **105.** I get physical reactions to reminders of abuse experiences (breaking out in cold sweat, trouble breathing, etc.)

_____ **106.** I engage in abusive relationships repeatedly.

_____ **107.** I have difficulty retreating from unhealthy relationships.

_____ **108.** I sometimes want to hurt myself physically.

_____ **109.** I need lots of stimulation so I will not be bored.

_____ **110.** I get "lost" in my work.

_____ **111.** I live a "double life."

_____ **112.** I vomit food or use diuretics to avoid weight gain.

_____ **113.** I feel anxious about being sexual.

_____ **114.** There is a certain age of children or adolescents that are sexually attractive to me.

_____ **115.** I continue contact with a person who has abused me.

_____ **116.** I often feel unworthy, unlovable, immoral, or sinful because of experiences I have had.

_____ **117.** I like sex when it is dangerous.

_____ **118.** I try to "slow down" my mind.

_____ **119.** I have a life of "compartments" that others do not know about.

_____ **120.** I experience periods of no interest in eating.

_____ **121.** I am scared about sex.

_____ **122.** There are activities that I have trouble stopping even though they are useless or destructive.

_____ **123.** I am in emotional fights (divorces, lawsuits) that seem endless.

_____ **124.** I often feel I should be punished for past behavior.

_____ **125.** I do sexual things that are risky.

_____ **126.** When I am anxious, I will do things to stop my feelings.

_____ **127.** I have a fantasy life that I retreat to when things are hard.

_____ **128.** I have difficulty with play.

_____ **129.** I wake up with upsetting dreams.

_____ **130.** My relationships seem to have the same dysfunctional pattern.

_____ **131.** There are certain people who I always allow to take advantage of me.

_____ **132.** I have a sense that others are always better off than me.

_____ **133.** I use cocaine or amphetamines to heighten "high risk" activities.

_____ **134.** I don't tolerate uncomfortable feelings.

_____ **135.** I am a daydreamer.

_____ **136.** At times, I see comfort, luxuries and play activities as frivolous.

_____ **137.** I hate it when someone approaches me sexually.

_____ **138.** Sometimes I find children more attractive than others.

_____ **139.** There are some people in my life who are hard to get over though they hurt or used me badly.

_____ **140.** I feel bad when something good happens.

_____ **141.** I get excited/aroused when faced with dangerous situations.

_____ **142.** I use anything to distract myself from my problems.

_____ **143.** Sometimes I live in an "unreal" world.

_____ **144.** There are long periods of time with no sexual activity for me.

# STRESS INDEX ANSWER GRID

❯ On the grid below, place an "X" by all the questions that you checked as true for you.

❯ Next, add up all the Xs in each column and place the total in the space at the bottom of each.

❯ Explanations of your scores appear in the PTSI Overview.

| 1 | 2 | 3 | 4 | 5 | 6 | 7 | 8 |
|---|---|---|---|---|---|---|---|
| 9 | 10 | 11 | 12 | 13 | 14 | 15 | 16 |
| 17 | 18 | 19 | 20 | 21 | 22 | 23 | 24 |
| 25 | 26 | 27 | 28 | 29 | 30 | 31 | 32 |
| 33 | 34 | 35 | 36 | 37 | 38 | 39 | 40 |
| 41 | 42 | 43 | 44 | 45 | 46 | 47 | 48 |
| 49 | 50 | 51 | 52 | 53 | 54 | 55 | 56 |
| 57 | 58 | 59 | 60 | 61 | 62 | 63 | 64 |
| 65 | 66 | 67 | 68 | 69 | 70 | 71 | 72 |
| 73 | 74 | 75 | 76 | 77 | 78 | 79 | 80 |
| 81 | 82 | 83 | 84 | 85 | 86 | 87 | 88 |
| 89 | 90 | 91 | 92 | 93 | 94 | 95 | 96 |
| 97 | 98 | 99 | 100 | 101 | 102 | 103 | 104 |
| 105 | 106 | 107 | 108 | 109 | 110 | 111 | 112 |
| 113 | 114 | 115 | 116 | 117 | 118 | 119 | 120 |
| 121 | 122 | 123 | 124 | 125 | 126 | 127 | 128 |
| 129 | 130 | 131 | 132 | 133 | 134 | 135 | 136 |
| 137 | 138 | 139 | 140 | 141 | 142 | 143 | 144 |
| **TRT** | **TR** | **TBD** | **TS** | **TP** | **TB** | **TSG** | **TA** |
| _____ | _____ | _____ | _____ | _____ | _____ | _____ | _____ |

❯ Transfer your score for each category to the appropriate section in the PTSI Overview.

# PTSI ANALYSIS OVERVIEW

Based on your scores for the Post-Traumatic Stress Index (PTSI), the following is a brief explanation of what the score measures. If you have been in recovery then these are possible "vulnerable" areas of which to be aware.

- If your score is **low (0-2)**, this is not an area of concern.
- If your score is **moderate (3-6)**, you may wish to explore strategies that might help resolve the past or how to reduce your vulnerability in this area.
- If your score is **severe (7-18)**, this is an area of potential intense focus or periodic significance.

Obviously, the higher the number, the more concern one has about the severity and chronicity of brain change. Please note that this screening instrument assists in beginning to think about the potential role of trauma or relational experiences in your life. Further assessment with your therapist will determine if these results "fit" and what protocols to consider.

........................................................................................................................................

## TRT - TRAUMA REACTIONS: MY SCORE ____

Experiencing current reactions to trauma events in the past. This relates to post-traumatic stress disorder (PTSD) symptoms and a tendency to over-react or under-react. Most individuals who score in this area experienced some kind of anxiety (stress) in their family of origin, or growing up and feeling a sense of fear or terror (lack of safety). This sense of uncertainty may be acute or chronic and longitudinal. The general idea is that perceived trauma by an individual results in the release of stress hormones, which may actually damage (rewire) the brain when stress is sustained.

### TYPICAL THERAPEUTIC STRATEGIES:
- Study and write down your automatic "knee jerk" reactions and distorted thinking.
- Write letters to those who facilitated less-than nurturing experiences for you, telling them of the long-term impact you are experiencing.
- Also write amends letters to those you know you have harmed.
- Decide with a therapist what is appropriate to send.
- You may need to wait until you are further along in your individual and coupleship (if applicable) recovery before attending to amends.

........................................................................................................................................

## TR - TRAUMA REPETITION: MY SCORE ____

Repeating behaviors or situations that parallel early relationally traumatic experiences. This relates to reenactment and the tendency to "do over." Individuals who score in this area often report OCD or OCPD features (hyper-focus, obsession, rumination).

### TYPICAL THERAPEUTIC STRATEGIES:
- Understand how history repeats itself in your life experiences.
- Develop habits which help to center yourself (e.g., breathing, journaling, meditation, light exercise) so you are doing what you intend—not the cycles of old.
- Work on boundaries, both external and internal. Boundary failure is key to repetition compulsion.

## TBD - TRAUMA BONDS: MY SCORE ____

Being connected (loyal, helpful or supportive) to people who are dangerous, shaming or exploitative. People who score in this area tend to trust those they should not and to mistrust those they should.

### TYPICAL THERAPEUTIC STRATEGIES:
- Learn to recognize trauma bonds by identifying those in your life.
- Look for patterns.
- Use "detachment" strategies in situations and with people who "trigger" your codependence.

........................................................................................................................................

## TS - TRAUMA SHAME: MY SCORE ____

Feeling unworthy, or helpless/hopeless/ worthless; having self-hate because of trauma experience. This relates to a sense of self, self-esteem and the experience of thinking "I'm not enough" and "I'm not safe" (e.g., "I can't be myself and be enough, and I'm not safe in this world … being who I am). Often, individuals will react to stress with extremes (under or overfunctioning, grandiosity or worthlessness, over-control or helplessness and avoidance or passive-aggressive behavior, excessive neediness or hopelessness).

### TYPICAL THERAPEUTIC STRATEGIES:
- Understand shame dynamics in your family of origin and how those patterns repeat in your relationships today.
- To whom was it important that you feel ashamed?
- Write a list of your secrets.
- Begin reprogramming yourself with 10 affirmations, 10 times a day (in front of the mirror is best).

........................................................................................................................................

## TP - TRAUMA PLEASURE NEUROPATHWAY: MY SCORE ____

This is one of the addictive neuropathways related to intensity. When the brain is triggered limbically, automatic reactions ensue and defenses (familiar coping mechanisms) result. Individuals who score in this area often find pleasure in the presence of extreme danger, violence, risk or shame. Thoughts/ behaviors primarily used to reduce pain and acted out with Intensity, Risk, Danger, Power/Control.

### TYPICAL THERAPEUTIC STRATEGIES:
- Write a history of how excitement and shame are linked to your trauma past.
- Note the costs and dangers to you over time.
- Write a First Step and relapse prevention plan about how powerful this is in your life.

### HOW THIS NEUROPATHWAY FACILITATES BEHAVIORAL SYMPTOMS IN VARIOUS AREAS:
❶ **Erotic (sexual):** All focus is on erotic behavior, excitement, sexual possibility and orgasm. High intensity, risk and danger are often associated. Trauma survivors may incorporate pain and trauma into behavior. Violent/Painful S&M. Voyeuristic Rape. Humiliation. Degradation. Anonymous. Prostitutes. One-night stands. Exhibitionism. Swinging/Swapping. Massage Parlors. Adult Bookstores. Frotterism. Masturbation w/or without porn or 900#.

**❷ Romance (sexual):** Romance junkies turn new love into a "fix." They fall into love repeatedly or simultaneously. Roller-coaster romances are highly sexual, volatile, and dangerous. Partners are often unreachable, unavailable or unreadable. Seduction. Exploitation. Conquest. Flirtation. Fatal Attraction syndrome. Having sex with employees and professional "relationships." Office romances. Affair with neighbor. Affairs. Harassment. Swinging/Swapping. Clubs/Bars.

**❸ Relationship (sexual):** Volatile, intense, controlling and often dangerous relationships. Traumatic bonding, stalking and codependency thrive in abandonment, fear-based or dangerous collaborations. Cycles of sex and breakups. High involvement with a stalker. Keep trying to "break it off." Seen in public with a lover. Domestic Violence Syndrome.

**❹ Drugs/Money/Food:** Methamphetamine, Cocaine, Ecstasy, Violence. Craps, Race Track. Over-eating. When facilitated in Health (ability to self-soothe): Life-Enhancing, Passion, Advocacy.

....................................................................................................................................

## TB - TRAUMA BLOCKING NEUROPATHWAY: MY SCORE ____

This is one of the addictive neuropathways related to numbing. When the brain is triggered limbically, automatic reactions ensue and defenses (familiar coping mechanisms) result. Patterns exist to numb and block out overwhelming feelings that stem from trauma in your life. The unconscious need is for satiation and trancing, which is used to soothe the anxiety and stress of daily life. Behavior is used to sleep, to calm down, or to manage internal discomfort. Anxiety occurs when highly ritualized behavior is frustrated or disturbed. Thoughts/Behaviors primarily used to reduce anxiety.

### TYPICAL THERAPEUTIC STRATEGIES:
- Work to identify experiences in which you felt pain or diminished.
- Re-experience the feelings in a safe place with the help of your therapist and make sense of them as an adult. This will reduce the power they have had in your life.
- Write a First Step if necessary.

### HOW THIS NEUROPATHWAY FACILITATES BEHAVIORAL SYMPTOMS IN VARIOUS AREAS:
**❶ Erotic (sexual):** Sex is used to soothe the anxiety and stress of daily life. Sex is used to sleep, to calm down high-risk takers, or to manage internal discomfort. Anxiety occurs when highly ritualized behavior is frustrated or disturbed. Masturbation to sleep. Adult Bookstores. Lounges. 900#. Internet. Voyeurism.

**❷ Romantic (sexual):** Romance becomes a way to manage anxiety. Person becomes anxious if not in love with someone or with the person loved. How you are and who the other is not as important as the comfort of being attached. The only goal is to be with someone. Avoid being alone/lonely at all costs. Serial or simultaneous dating/ marriage. CoSA/S-Anon.

**❸ Relationship (sexual):** Compulsive relationships include tolerating the intolerable – battering, addiction, abuse and deprivation. Person will distort reality rather than face abandonment. Domestic Violence.

**❹ Drugs/Money/Food:** Alcohol, Valium, Heroin. Slot Machines. Over-eating. When facilitated in Health (ability to self-soothe): Reflective, Calming, Solitude.

## TSG - TRAUMA SPLITTING NEUROPATHWAY: MY SCORE ____

This is one of the addictive neuropathways related to dissociation. Dissociation exists on a continuum from "simply spacing out sometimes when driving" to severe Dissociative Identity Disorder. When the brain is triggered limbically, automatic reactions ensue and defenses (familiar coping mechanisms) result. Ignoring traumatic realities by dissociating or compartmentalizing experiences or parts of the self. Flighting in to fantasy and unreality as an escape. Dissociation and OCD symptoms are typical. Obsession and preoccupation become the solution to painful reality. Fantasy is an escape used to procrastinate, avoid grief and ignore pain. The neurochemicals involved are typically estrogens and androgens that occur naturally for libido, lust and the drive to procreate. In terms of courtship disorder, this results in dysfunctional patterns of noticing, attraction, touching and foreplay. Thoughts/behaviors primarily used to reduce shame. Acting out with Dissociation, Compartmentalizing, Escape, Obsession.

### TYPICAL THERAPEUTIC STRATEGIES:
- Learn that dissociating is a "normal" response to trauma.
- Identify ways you split reality and the triggers that cause that to happen.
- Cultivate a "caring" adult who stays present so you can remain whole.
- Notice any powerlessness you feel and how you're drawn to control or having to know exactly what/how/why, or managing the outcome, and may experience difficulty with flexibility and trusting the process.

### HOW THIS NEUROPATHWAY FACILITATES BEHAVIORAL SYMPTOMS IN VARIOUS AREAS:
❶ **Erotic (sexual):** Obsession and preoccupation become the solution to painful reality. Fantasy is an escape used to procrastinate, avoid grief and ignore pain. Ultimate orgasm, Strip clubs. Swinging/Swapping. Cruising. Cybersex. Porn. 900#. High ritualization.

❷ **Romance (sexual):** Person avoids life problems through romantic preoccupation. Planning, intrigue and research fill the void. Emails and chats, magical romance and stalking are more real than family. Erotic Stories. Sexual misconduct. Stalking. Internet "soulmate".

❸ **Relationship (sexual):** Compulsive relationships are built on distorted fantasy. Charisma, role, cause, gratitude play role in cults, sexual misconduct and betrayal. Mystique is built on secrecy, belief in uniqueness, and "special" needs/wants. "Cosmic Relationship".

❹ **Drugs/Money/Food:** Cannabis, LSD. Internet Lottery. Binge-Purge. When facilitated in Health (ability to self-soothe): Focus(ed).

........................................................................................................................................

## TA - TRAUMA ABSTINENCE: MY SCORE ____

As a result of traumatic experience, individuals who score in this area tend to deprive (also noted as Trauma Deprivation or TD) themselves of things that are wanted, needed or deserved. There is difficulty in meeting for, or asking for help in meeting, one's needs and wants. Trauma Aversion is used to reduce terror/fear by providing a false sense of control. Individuals will often experience or act out in extremes or binge/purge patterns. Thoughts/Behaviors used primarily to reduce terror/fear. Acted out with Control and Binge-Purge.

## TYPICAL THERAPEUTIC STRATEGIES:

- Understand how deprivation is a way to continue serving your perpetrators.

- Write a letter to the victim that was you in the past about how you learned to tolerate pain and deprivation.

- Work on strategies to self-nurture and protect/comfort your inner child.

- Visualize yourself as a precious child of the universe.

## HOW THIS NEUROPATHWAY FACILITATES BEHAVIORAL SYMPTOMS IN VARIOUS AREAS:

❶ **Erotic (sexual):** Anything erotic or suggestive is rejected. Sex is threatening, mundane, tolerable; not pleasurable. Sex may be okay if the other person does not matter (objectified). Self-mutilation. Objectification of self, being used (prostitution).

❷ **Romance (sexual):** Extreme distrust of romantic feelings or initiatives. At best person seeks "arrangement." Marriage without sex. Suspicious of kindness (seeks ulterior motives). Avoid and withdraw.

❸ **Relationship (sexual):** Avoids. Isolated, lonely, restricted emotions and poor or nonexistent communication skills. May be overly intellectual/analytical. Secret attachments (nobody can know that I care about …)

❹ **Drugs/Money/Food:** Under-earning, Hoarding. When facilitated in Health (ability to self-soothe): Ascetic (for a higher purpose – as in choosing celibacy as a spiritual way of life, or abstinence for a specific period of time to promote self-awareness and healthy nurturing).

# APPENDIX THREE

## ENDNOTES

### ENDNOTES FOR THE INTRODUCTION

1 http://www.airspacemag.com/need-to-know/NEED-helmets.html

### ENDNOTES FOR PILLAR OF FREEDOM ONE

2 Peck, M.S., M.D. (1978). *The Road Less Traveled: A New Psychology of Love, Traditional Values and Spiritual Growth.* New York, NY: Simon & Schuster, Inc.

3 CSAT Certification Intensive Training Manual Week One –day one, page 4 of 15

4 Nikolas Westerhoff, *Why Do Men Buy Sex?*, Scientific American Mind (Dec/Jan 2008), pg 62-67

5 Naval Air Training and Operating Procedures Standardization (NATOPS)

6 Louis Cozolino, *The Neuroscience of Human Relationships* (New York: W.W. Norton & Company, 2006) 304.

7 Patrick Carnes, *Facing the Shadow* (Carefree, Arizona: Gentle Path Press, 2005) 91.

8 Mary Sykes Wylie, *Mindsight, Dan Siegel Offers Therapist a New Vision of the Brain*, Networker U Online Course, No.102: Getting Comfortable with the Brain. http://www.gotomylist.com/cme/networker/OHS/0102/102_3.html

9 Daniel Siegel, *The Developing Mind*. (New York: Guilford Press, 1999) 50-69.

10 Patrick Carnes, ed., *Clinical Management of Sex Addiction* (New York: Brunner-Routledge, 2002) 14-18.

11 Samuel Greenfield, *The Human Brain: A Guided Tour* (New York: Basic Books, 1996) 16-45.

### ENDNOTES FOR PILLAR OF FREEDOM TWO

12 Michael Dye, CADC, NCAC, and Patricia Fancher, CAC III, MFCC, Ph.D. *The Genesis Process. A Relapse Prevention Workbook for Addictive/Compulsive Behaviors*, (Auburn, CA: Michael Dye, 1998; 3rd Edition 2007). www.genesisprocess.org. 160.

13 Jeff Van Vonderen, *Tired of Trying to Measure Up* (Minneapolis: Bethany House Publishers, 1989).

14 Philip Yancey, *What's So Amazing About Grace?* (Grand Rapids: Zondervan, 1997) 209.

15 Ted Roberts, *Pure Desire* (Ventura, CA: Regal, 1999) 83.

16 Ibid. 83.

17 http://dictionary.reference.com/browse/individualism. 2009.

18 Leonard Ravenhill. August 3, 2005. http://dailychristianquote.com/dcqravenhill.html, 2009.

## ENDNOTES FOR PILLAR OF FREEDOM THREE

19 Jerry L. Sittser, *A Grace Disguised: How the Soul Grows Through Loss* (Grand Rapids: Zondervan, 2004) 32.

20 Michael Dye, CADC, NCAC, and Patricia Fancher, CAC III, MFCC, Ph.D. *The Genesis Process. A Relapse Prevention Workbook for Addictive/Compulsive Behaviors*, (Auburn, CA: Michael Dye, 1998; 3rd Edition 2007). www.genesisprocess.org; 115.

21 Adapted from Michael Dye, *The Genesis Process* (Auburn, CA: Michael Dye, 2006). www.genesisprocess.org

22 "Assertiveness." Wikipedia. Wikimedia Foundation, n.d. Web. 03 Aug. 2015. https://en.wikipedia.org/wiki/Assertiveness

23 Robert Alberti, Ph.D. & Michael Emmons, Ph.D. *Your Perfect Right: Assertiveness & Equality in Your Life* (Newberg, OR: Impact Publishers, 2008).

24 Brown, B., Ph.D. (2010). *The Gifts of Imperfection: Let Go of Who You Think You're Supposed to Be and Embrace Who You Are.* Center City, MN: Hazelden.

25 Ted Roberts, created & recommended by Ted Roberts, Pure Desire Ministries International. 310 Seven Pillars of Freedom

## ENDNOTES FOR PILLAR OF FREEDOM FOUR

26 Patrick Carnes, *Facing the Shadow* (Carefree, Arizona: Gentle Path Press, 2005) 268.

27 Patrick Carnes, *Don't Call It Love* (New York: Bantam Books, 1992) 207.

## ENDNOTES FOR PILLAR OF FREEDOM FIVE

28 Jamie Buckingham, *"The Journey to Spiritual Maturity,"* ( Orleans, MA: Paraclete Press, 1985), pg. 9-15. 36

29 Harry Potter and the Sorcerer's Stone. Dir. Chris Columbus. 2001.

30 The concept of the Mirror of Erised comes from the sexual addiction therapist training I (Ted Roberts) received through IITAP. www.IITAP.com

31 Norman Doidge, *The Brain that Changes Itself*, (New York: Viking, 2007) 60.

32 The concept of the Arousal Template comes from Dr. Patrick Carnes and Anna Valenti. Many men I have counseled through the years have been set free to win the battle through the brilliance of their therapeutic insight.

33 *The Karate Kid*. Dir. John G. Avildsen. Perf. Pat Morita and Ralph Macchio. Columbia Pictures, 1984.

34 Robin Williams. www.Great-Quotes.com. 2009.

35 Ted Roberts. *Living Life Boldly Study Guide*. (Gresham, OR: East Hill Church, 2005) 75-76. Used by permission.

# ENDNOTES FOR PILLAR OF FREEDOM SIX

36 Pedersen JM, Torsting K. Armadillo. Fridthjof Film. Denmark; 2010.

37 Dorthe Bernsten, Kim B. Johannessen, Yvonne D. Thomsen, Mette Bertelsen, Rick H. Hoyle, David C. Rubin. "Peace and War: Trajectories of Posttraumatic Stress Disorder Symptoms Before, During, and After Military Deployment in Afghanistan." *Psychological Science.* First published on November 5, 2012.

38 Center for Substance Abuse Treatment (US). Trauma-Informed Care in Behavioral Health Services. Rockville (MD): Substance Abuse and Mental Health Services Administration (US); 2014. (Treatment Improvement Protocol (TIP) Series, No. 57.) Chapter 3, Understanding the Impact of Trauma. Available from: http://www.ncbi.nlm.nih.gov/books/NBK207191/

39 Jie Tang, Yizhen Yu, Yukai Du, Ying Ma, Dongying Zhang, Jiaji Wang. Prevalence of Internet addiction and its association with stressful life events and psychological symptoms among adolesent internet users. *Addictive Behaviors*, Volume 39, Issue 3, March 2014. 744-747

40 John Pennebaker. *Opening Up: The Healing Power of Confiding in Others.* (New York: The Guilford Press, 1990) 79-92.

41 A. N. Schore. *Affect Regulation and the Origin of the Self.* (Hove, U.K.: Lawrence Erlbaum Associates Publishers, 1994).

42 Bessel A. Van der Kolk, Alexander C. McFarlane, & Lars Weisaeth (Editors), *Traumatic Stress: The Effects of Overwhelming Experience on Mind, Body, and Society.* (New York: The Guilford Press, 1st Edition, November 2006).

43 Peter A. Levine, *In an Unspoken Voice: How the body release trauma and restores goodness.* (Berkeley, CA: North Atlantic Books, 2012) 50.

44 Schneider, JP (2000). Compulsive and Addictive Sexual Disorders and the Family. *CNS Spectrums, 5*(10), 53-62.

45 Smith, D. (2002). *A Beautiful Mind, Part 3.* Abilene, TX: Heartlight, Inc. Available from: www.heartlight.org/articles/200206/20020602_mind3.html

46 Little, BL (2008). *The Secret and Spirituality.* Gretna, LA: Dove Inspirational Press.

47 Viktor Frankl, *Man's Search for Meaning* (New York: Pocket Books, 1997) 123.

48 Frank Laubach, *Letters by a Modern Mystic* (Colorado Springs: Purposeful Design Publications, 2007) 3.

49 Ibid. 33.

50 Ibid. 23.

51 Jeffrey Schwartz, "Brain Lock: Free yourself from obsessive-compulsive behavior." (New York: Harper Perennial, 1997).

52 Richard Davidson and Sharon Begley, *The Emotional Life of Your Brain* (New York: Hudson Street Press, 2012) 10.

53 Daniel Siegel, *Mindsight* (New York: Bantam Books, 2010) 133.

54 Davidson, R.J.,Kabat-Zinn, J. et. al. (2003) Alterations in brain and immune function produced by mindfulness meditations. *Psychosomatic Medicine*. 65:564-570.

55 Creswell, J. D., et. al. (2007) Neural correlates of dispositional mindfulness during affect labeling. *Psychosomatic Medicine*. 69: 560-565.

56 Wolf, O.T. (2009, October 13). *"Stress and memory in humans: Twelve years of progress?"* Brain Research. 1293: 142-54.

57 Jaffe, E. (2010, May/June) "This side of paradise: Discovering why the human mind needs nature." *Association for Psychological Sciences*. 23(5):11-15.

## ENDNOTES FOR PILLAR OF FREEDOM SEVEN

58 A significant portion of this portion of the lesson is drawn from a presentation by Dr. Stefanie Carnes as part of Module 3, CSAT certification process, 2008.

59 Dr. Omar Minwalla, Licensed Psychologist and Clinical Sexologist. http://understandingher-sideofthestory.com/The_Sexual_Trauma_Model.html. 2008.

60 Deborah Corley & Jennifer Schneider, *"Disclosing Secrets"*, (Wickenburg, Arizona; Gentle Path Press: 2002)

61 Ibid.

62 Ibid. 141.

63 Statistics from Dr. Doug Weiss at Spring Conference 2005, Heart to Heart Counseling Center, Colorado Springs, CO. www.sexaddict.com

64 Gert Holstege, Holland Researcher, published in Scientific American Mind, April/May 2008, 71.

65 Ted Roberts, *Pure Desire* (Ventura, CA: Regal, 2008) 287.

66 Ibid. 287.

67 Diane Roberts, *Betrayal & Beyond Workbook III* (Gresham, OR: Pure Desire Ministries International, 2010) 97-98.

68 Ted and Diane Roberts, Sexy Christians Seminar, Pure Desire Ministries International, www.puredesire.org

69 Patrick Carnes, ed., *Clinical Management of Sex Addiction* (New York: Brunner-Routledge, 2002) 14-18.

70 McGonigal, K., Ph.D. (2012). *The Willpower Instinct: How Self-Control Works, Why It Matters, and What You Can Do to Get More of It.* New York, NY: The Penguin Group.

71 McGonigal, K., Ph.D. (2012). *The Willpower Instinct: How Self-Control Works, Why It Matters, and What You Can Do to Get More of It.* New York, NY: The Penguin Group.

72 Muraven, M., & Slessareva, E. (2003). Mechanisms of self-control failure: Motivation and limited resources. *Personality and Social Psychology Bulletin*, 29(7), 894-906.

73 Beer, J.S., John, O.P., Scabini, D. & Knight, R.T., (2006). Orbitofrontal Cortex and Social Behavior: Integrating Self-monitoring and Emotion-Cognition Interactions. *Journal of Cognitive Neuroscience,* 18(6), 871-879.

74 Michael Dye, CADC, NCAC II, *The Genesis Process for Change Groups* (Auburn, CA: Michael Dye, 2006). www.genesisprocess.org

75 Ted and Diane Roberts, *Sexy Christians*. (Grand Rapids: Baker Publishing Group, 2010) www.puredesire.org

## ENDNOTES FOR APPENDICES

76 John Demos, *"Neurofeedback,"* (New York; W.W. Norton: 2005) 22-56.

77 Earl Henslin, *"This is your Brain on Joy,"* (Nashville: Thomas Nelson: 2008) 172-192.

78 Dr. Louis Cozolino, Lecture Notes, IITP Symposium, Feb. 2008.

79 Louis Cozolino, *"The Neuroscience of Human Relationships,"* (New York; W.W. Norton: 2006) 96.

80 Aron Fisher, (2005) "Reward, Motivation and Emotional Systems Associated with Early-Stage Intense Romantic Love," Journal of Neurophysiology 94 (1) 327-337.

81 Emily Anthes, "Instant Egghead Guide to the Brain," (New York; St. Martin's Griffin: 2009) pg. 202.

82 John Ratey, *"A User's Guide to the Brain,"* (New York; Vintage Books: 2001) 227.

83 Patrick Carnes, *The 40-Day Focus: Book One* (Carefree, Arizona; Gentle Path Press: 2005), pg 20.

84 Joseph LeDoux, *The Emotional Brain* (New York: Simon & Schuster, 1996)

85 *"Process Addictions: Approaches for Professionals"* notes from seminar presented by Foundations Recovery Network, April 22-24, 2009.

86 Eric Nestler, (2001). *"Psychogenomics: Opportunities for understanding addictions"*. Journal of Neuroscience, 21 (21), 8324-8327.

87 Markus Barth, *"Ephesians 4-6,"* (New York; Doubleday: 1974) 777.

88 Post Traumatic Stress Index Test & Analysis. Copyright Patrick J. Carnes, PhD,CAS 1999. Used by permission of Patrick J. Carnes.